RECENT TOPICS IN NONLINEAR PDE III

NORTH-HOLLAND
MATHEMATICS STUDIES **148**

Lecture Notes in Numerical and Applied Analysis Vol. 9
General Editors:
H. Fujita (University of Tokyo) and M. Yamaguti (Kyoto University)

Recent Topics in Nonlinear PDE III

Edited by

KYÛYA MASUDA (University of Tokyo)
TAKASHI SUZUKI (University of Tokyo)

KINOKUNIYA

KINOKUNIYA COMPANY LTD.
TOKYO JAPAN

NORTH-HOLLAND
AMSTERDAM·NEW YORK·OXFORD

KINOKUNIYA COMPANY-TOKYO
NORTH-HOLLAND-AMSTERDAM·NEW YORK·OXFORD

ISBN: 0 444 70317 9

Publishers
KINOKUNIYA COMPANY LTD.
TOKYO JAPAN

* * *

ELSEVIER SCIENCE PUBLISHERS B.V.
P.O. Box 1991
1000 BZ Amsterdam
The Netherlands

Sole distributors for the U.S.A. and Canada
ELSEVIER SCIENCE PUBLISHING COMPANY, INC.
52 VANDERBILT AVENUE
NEW YORK, N.Y. 10017

Distributed in Japan by KINOKUNIYA COMPANY LTD.
Distributed outside Japan by ELSEVIER SCIENCE PUBLISHERS B. V. (NORTH-HOLLAND)

Lecture Notes in Numerical and Applied Analysis Vol. 9

PRINTED IN JAPAN

PREFACE

This volume is an outgrowth of lectures delivered at the fourth meeting on "Nonlinear Partial Differential Equations", held at the University of Tokyo, February 24-26, 1986. Many mathematicians in Japan were invited to talk on their current research interests in nonlinear PDE's occuring in the areas of fluid dynamics, free boundary problems, population dynamics and mathematical physics.

We would like to take the opportunity to thank all the participants of the meeting, and the contributors to these proceedings.

K. Masuda

T. Suzuki

CONTENTS

Recent Topics in Nonlinear PDE III, Tokyo, 1986
Lecture Notes in Num. Appl. Anal., 9, 1–73 (1987)

Slow Traveling Wave Solutions to The Hodgkin-Huxley Equations

Hideo IKEDA*, Masayasu MIMURA** and Tohru TSUJIKAWA***

*Faculty of Economics, Toyama University
Toyama 930, Japan

**Department of Mathematics, Hiroshima University
Hiroshima 730, Japan

***Hiroshima Junior College of Automotive Engineering
Hiroshima 739-03, Japan

1. Introduction

The most important mathematical model describing nerve impulses on an unmyelinated axon was proposed by Hodgkin and Huxley [11]. It consists of a set of reaction - diffusion equations

$$(1.1)\quad \begin{cases} \dfrac{\partial v}{\partial t} = \dfrac{\partial^2 v}{\partial x^2} - \bar{g}_K n^4(v-V_K) - \bar{g}_{Na} m^3 h(v-V_{Na}) - \bar{g}_\ell (v-V_\ell) \\ \dfrac{\partial m}{\partial t} = \gamma_m(v)(m_\infty(v) - m) \\ \dfrac{\partial n}{\partial t} = \gamma_n(v)(n_\infty(v) - n) \\ \dfrac{\partial h}{\partial t} = \gamma_h(v)(h_\infty(v) - h) . \end{cases}$$

Here $v(x,t)$ denotes the potential across the membrane at time t and distance x along the axon. m, n, and h denote local changes in the membrane permeability to N_a^+ and K^+ in response to changes in v. $\bar{g}_K$, $\bar{g}_{Na}$ and $\bar{g}_\ell$ are respectively the maximum potassium conductance, the maximum sodium conductance and the nonspecific leakage conductance. V_K, V_{Na} and V_ℓ are the potassium equilibrium potential, the sodium equilibrium potential and the equilibrium potential of leakage current. γ_m, γ_n, γ_h, m_∞, n_∞ and h_∞ are empirically determined functions of the potential (for a more complete account, see [11]).

Hodgkin and Huxley considered traveling wave solutions of the type $(v(z), m(z), n(z), h(z))$ $(z = x+ct)$ which tend to the resting state π as $|z| \to +\infty$. These solutions satisfy

$$(1.2)\quad \begin{cases} \dfrac{d^2v}{dz^2} - c\dfrac{dv}{dz} - \bar{g}_K n^4(v-V_K) - \bar{g}_{Na} m^3 h(v-V_{Na}) - \bar{g}_\ell(v-V_\ell) = 0 \\ c\dfrac{dm}{dz} - \gamma_m(v)(m_\infty(v) - m) = 0 \\ c\dfrac{dn}{dz} - \gamma_n(v)(n_\infty(v) - n) = 0 \qquad\qquad , \; z \in \mathbb{R} \\ c\dfrac{dh}{dz} - \gamma_h(v)(h_\infty(v) - h) = 0 \\ (v(\pm\infty), m(\pm\infty), n(\pm\infty), h(\pm\infty)) = \pi . \end{cases}$$

With experimentally specified data in (1.1), Hodgkin and Huxley [11], Huxley [12], [13], Miller and Rinzel [15] and Cooley and Dodge [3] numerically found that there are evidently two different values of c for which there is a solution of (1.2): a fast velocity solution and a slow velocity solution. Furthermore, it is numerically supported that the fast velocity solution corresponds to a stable impulse, while the slow velocity one does to an unstable one.

From a theoretical point of view, Hastings [10] and Carpenter [1] proved the existence of the fast velocity solution (excitable impulse) by using singular perturbation methods in phase space when the rate differences $\gamma_n(v)/\gamma_m(v)$ and $\gamma_h(v)/\gamma_m(v)$ are sufficiently small. On the other hand, the existence of slow velocity solutions has not yet been proved, although it is important in playing a role of a " separator " of an excitable impulse and the resting state. For stability of these traveling wave solutions, we should refer the reader to the most important works by Evans [4], [5], [6] and [7], who showed that the linearized stability criterion is valid to discuss stability of these solutions. He and later Maginu [14] showed that the transition at which the unstable manifold passes through the stable manifold with respect to the resting state when the velocity parameter c increases through the critical value gives information about instability of the slow traveling wave solution. Evans and Feroe [8] numerically studied this transition and asserted that the slow traveling wave solution is unstable.

In this paper, motivated by the above studies, we construct a slow velocity solution by using singular perturbation methods which are different from the approaches by Hastings [10] and Carpenter [1], and then prove that it is unstable.

Following [10] and [1], we introduce a small parameter ε into (1.1) to emphasize the fast and slow time scales. The resulting Hodgkin and Huxley's model becomes

$$(1.3)\qquad \begin{cases} \dfrac{\partial v}{\partial t} = \dfrac{\partial^2 v}{\partial x^2} - F(v,m,n,h) \\[2ex] \dfrac{\partial m}{\partial t} = \gamma_m(v)(m_\infty(v) - m) \\[2ex] \dfrac{\partial n}{\partial t} = \varepsilon^2 \gamma_n(v)(n_\infty(v) - n) \\[2ex] \dfrac{\partial h}{\partial t} = \varepsilon^2 \gamma_h(v)(h_\infty(v) - h) , \end{cases}$$

where $F(v,m,n,h) = g_K(n)(v-V_K) + g_1(m)g_2(h)(v-V_{Na}) + \bar{g}_\ell(v-V_\ell)$ and $\gamma_m(v)$, $\gamma_n(v)$ and $\gamma_h(v)$ are rescaled to be about the same magnitude in v.

Following Hodgkin and Huxley [11], we impose several assumptions on (1.3).

(A-1) $V_K < 0 < V_\ell < V_{Na}$ and $\bar{g}_\ell > 0$ are constants.

(A-2) $g_1(m)$, $g_2(h)$ and $g_K(n)$ are nonnegative functions in $C^2[0,1]$ satisfying $g_1', g_2', g_K' > 0$ on $(0,1)$ and $g_2(0) = 0$, where $'$ means the derivative of its argument.

(A-3) $\gamma_m(v)$, $\gamma_n(v)$, $\gamma_h(v)$, $m_\infty(v)$, $n_\infty(v)$ and $h_\infty(v)$ are positive functions in $C^2(\mathbb{R})$ satisfying $m_\infty', n_\infty', -h_\infty' > 0$ on $\mathbb{R}$ and

$m_\infty(+\infty) = n_\infty(+\infty) = h_\infty(-\infty) = 1$,

$m_\infty(-\infty) = n_\infty(-\infty) = h_\infty(+\infty) = 0$.

(A-4) (1.3) has a unique (spatially homogeneous) resting state $\pi = (0,\bar{m},\bar{n},\bar{h})$, that is,

$F(0,\bar{m},\bar{n},\bar{h}) = 0$, $m_\infty(0) = \bar{m}$, $n_\infty(0) = \bar{n}$ and $h_\infty(0) = \bar{h}$.

(A-5) For each $n,h \in [0,1]$, $F(v,m_\infty(v),n,h) = 0$ has at most three roots. If there are exactly three roots, say $\omega(n,h) < \mu(n,h) < \lambda(n,h)$, all are nondegenerate. In particular, when $n = \bar{n}$ and $h = \bar{h}$, it has three roots, say $0 = \omega(\bar{n},\bar{h}) < \mu(\bar{n},\bar{h}) < \lambda(\bar{n},\bar{h})$.

(A-6) $\displaystyle\int_0^{\lambda(\bar{n},\bar{h})} F(v,m_\infty(v),\bar{n},\bar{h})dv < 0$.

Theorem A. *Under the assumptions* (A-1) - (A-6), *there are* $\varepsilon_0 > 0$ *and* $c_* > 0$ *such that for any* $0 < \varepsilon < \varepsilon_0$, (1.3) *has a single pulse traveling wave solution* $(v(x+\varepsilon c(\varepsilon)t), m(x+\varepsilon c(\varepsilon)t), n(x+\varepsilon c(\varepsilon)t), h(x+\varepsilon c(\varepsilon)t))$ *with* $(v,m,n,h)(\pm\infty) = \pi$, *where the velocity* $\varepsilon c(\varepsilon)$ *satisfies* $\varepsilon c(\varepsilon) = \varepsilon(c_* + o(1))$ *as* $\varepsilon \to 0$.

We next show the instability of this traveling wave solution. To state it, we introduce the traveling coordinate system $(z,t) = (x + \varepsilon c(\varepsilon)t, t)$ into (1.3). Then (1.3) takes the form

$$(1.4) \qquad \begin{cases} \dfrac{\partial v}{\partial t} = \dfrac{\partial^2 v}{\partial z^2} - \varepsilon c(\varepsilon)\dfrac{\partial v}{\partial z} - F(v,m,n,h) \\[2mm] \dfrac{\partial m}{\partial t} = -\varepsilon c(\varepsilon)\dfrac{\partial m}{\partial z} + \gamma_m(v)(m_\infty(v) - m) \\[2mm] \dfrac{\partial n}{\partial t} = -\varepsilon c(\varepsilon)\dfrac{\partial n}{\partial z} + \varepsilon^2\gamma_n(v)(n_\infty(v) - n) \\[2mm] \dfrac{\partial h}{\partial t} = -\varepsilon c(\varepsilon)\dfrac{\partial h}{\partial z} + \varepsilon^2\gamma_h(v)(h_\infty(v) - h) . \end{cases}$$

We call the traveling wave solution $(v(z),m(z),n(z),h(z))$ to be *unstable* when there is some point with a positive real part in the spectrum of the linearized operator about the solution $(v(z),m(z),n(z),h(z))$ to (1.4).

Theorem B. *The traveling wave solution constructed in Theorem* A *is unstable.*

Throughout this paper we use the following function spaces: Let $I = (a,b)$ $(-\infty < a < b < +\infty)$, $J = \mathbb{R}_-$ or $\mathbb{R}_+$, σ be a nonnegative number, δ be a positive number and n be a nonnegative integer.

$$X^n_{\sigma,\delta}(J) = \{u \in C^n(J) \mid \|u\|_{X^n_{\sigma,\delta}} \equiv \sum_{i=0}^{n} \sup_{x\in J} e^{\sigma|x|}|(\delta\frac{d}{dx})^i u(x)| < +\infty\} .$$

$$\mathring{X}^n_{\sigma,\delta}(J) = \{u \in X^n_{\sigma,\delta}(J) \mid u(0) = 0\} .$$

$$\mathring{E}^n_\delta(J) = \{u \in C^n(J) \mid u(0) = 0, \ \|u\|_{E^n_\delta} \equiv \|u\|_{C^0} + \sum_{i=0}^{n} \|\delta^{i-1}(\frac{d}{dx})^i u\|_{C^0} < +\infty\}.$$

$$C^n_\delta(I) = \{u \in C^n(I) \mid \|u\|_{C^n_\delta} \equiv \sum_{i=0}^{n} \|(\delta\frac{d}{dx})^i u\|_{C^0} < +\infty\} .$$

$$\mathring{C}^n_\delta(I) = \{u \in C^n_\delta(I) \mid u(a) = 0\} .$$

$$\overset{\circ}{C}{}^n_-(I) = \{u \in C^n(I) \mid u(a) = \frac{d}{dx} u(b) = 0\} .$$

$$\overset{\circ}{C}{}^n_+(I) = \{u \in C^n(I) \mid \frac{d}{dx} u(a) = u(b) = 0\} .$$

2. Existence of slow traveling wave solutions

Introduce the traveling coordinate $z = \varepsilon(x + \varepsilon ct)$ into (1.3). Then we have

$$(2.1) \quad \begin{cases} \varepsilon^2 \dfrac{d^2v}{dz^2} - \varepsilon^2 c \dfrac{dv}{dz} - F(v,m,n,h) = 0 \\[2ex] \varepsilon^2 c \dfrac{dm}{dz} - \gamma_m(v)(m_\infty(v) - m) = 0 \\[2ex] c \dfrac{dn}{dz} - \gamma_n(v)(n_\infty(v) - n) = 0 \\[2ex] c \dfrac{dh}{dz} - \gamma_h(v)(h_\infty(v) - h) = 0 \end{cases} , z \in \mathbb{R} .$$

The boundary conditions to (2.1) are assumed to be

$$(2.2) \qquad v(\pm\infty) = 0,\ m(\pm\infty) = \overline{m},\ n(\pm\infty) = \overline{n},\ h(\pm\infty) = \overline{h} .$$

We look for a single pulse solution $(v(z),m(z),n(z),h(z))$ satisfying (2.1), (2.2). Without a loss of generality, we assume $c > 0$. This implies that the pulse is traveling to the left with a velocity εc.

We first divide the whole interval $\mathbb{R}$ into four subintervals $I_1 = (-\infty,-\varepsilon\kappa]$, $I_2 = [-\varepsilon\kappa,0]$, $I_3 = [0,\varepsilon\tau]$ and $I_4 = [\varepsilon\tau,+\infty)$ for arbitrarily fixed $\kappa > 0$ and $\tau > 0$, and fix the phase of the solution by setting the condition

$$\frac{d}{dz} v(0) = 0 .$$

2.1. Construction of solutions on $I_1 = (-\infty,-\varepsilon\kappa]$

First we consider the system (2.1) on I_1 with the boundary conditions

$$(2.3)\qquad \begin{cases} v(-\infty) = 0, \quad v(-\varepsilon\kappa) = \nu_1 \\ m(-\infty) = \overline{m}, \quad n(-\infty) = \overline{n}, \quad h(-\infty) = \overline{h}\ . \end{cases}$$

Here ν_1 is an arbitrarily fixed number satisfying $\mu(\overline{n},\overline{h}) < \nu_1 < v^*$ where v^* is a positive constant determined by $\int_0^{v^*} F(v,m_\infty(v),\overline{n},\overline{h})dv = 0$. v^* is uniquely determined by (A-5) and (A-6). Using the transformation $y = z + \varepsilon\kappa$, we have

$$(2.4)\qquad \begin{cases} \varepsilon^2 v'' - \varepsilon^2 cv' - F(v,m,n,h) = 0 \\ \varepsilon^2 cm' - \gamma_m(v)(m_\infty(v) - m) = 0 \\ cn' - \gamma_n(v)(n_\infty(v) - n) = 0 \\ ch' - \gamma_h(v)(h_\infty(v) - h) = 0 \end{cases} , \ y \in \mathbb{R}_- ,$$

where $'$ means $\frac{d}{dy}$. The boundary conditions are

$$(2.5)\qquad \begin{cases} v(-\infty) = 0, \quad v(0) = \nu_1 \\ m(-\infty) = \overline{m}, \ n(-\infty) = \overline{n}, \ h(-\infty) = \overline{h}\ . \end{cases}$$

We seek an approximation of (2.4),(2.5) in the form of a formal power series of ε

$$(2.6)\qquad \begin{cases} v(y) = v_0(y) + \varepsilon v_1(y) + \cdots + \varepsilon^i v_i(y) + \cdots \\ m(y) = m_0(y) + \varepsilon m_1(y) + \cdots + \varepsilon^i m_i(y) + \cdots \\ n(y) = n_0(y) + \varepsilon n_1(y) + \cdots + \varepsilon^i n_i(y) + \cdots \\ h(y) = h_0(y) + \varepsilon h_1(y) + \cdots + \varepsilon^i h_i(y) + \cdots \quad . \end{cases}$$

Substituting (2.6) into (2.4), (2.5) and equating like powers of ε^0, we obtain

$$
(2.7) \qquad \begin{cases} F(v_0,m_0,n_0,h_0) = 0 \\ \gamma_m(v_0)(m_\infty(v_0) - m_0) = 0 \end{cases}
$$

and

$$
(2.8) \qquad \begin{cases} cn_0' - \gamma_n(v_0)(n_\infty(v_0) - n_0) = 0 \\ ch_0' - \gamma_h(v_0)(h_\infty(v_0) - h_0) = 0 \\ n_0(-\infty) = \bar{n}, \ h_0(-\infty) = \bar{h} \,. \end{cases} , \quad y \in \mathbb{R}_-
$$

Since (2.7) reduces to $F(v_0,m_\infty(v_0),n_0,h_0) = 0$, which leads to $v_0 = \omega(n_0,h_0)$ from the boundary conditions in (2.5). Then (2.8) is written as

$$
(2.9) \qquad \begin{cases} cn_0' - \gamma_n(\omega(n_0,h_0))(n_\infty(\omega(n_0,h_0)) - n_0) = 0 \\ ch_0' - \gamma_h(\omega(n_0,h_0))(h_\infty(\omega(n_0,h_0)) - h_0) = 0 \\ n_0(-\infty) = \bar{n}, \ h_0(-\infty) = \bar{h} \,. \end{cases} , \quad y \in \mathbb{R}_-
$$

Lemma 1. *Let* $c > 0$ *be arbitrarily fixed.* (2.9) *has a unique solution* $(n_0(y),h_0(y)) \equiv (\bar{n},\bar{h})$.

Noting that $\frac{\partial\omega}{\partial n} < 0$ and $\frac{\partial\omega}{\partial h} > 0$ in some neighborhood of $(\bar{n},\bar{h})$ (Hastings [Lemma 1 : 10]), we find that the linearized matrix around $(\bar{n},\bar{h})$ to (2.9) has two negative eigenvalues. Therefore, the proof of Lemma 1 is obvious.

Thus, it turns out by (A-4) that (2.7) and (2.8) have a unique solution $(v_0,m_0,n_0,h_0) = (0,\bar{m},\bar{n},\bar{h})$.

Next, equating like powers of ε in (2.4), (2.5), we obtain

$$(2.10)\qquad \begin{cases} F_v(0,\bar{m},\bar{n},\bar{h})v_1 + F_m(0,\bar{m},\bar{n},\bar{h})m_1 + F_n(0,\bar{m},\bar{n},\bar{h})n_1 \\ + F_h(0,\bar{m},\bar{n},\bar{h})h_1 = 0 \\ \gamma_m(0)(m_\infty'(0)v_1 - m_1) = 0 \end{cases}$$

and

$$(2.11)\qquad \begin{cases} cn_1' - \gamma_n(0)(n_\infty'(0)v_1 - n_1) = 0 \\ ch_1' - \gamma_h(0)(h_\infty'(0)v_1 - h_1) = 0 \\ n_1(-\infty) = h_1(-\infty) = 0 . \end{cases} , \ y \in \mathbb{R}_-$$

Here we write $F_v = \frac{\partial F}{\partial v}$, $F_m = \frac{\partial F}{\partial m}$, $F_n = \frac{\partial F}{\partial n}$ and $F_h = \frac{\partial F}{\partial h}$ for simplicity. (2.10) is simply written as

$$(2.12)\qquad \begin{cases} v_1 = -(F_n^0 n_1 + F_h^0 h_1) \\ m_1 = m_\infty'(0)v_1 , \end{cases}$$

where

$$\begin{cases} F_n^0 = F_n(0,\bar{m},\bar{n},\bar{h})/\{F_v(0,\bar{m},\bar{n},\bar{h}) + m_\infty'(0)F_m(0,\bar{m},\bar{n},\bar{h})\} \\ F_h^0 = F_h(0,\bar{m},\bar{n},\bar{h})/\{F_v(0,\bar{m},\bar{n},\bar{h}) + m_\infty'(0)F_m(0,\bar{m},\bar{n},\bar{h})\}. \end{cases}$$

Substituting (2.12) into (2.11), we have

$$(2.13)\qquad \begin{cases} cn_1' + \gamma_n(0)\{(n_\infty'(0)F_n^0 + 1)n_1 + n_\infty'(0)F_h^0 h_1\} = 0 \\ ch_1' + \gamma_h(0)\{h_\infty'(0)F_n^0 n_1 + (h_\infty'(0)F_h^0 + 1)h_1\} = 0 \\ n_1(-\infty) = h_1(-\infty) = 0 . \end{cases} , \ y \in \mathbb{R}_-$$

Lemma 2. *Let* $c > 0$ *be arbitrarily fixed. Then* (2.13) *has a unique solution* $(n_1(y),h_1(y)) \equiv (0,0)$.

Since $F_n^0 > 0$, $F_h^0 < 0$, $n_\infty'(0) > 0$ and $h_\infty'(0) < 0$, the proof is obvious, so we omit it.

From Lemma 2 and (2,12), it follows that $(v_1,m_1,n_1,h_1) = (0,0,0,0)$. In a similar way, we find that $(v_i,m_i,n_i,h_i) = (0,0,0,0)$ for any $i\ (\geq 2)$. Thus, the approximation up to order ε^i $(i \geq 0)$ of (2.4) is $(v,m,n,h) = (0,\bar{m},\bar{n},\bar{h})$, but it does not satisfy $v(0) = \nu_1$ of (2.5). So, in a neighborhood of $y = 0$, we look for an approximation of the form

$$
(2.14)\qquad \begin{cases} v(y;\varepsilon) = \phi_0(y/\varepsilon) + \varepsilon\phi_1(y/\varepsilon) + \cdots + \varepsilon^i\phi_i(y/\varepsilon) + \cdots \\ m(y;\varepsilon) = \bar{m} + \psi_0(y/\varepsilon) + \varepsilon\psi_1(y/\varepsilon) + \cdots + \varepsilon^i\psi_i(y/\varepsilon) + \cdots \\ n(y;\varepsilon) = \bar{n} + \pi_0(y/\varepsilon) + \varepsilon\pi_1(y/\varepsilon) + \cdots + \varepsilon^i\pi_i(y/\varepsilon) + \cdots \\ h(y;\varepsilon) = \bar{h} + \omega_0(y/\varepsilon) + \varepsilon\omega_1(y/\varepsilon) + \cdots + \varepsilon^i\omega_i(y/\varepsilon) + \cdots \end{cases} .
$$

Using $\xi = y/\varepsilon$, we rewrite (2.4) as

$$
(2.15)\qquad \begin{cases} v^{\cdot\cdot} - \varepsilon c v^{\cdot} - F(v,m,n,h) = 0 \\ \varepsilon c m^{\cdot} - \gamma_m(v)(m_\infty(v) - m) = 0 \\ c n^{\cdot} - \varepsilon\gamma_n(v)(n_\infty(v) - n) = 0 \\ c h^{\cdot} - \varepsilon\gamma_h(v)(h_\infty(v) - h) = 0 \end{cases} , \quad \xi \in \mathbb{R}_- ,
$$

where $\cdot$ means $\frac{d}{d\xi}$. Substituting (2.14) into (2.15), (2.5) and equating like powers of ε^0, we have

$$
(2.16)\qquad \begin{cases} \phi_0^{\cdot\cdot} - F(\phi_0,\bar{m}+\psi_0,\bar{n}+\pi_0,\bar{h}+\omega_0) = 0 \\ \gamma_m(\phi_0)(m_\infty(\phi_0) - \bar{m} - \psi_0) = 0 \end{cases} , \quad \xi \in \mathbb{R}_-
$$

$$\phi_0(-\infty) = 0,\ \phi_0(0) = \nu_1,\ \phi_0(-\infty) = 0$$

and

$$(2.17)\qquad \begin{cases} c\pi_0^{\cdot} = 0, \quad c\omega_0^{\cdot} = 0 & ,\ \xi \in \mathbb{R}_- \\ \pi_0(-\infty) = \omega_0(-\infty) = 0\ . \end{cases}$$

It is easy to see that $(\pi_0(\xi),\omega_0(\xi)) \equiv (0,0)$. Since the second equation in (2.16) becomes $\psi_0 = m_\infty(\phi_0) - \overline{m}$, (2.16) is simply written as

$$(2.18)\qquad \begin{cases} \phi_0^{\cdot\cdot} - F(\phi_0,m_\infty(\phi_0),\overline{n},\overline{h}) = 0 & ,\ \xi \in \mathbb{R}_- \\ \phi_0(-\infty) = 0,\ \phi_0(0) = \nu_1 . \end{cases}$$

Lemma 3 (Fife [Lemma 2.1 : 9]). (2.18) *has a unique strictly monotone increasing solution* $\phi_0(\xi) \in X^2_{\sigma_-,1}(\mathbb{R}_-)$ *satisfying*

$$\frac{d}{d\xi}\phi_0(0) = \{\ 2\int_0^{\nu_1} F(v,m_\infty(v),\overline{n},\overline{h})dv\ \}^{1/2}\ ,$$

where $\sigma_- = \{F_v(0,\overline{m},\overline{n},\overline{h}) + m_\infty{}'(0)F_m(0,\overline{m},\overline{n},\overline{h})\}^{1/2}$.

From Lemma 3, we find that (2.16) and (2.17) have a solution $(\phi_0,\psi_0,\pi_0,\omega_0)$ of the form

$$(2.19)\qquad \begin{cases} \phi_0 = \phi_0(\xi) \\ \psi_0 = m_\infty(\phi_0(\xi)) - \overline{m} = \psi_0(\xi) \\ \pi_0 = 0 \\ \omega_0 = 0\ . \end{cases}$$

Here we note that $(\phi_0(\xi),\psi_0(\xi)) \in X^2_{\sigma_-,1}(\mathbb{R}_-) \times X^1_{\sigma_-,1}(\mathbb{R}_-)$.

Using (2.19) and equating like powers of ε in (2.15), (2.5), we have

$$(2.20)\quad \begin{cases} \phi_1^{\cdot\cdot} - F_v(\phi_0,m_\infty(\phi_0),\bar{n},\bar{h})\phi_1 - F_m(\phi_0,m_\infty(\phi_0),\bar{n},\bar{h})\psi_1 \\ \qquad = c\phi_0^{\cdot} + F_n(\phi_0,m_\infty(\phi_0),\bar{n},\bar{h})\pi_1 + F_h(\phi_0,m_\infty(\phi_0),\bar{n},\bar{h})\omega_1 \ , \ \xi \in \mathbb{R}_- \\ m_\infty'(\phi_0)\phi_1 - \psi_1 = c\psi_0^{\cdot}/\gamma_m(\phi_0) \\ \phi_1(-\infty) = \phi_1(0) = \psi_1(-\infty) = 0 \end{cases}$$

and

$$(2.21)\quad \begin{cases} c\pi_1^{\cdot} - \gamma_n(\phi_0)(n_\infty(\phi_0) - \bar{n}) = 0 \\ c\omega_1^{\cdot} - \gamma_h(\phi_0)(h_\infty(\phi_0) - \bar{h}) = 0 \\ \pi_1(-\infty) = \omega_1(-\infty) = 0 \ . \end{cases} \quad , \ \xi \in \mathbb{R}_-$$

Since a solution (π_1,ω_1) of (2.21) is represented as

$$(2.22)\quad \begin{cases} \pi_1 = \dfrac{1}{c}\displaystyle\int_{-\infty}^{\xi} \gamma_n(\phi_0(\zeta))(n_\infty(\phi_0(\zeta)) - \bar{n})d\zeta \equiv \pi_1(\xi;c) \\ \omega_1 = \dfrac{1}{c}\displaystyle\int_{-\infty}^{\xi} \gamma_h(\phi_0(\zeta))(h_\infty(\phi_0(\zeta)) - \bar{h})d\zeta \equiv \omega_1(\xi;c) \ , \end{cases}$$

by substituting (2.22) into (2.20), we have the boundary value problem for ϕ_1 only :

$$(2.23)\quad \begin{cases} \phi_1^{\cdot\cdot} - F_1(\xi)\phi_1 = G_1(\xi;c) \qquad , \ \xi \in \mathbb{R}_- \\ \phi_1(-\infty) = \phi_1(0) = 0 \ , \end{cases}$$

where

$$F_1(\xi) = F_v(\phi_0,m_\infty(\phi_0),\bar{n},\bar{h}) + m_\infty'(\phi_0)F_m(\phi_0,m_\infty(\phi_0),\bar{n},\bar{h})$$

and

$$G_1(\xi;c) = c\phi_0^{\cdot} + F_n(\phi_0,m_\infty(\phi_0),\bar{n},\bar{h})\pi_1 + F_h(\phi_0,m_\infty(\phi_0),\bar{n},\bar{h})\omega_1$$

$$- cF_m(\phi_0,m_\infty(\phi_0),\bar{n},\bar{h})\psi_0^{\cdot}/\gamma_m(\phi_0) .$$

Lemma 3 shows that $\phi_0^{\cdot}$ is a positive solution of $\phi^{\cdot\cdot} - F_1(\xi)\phi = 0$, and therefore, a solution ϕ_1 of (2.23) is explicitly represented as

$$\phi_1(\xi;c) = - \phi_0^{\cdot}(\xi)\int_\xi^0 (\phi_0^{\cdot}(\eta))^{-2}\int_{-\infty}^{\eta}\phi_0^{\cdot}(\zeta)G_1(\zeta;c)d\zeta d\eta .$$

Thus, we obtain a solution (ϕ_1,ψ_1) of (2.20), which is of the form

$$(2.24) \qquad \begin{cases} \phi_1 = \phi_1(\xi;c) \\ \psi_1 = m_\infty'(\phi_0(\xi))\phi_1(\xi;c) - c\psi_0^{\cdot}(\xi)/\gamma_m(\phi_0(\xi)) \equiv \psi_1(\xi;c) . \end{cases}$$

Equating like powers of ε^2 in (2.15) with (2.5), we have

$$(2.25) \qquad \begin{cases} \phi_2^{\cdot\cdot} - F_v(\phi_0,\psi_0,\bar{n},\bar{h})\phi_2 - F_m(\phi_0,\psi_0,\bar{n},\bar{h})\psi_2 = \\ \quad c\phi_1^{\cdot} + F_n(\phi_0,\psi_0,\bar{n},\bar{h})\pi_2 + F_h(\phi_0,\psi_0,\bar{n},\bar{h})\omega_2 + \\ \quad \frac{1}{2}[\,\{F_{vv}(\phi_0,\psi_0,\bar{n},\bar{h})\phi_1 + (F_{vm}(\phi_0,\psi_0,\bar{n},\bar{h}) + \\ \quad F_{mv}(\phi_0,\psi_0,\bar{n},\bar{h}))\psi_1 + (F_{vn}(\phi_0,\psi_0,\bar{n},\bar{h}) + \\ \quad F_{nv}(\phi_0,\psi_0,\bar{n},\bar{h}))\pi_1 + (F_{vh}(\phi_0,\psi_0,\bar{n},\bar{h}) + \\ \quad F_{hv}(\phi_0,\psi_0,\bar{n},\bar{h}))\omega_1\}\phi_1 + \{F_{mm}(\phi_0,\psi_0,\bar{n},\bar{h})\psi_1 + \\ \quad (F_{mn}(\phi_0,\psi_0,\bar{n},\bar{h}) + F_{nm}(\phi_0,\psi_0,\bar{n},\bar{h}))\pi_1 + \\ \quad (F_{mh}(\phi_0,\psi_0,\bar{n},\bar{h}) + F_{hm}(\phi_0,\psi_0,\bar{n},\bar{h}))\omega_1\}\psi_1 + \end{cases}$$

$$\left|\begin{array}{l} \{F_{nn}(\phi_0,\psi_0,\bar{n},\bar{h})\pi_1 + (F_{nh}(\phi_0,\psi_0,\bar{n},\bar{h}) + \\ F_{hn}(\phi_0,\psi_0,\bar{n},\bar{h}))\omega_1\}\pi_1 + F_{hh}(\phi_0,\psi_0,\bar{n},\bar{h})\omega_1{}^2] \\ m_\infty'(\phi_0)\phi_2 - \psi_2 = (c\psi_1{}^{\cdot} - \gamma_m'(\phi_0)(m_\infty'(\phi_0)\phi_1 - \\ \qquad \psi_1)\phi_1)/\gamma_m(\phi_0) - m_\infty''(\phi_0)\phi_1{}^2/2 \\ \phi_2(-\infty) = \phi_2(0) = \psi_2(-\infty) = 0 \end{array}\right. \quad \xi \in \mathbb{R}_-$$

and

$$(2.26)\quad \left\{\begin{array}{l} c\pi_2{}^{\cdot} - \{\gamma_n(\phi_0)n_\infty'(\phi_0) + \gamma_n'(\phi_0)(n_\infty(\phi_0) - \bar{n})\}\phi_1 + \gamma_n(\phi_0)\pi_1 = 0 \\ c\omega_2{}^{\cdot} - \{\gamma_h(\phi_0)h_\infty'(\phi_0) + \gamma_h'(\phi_0)(h_\infty(\phi_0) - \bar{h})\}\phi_1 + \gamma_h(\phi_0)\omega_1 = 0 \\ \pi_2(-\infty) = \omega_2(-\infty) = 0\ . \end{array}\right. , \ \xi \in \mathbb{R}_-$$

We easily solve (2.26) and obtain a solution $(\pi_2,\omega_2) = (\pi_2(\xi;c),\omega_2(\xi;c))$. Substituting this into (2.25), we obtain a solution (ϕ_2,ψ_2) of (2.25) by an argument similar to (ϕ_1,ψ_1). Thus, we have a solution $(\phi_2,\psi_2,\pi_2,\omega_2)$ of (2.25) and (2.26). Analogously, $(\phi_i,\psi_i,\pi_i,\omega_i)$ $(i \geq 3)$ can be also obtained.

Using the above approximations, we look for an exact solution (v,m,n,h) of (2.4), (2.5), which is of the form

$$\left\{\begin{array}{l} v(y;\varepsilon,c) = \phi_0(y/\varepsilon) + \varepsilon\phi_1(y/\varepsilon;c) + \varepsilon p(y/\varepsilon;\varepsilon,c) \\ m(y;\varepsilon,c) = \bar{m} + \psi_0(y/\varepsilon) + \varepsilon\psi_1(y/\varepsilon;c) + \varepsilon m_\infty'(\phi_0)p(y/\varepsilon;\varepsilon,c) \\ \qquad + \varepsilon q(y/\varepsilon;\varepsilon,c) \\ n(y;\varepsilon,c) = \bar{n} + \varepsilon\pi_1(y/\varepsilon;c) + \varepsilon^2\pi_2(y/\varepsilon;c) + \varepsilon^2 r(y/\varepsilon;\varepsilon,c) \\ h(y;\varepsilon,c) = \bar{h} + \varepsilon\omega_1(y/\varepsilon;c) + \varepsilon^2\omega_2(y/\varepsilon;c) + \varepsilon^2 s(y/\varepsilon;\varepsilon,c)\ . \end{array}\right.$$

Substituting this into (2.4), we have

$$(2.27)\quad \begin{cases} 0 = p^{\cdot\cdot} - \varepsilon c p^{\cdot} - \varepsilon^{-1}F(\phi_0 + \varepsilon\phi_1 + \varepsilon p, \bar{m} + \psi_0 + \varepsilon\psi_1 + \varepsilon m_\infty'(\phi_0)p + \varepsilon q, \\ \quad \bar{n} + \varepsilon\pi_1 + \varepsilon^2\pi_2 + \varepsilon^2 r, \bar{h} + \varepsilon\omega_1 + \varepsilon^2\omega_2 + \varepsilon^2 s) + \varepsilon^{-1}F(\phi_0, \bar{m} + \psi_0, \bar{n}, \bar{h}) \\ \quad + \phi_1^{\cdot\cdot} - c\phi_0^{\cdot} - \varepsilon c\phi_1^{\cdot} \\ 0 = \varepsilon c(m_\infty'(\phi_0)p^{\cdot} + q^{\cdot}) - \varepsilon^{-1}\gamma_m(\phi_0 + \varepsilon\phi_1 + \varepsilon p)(m_\infty(\phi_0 + \varepsilon\phi_1 + \varepsilon p) - \\ \quad \bar{m} - \psi_0 - \varepsilon\psi_1 - \varepsilon m_\infty'(\phi_0)p - \varepsilon q) + c\psi_0^{\cdot} + \varepsilon c\psi_1^{\cdot} + \varepsilon c m_\infty''(\phi_0)\phi_0^{\cdot} p \\ 0 = cr^{\cdot} + \varepsilon\gamma_n(\phi_0 + \varepsilon\phi_1 + \varepsilon p)r + c\varepsilon^{-1}\pi_1^{\cdot} + c\pi_2^{\cdot} - \varepsilon^{-1}\gamma_n(\phi_0 + \varepsilon\phi_1 \\ \quad + \varepsilon p)(n_\infty(\phi_0 + \varepsilon\phi_1 + \varepsilon p) - \bar{n} - \varepsilon\pi_1 - \varepsilon^2\pi_2) \\ 0 = cs^{\cdot} + \varepsilon\gamma_h(\phi_0 + \varepsilon\phi_1 + \varepsilon p)s + c\varepsilon^{-1}\omega_1^{\cdot} + c\omega_2^{\cdot} - \varepsilon^{-1}\gamma_h(\phi_0 + \varepsilon\phi_1 \\ \quad + \varepsilon p)(h_\infty(\phi_0 + \varepsilon\phi_1 + \varepsilon p) - \bar{h} - \varepsilon\omega_1 - \varepsilon^2\omega_2) . \end{cases}$$

By (2.5), the boundary conditions for (p,q,r,s) become

$$(2.28)\qquad p(-\infty) = p(0) = q(-\infty) = r(-\infty) = s(-\infty) = 0 .$$

For simplicity, we write (2.27), (2.28) as

$$(2.29)\qquad T(t;\varepsilon,c) = 0$$

for $t = {}^t(p,q,r,s)$, where the superscript ^{t} denotes the transposition. Let T be a mapping from $\mathring{Y}_{\sigma,\varepsilon}$ into Z_σ, where

$$\mathring{Y}_{\sigma,\varepsilon} = \mathring{X}^2_{\sigma,1}(\mathbb{R}_-) \times X^1_{\sigma,\varepsilon}(\mathbb{R}_-) \times X^1_{\sigma,1}(\mathbb{R}_-) \times X^1_{\sigma,1}(\mathbb{R}_-)$$

and

$$Z_\sigma = X^0_{\sigma,1}(\mathbb{R}_-) \times X^0_{\sigma,1}(\mathbb{R}_-) \times X^0_{\sigma,1}(\mathbb{R}_-) \times X^0_{\sigma,1}(\mathbb{R}_-)$$

with any fixed σ satisfying $0 < \sigma < \sigma_-$, where σ_- is a known constant in Lemma 3.

Lemma 4. *For an arbitrarily given positive constant* c_*, *there are* $\varepsilon_1 > 0$ *and* $\rho_1 > 0$ *and* $K > 0$ *such that for any* $\varepsilon \in (0,\varepsilon_1)$ *and* $c \in \Lambda_{\rho_1} = \{c \in \mathbb{R}_+ \,|\, |c - c_*| \le \rho_1\}$,

(i) $\|T(0;\varepsilon,c)\|_{Z_\sigma} = O(\varepsilon)$ *uniformly in* c ;

(ii) *for any* $t_1, t_2 \in \mathring{Y}_{\sigma,\varepsilon}$,

$$\|T_t(t_1;\varepsilon,c) - T_t(t_2;\varepsilon,c)\|_{\mathring{Y}_{\sigma,\varepsilon} \to Z_\sigma} \le K\,\|t_1 - t_2\|_{\mathring{Y}_{\sigma,\varepsilon}} ;$$

(iii) $\|T_t^{-1}(0;\varepsilon,c)\|_{Z_\sigma \to \mathring{Y}_{\sigma,\varepsilon}} \le K$.

Moreover the results (i) - (iii) *hold for* $\frac{\partial T}{\partial c}$ *in place of* T.

The proof will be stated in the appendix.

By Lemma 4, we can apply the Implicit Function Theorem to (2.29). Thus, we have immediately

Theorem 1. *Let* c_* *be the same constant as in* Lemma 4. *Then there are* $\varepsilon_2 > 0$ *and* $\rho_2 > 0$ *such that for any* $\varepsilon \in (0,\varepsilon_2)$ *and* $c \in \Lambda_{\rho_2}$, *there exists* $t(\varepsilon,c) \in \mathring{Y}_{\sigma,\varepsilon}$ *satisfying* (2.29). $t(\varepsilon,c)$ *and* $\frac{\partial}{\partial c} t(\varepsilon,c)$ *are uniformly continuous with respect to* $(\varepsilon,c) \in (0,\varepsilon_2) \times \Lambda_{\rho_2}$ *in the* $\mathring{Y}_{\sigma,\varepsilon}$ - *topology and satisfy*

$$\begin{cases} \| t(\varepsilon,c) \|_{\overset{\circ}{Y}_{\sigma,\varepsilon}} = O(\varepsilon) \\ \| \frac{\partial t}{\partial c}(\varepsilon,c) \|_{\overset{\circ}{Y}_{\sigma,\varepsilon}} = O(\varepsilon) \end{cases} \quad \textit{uniformly in } c .$$

Thus, we obtain a solution of (2.1), (2.3) on I_1, which takes the form

$$\begin{cases} v(z;\varepsilon,c) = \phi_0(z/\varepsilon+\kappa) + \varepsilon\phi_1(z/\varepsilon+\kappa;c) + \varepsilon p(z/\varepsilon+\kappa;\varepsilon,c) \\ m(z;\varepsilon,c) = \bar{m} + \psi_0(z/\varepsilon+\kappa) + \varepsilon\psi_1(z/\varepsilon+\kappa;c) \\ \qquad + \varepsilon m_\infty{}'(\phi_0(z/\varepsilon+\kappa))p(z/\varepsilon+\kappa;\varepsilon,c) + \varepsilon q(z/\varepsilon+\kappa;\varepsilon,c) \\ n(z;\varepsilon,c) = \bar{n} + \varepsilon\pi_1(z/\varepsilon+\kappa;c) + \varepsilon^2\pi_2(z/\varepsilon+\kappa;c) + \varepsilon^2 r(z/\varepsilon+\kappa;\varepsilon,c) \\ h(z;\varepsilon,c) = \bar{h} + \varepsilon\omega_1(z/\varepsilon+\kappa;c) + \varepsilon^2\omega_2(z/\varepsilon+\kappa;c) + \varepsilon^2 s(z/\varepsilon+\kappa;\varepsilon,c) , \end{cases}$$

where p, q, r and s are the remainder terms given in Theorem 1. To emphasize that (v,m,n,h), $(\phi_i,\psi_i,\pi_{i+1},\omega_{i+1})$ ($i = 0,1$) and (p,q,r,s) are the functions constructed on I_1, we write them as $(v^{(1)},m^{(1)},n^{(1)},h^{(1)})$, $(\phi_i{}^{(1)},\psi_i{}^{(1)},\pi_{i+1}{}^{(1)},\omega_{i+1}{}^{(1)})$ ($i = 0,1$) and $(p^{(1)},q^{(1)},r^{(1)},s^{(1)})$, respectively.

2.2. Construction of solutions on $I_2 = [-\varepsilon\kappa,0]$

Let $\kappa = \kappa_0 + \varepsilon\kappa_1$, where κ_0 (> 0) and κ_1 will be determined later. We consider the system (2.1) on I_2 with the boundary conditions

$$(2.30) \quad \begin{cases} v(-\varepsilon\kappa) = \nu_1, \ \frac{d}{dz} v(0) = 0, \ m(-\varepsilon\kappa) = m^{(1)}(-\varepsilon\kappa;\varepsilon,c) \\ n(-\varepsilon\kappa) = n^{(1)}(-\varepsilon\kappa;\varepsilon,c), \ h(-\varepsilon\kappa) = h^{(1)}(-\varepsilon\kappa;\varepsilon,c) . \end{cases}$$

We recall that

$$
(2.31)\quad \begin{cases} m^{(1)}(-\varepsilon\kappa;\varepsilon,c) = \overline{m} + \psi_0{}^{(1)}(0) + \varepsilon\psi_1{}^{(1)}(0;c) + \varepsilon q^{(1)}(0;\varepsilon,c) \\ n^{(1)}(-\varepsilon\kappa;\varepsilon,c) = \overline{n} + \varepsilon\pi_1{}^{(1)}(0;c) + \varepsilon^2\pi_2{}^{(1)}(0;c) + \varepsilon^2 r^{(1)}(0;\varepsilon,c) \\ h^{(1)}(-\varepsilon\kappa;\varepsilon,c) = \overline{h} + \varepsilon\omega_1{}^{(1)}(0;c) + \varepsilon^2\omega_2{}^{(1)}(0;c) + \varepsilon^2 s^{(1)}(0;\varepsilon,c) . \end{cases}
$$

By using $z = \varepsilon\kappa y$, (2.1) with (2.30) can be written as

$$
(2.32)\quad \begin{cases} v'' - \varepsilon c\kappa v' - \kappa^2 F(v,m,n,h) = 0 \\ \varepsilon c m' - \kappa\gamma_m(v)(m_\infty(v) - m) = 0 \\ c n' - \varepsilon\kappa\gamma_n(v)(n_\infty(v) - n) = 0 \\ c h' - \varepsilon\kappa\gamma_h(v)(h_\infty(v) - h) = 0 \end{cases} , \; y \in (-1,0)
$$

with

$$
(2.33)\quad \begin{cases} v(-1) = \nu_1, \quad v'(0) = 0, \quad m(-1) = m^{(1)}(-\varepsilon\kappa;\varepsilon,c) \\ n(-1) = n^{(1)}(-\varepsilon\kappa;\varepsilon,c), \quad h(-1) = h^{(1)}(-\varepsilon\kappa;\varepsilon,c) . \end{cases}
$$

Let us construct an approximate function to (2.32), (2.33), which is of the form

$$
(2.34)\quad \begin{cases} v(y) = \phi_0(y) + \varepsilon\phi_1(y) \\ m(y) = \psi_0(y) + \varepsilon\psi_1(y) \\ n(y) = \pi_0(y) + \varepsilon\pi_1(y) + \varepsilon^2\pi_2(y) \\ h(y) = \omega_0(y) + \varepsilon\omega_1(y) + \varepsilon^2\omega_2(y) . \end{cases}
$$

Substituting (2.34) into (2.32), (2.33) and equating like powers of ε^0, we have

$$(2.35)\qquad \begin{cases} \phi_0'' - \kappa_0^2 F(\phi_0,\psi_0,\pi_0,\omega_0) = 0 & \\ & , \ y \in (-1,0) \\ \gamma_m(\phi_0)(m_\infty(\phi_0) - \psi_0) = 0 & \\ \phi_0(-1) = \nu_1, \quad \phi_0'(0) = 0, \quad \psi_0(-1) = \bar{m} + \psi_0^{(1)}(0) & \end{cases}$$

and

$$(2.36)\qquad \begin{cases} c\pi_0' = 0, \quad c\omega_0' = 0 & , \ y \in (-1,0) \\ \pi_0(-1) = \bar{n}, \quad \omega_0(-1) = \bar{h} \ . & \end{cases}$$

It directly follows from (2.36) that $(\pi_0(y),\omega_0(y)) \equiv (\bar{n},\bar{h})$. Then (2.35) is rewritten as

$$(2.37)\qquad \begin{cases} \phi_0'' - \kappa_0^2 F(\phi_0, m_\infty(\phi_0),\bar{n},\bar{h}) = 0 & , \ y \in (-1,0) \\ \phi_0(-1) = \nu_1, \quad \phi_0'(0) = 0 \ . & \end{cases}$$

Lemma 5. *For any fixed* $\kappa_0 > 0$, *(2.37) has a unique strictly monotone increasing solution* $\phi_0(y;\kappa_0)$. *Furthermore, if* ν_2 *is defined by* $\phi_0(0;\kappa_0) = \nu_2$, κ_0 *is related with* ν_2 *by*

$$(2.38)\qquad \kappa_0 = \int_{\nu_1}^{\nu_2} \left(2\int_{\nu_2}^{v} F(t,m_\infty(t),\bar{n},\bar{h})dt\right)^{-1/2} dv$$

and

$$(2.39)\qquad \frac{d}{dy}\phi_0(-1;\kappa_0) = \kappa_0\left(2\int_{\nu_2}^{\nu_1} F(v,m_\infty(v),\bar{n},\bar{h})dv\right)^{1/2} .$$

The proof is easily achieved by using phase plane methods. So we omit it.

From Lemma 5, we find that (2.35) and (2,36) have a solution $(\phi_0,\psi_0,$

$\pi_0,\omega_0)$ of the form

$$(2.40)\qquad \begin{cases} \phi_0 = \phi_0(y;\kappa_0) \\ \psi_0 = m_\infty(\phi_0(y;\kappa_0)) \equiv \psi_0(y;\kappa_0) \\ \pi_0 = \overline{n} \\ \omega_0 = \overline{h}\ . \end{cases}$$

Using (2.40) and equating like powers of ε in (2.32), (2.33), we obtain

$$(2.41)\qquad \begin{cases} \phi_1'' - \kappa_0^2(F_v(\phi_0,\psi_0,\overline{n},\overline{h})\phi_1 + F_m(\phi_0,\psi_0,\overline{n},\overline{h})\psi_1) = c\kappa_0\phi_0' \\ \quad + 2\kappa_0\kappa_1 F(\phi_0,\psi_0,\overline{n},\overline{h}) + \kappa_0^2 F_n(\phi_0,\psi_0,\overline{n},\overline{h})\pi_1 + \kappa_0^2 F_h(\phi_0,\psi_0,\overline{n},\overline{h})\omega_1 \\ \kappa_0\gamma_m(\phi_0)(m_\infty'(\phi_0)\phi_1 - \psi_1) = c\psi_0' \qquad , y \in (-1,0) \\ \phi_1(-1) = \phi_1'(0) = 0, \quad \psi_1(-1) = \psi_1^{(1)}(0;c) \end{cases}$$

and

$$(2.42)\qquad \begin{cases} c\pi_1' - \kappa_0\gamma_n(\phi_0)(n_\infty(\phi_0) - \overline{n}) = 0 \\ \qquad\qquad\qquad\qquad\qquad\qquad , y \in (-1,0) \\ c\omega_1' - \kappa_0\gamma_h(\phi_0)(h_\infty(\phi_0) - \overline{h}) = 0 \\ \pi_1(-1) = \pi_1^{(1)}(0;c), \quad \omega_1(-1) = \omega_1^{(1)}(0;c)\ . \end{cases}$$

Since a solution (π_1,ω_1) of (2.42) is represented as

$$(2.43)\qquad \begin{cases} \pi_1 = \dfrac{\kappa_0}{c}\displaystyle\int_{-1}^{y} \gamma_n(\phi_0(\zeta;\kappa_0))(n_\infty(\phi_0(\zeta;\kappa_0)) - \overline{n})d\zeta \\ \qquad + \pi_1^{(1)}(0;c) \equiv \pi_1(y;c,\kappa_0) \\ \omega_1 = \dfrac{\kappa_0}{c}\displaystyle\int_{-1}^{y} \gamma_h(\phi_0(\zeta;\kappa_0))(h_\infty(\phi_0(\zeta;\kappa_0)) - \overline{h})d\zeta \end{cases}$$

$$+ \omega_1^{(1)}(0;c) \equiv \omega_1(y;c,\kappa_0) ,$$

by substituting (2.43) into (2.41), we have the problem for ϕ_1 only :

$$(2.44) \quad \begin{cases} \phi_1'' - F_2(y;\kappa_0)\phi_1 = G_2(y;c,\kappa_0,\kappa_1) & , y \in (-1,0) \\ \phi_1(-1) = \phi_1'(0) = 0 , \end{cases}$$

where

$$F_2(y;\kappa_0) = \kappa_0^2(F_v(\phi_0,\psi_0,\bar{n},\bar{h}) + m_\infty'(\phi_0)F_m(\phi_0,\psi_0,\bar{n},\bar{h}))$$

and

$$G_2(y;c,\kappa_0,\kappa_1) = c\kappa_0\phi_0' + 2\kappa_0\kappa_1 F(\phi_0,\psi_0,\bar{n},\bar{h}) + \kappa_0^2 F_n(\phi_0,\psi_0,\bar{n},\bar{h})\pi_1$$

$$+ \kappa_0^2 F_h(\phi_0,\psi_0,\bar{n},\bar{h})\omega_1 - c\kappa_0 F_m(\phi_0,\psi_0,\bar{n},\bar{h})\psi_0'/\gamma_m(\phi_0) .$$

Noting that ϕ_0' is a positive solution of $\phi'' - F_2(y;\kappa_0)\phi = 0$, one finds that Green's function of (2.44) is given by

$$(2.45) \qquad G(y,z;\kappa_0) = \begin{cases} g_1(y;\kappa_0)g_2(z;\kappa_0) & (-1 \le y \le z) \\ g_2(y;\kappa_0)g_1(z;\kappa_0) & (z \le y \le 0) , \end{cases}$$

where $g_0(y;\kappa_0) = \phi_0'(y;\kappa_0)$, $g_1(y;\kappa_0) = g_0(y;\kappa_0)\int_{-1}^{y} \frac{dz}{g_0(z;\kappa_0)^2}$ and $g_2(y;\kappa_0) = g_0(y;\kappa_0) - g_0'(0;\kappa_0)g_1(y;\kappa_0)/g_1'(0;\kappa_0)$. Therefore a solution (ϕ_1,ψ_1) of (2.41) is represented as

$$(2.46) \quad \begin{cases} \phi_1 = -\int_{-1}^{0} G(y,z;\kappa_0)G_2(z;c,\kappa_0,\kappa_1)\, dz \equiv \phi_1(y;c,\kappa_0,\kappa_1) \\ \psi_1 = m_\infty'(\phi_0(y;\kappa_0))\phi_1(y;c,\kappa_0,\kappa_1) - c\psi_0'(y;\kappa_0)/(\kappa_0\gamma_m(\phi_0(y;\kappa_0))) \end{cases}$$

$$\Big| \equiv \psi_1(y;c,\kappa_0,\kappa_1) .$$

Here we determine ν_2 such that $\psi_1(-1;c,\kappa_0,\kappa_1) = \psi_1^{(1)}(0;c)$, which leads to $\int_0^{\nu_2} F(v,m_\infty(v),\bar{n},\bar{h})dv = 0$, by (2.24) and (2.46). It gives $\nu_2 = v^*$ and hence $\kappa_0 = \kappa_0^* = \int_{\nu_1}^{v^*} (2\int_{v^*}^{v} F(t,m_\infty(t),\bar{n},\bar{h})dt)^{-1/2}dv$ (> 0) by (2.38) .

Using (2.43) and (2.46) with $\kappa_0 = \kappa_0^*$ are equating like powers of ε^2 in (2.32), (2.33), we obtain

$$(2.47)\quad \begin{cases} c\pi_2' - \kappa_0^*\gamma_n(\phi_0)(n_\infty'(\phi_0)\phi_1 - \pi_1) - \kappa_0^*\gamma_n'(\phi_0)(n_\infty(\phi_0) - \bar{n})\phi_1 \\ \quad - \kappa_1\gamma_n(\phi_0)(n_\infty(\phi_0) - \bar{n}) = 0 \\ \qquad\qquad\qquad\qquad\qquad\qquad\qquad\qquad , \ y \in (-1,0) \\ c\omega_2' - \kappa_0^*\gamma_h(\phi_0)(h_\infty'(\phi_0)\phi_1 - \omega_1) - \kappa_0^*\gamma_h'(\phi_0)(h_\infty(\phi_0) - \bar{h})\phi_1 \\ \quad - \kappa_1\gamma_h(\phi_0)(h_\infty(\phi_0) - \bar{h}) = 0 \\ \pi_2(-1) = \pi_2^{(1)}(0;c), \quad \omega_2(-1) = \omega_2^{(1)}(0;c) . \end{cases}$$

By using (2.46), we obtain a solution of (2.47) as $(\pi_2,\omega_2) \equiv (\pi_2(y;c,\kappa_0^*,\kappa_1), \omega_2(y;c,\kappa_0^*,\kappa_1))$.

Using the above approximation, we look for an exact solution (v,m,n,h) of (2.32), (2.33) which takes the form

$$\begin{cases} v(y;\varepsilon,c,\kappa_1) = \phi_0(y;\kappa_0^*) + \varepsilon\phi_1(y;c,\kappa_0^*,\kappa_1) + \varepsilon p(y;\varepsilon,c,\kappa_1) \\ m(y;\varepsilon,c,\kappa_1) = \psi_0(y;\kappa_0^*) + \varepsilon\psi_1(y;c,\kappa_0^*,\kappa_1) + \varepsilon m_\infty'(\phi_0(y;\kappa_0^*))p(y;\varepsilon,c,\kappa_1) \\ \qquad\qquad + \varepsilon q(y;\varepsilon,c,\kappa_1) + \varepsilon q^{(1)}(0;\varepsilon,c) \\ n(y;\varepsilon,c,\kappa_1) = \bar{n} + \varepsilon\pi_1(y;c,\kappa_0^*) + \varepsilon^2\pi_2(y;c,\kappa_0^*,\kappa_1) \end{cases}$$

$$
\begin{aligned}
&\quad + \varepsilon^2 r(y;\varepsilon,c,\kappa_1) + \varepsilon^2 r^{(1)}(0;\varepsilon,c) \\
&h(y;\varepsilon,c,\kappa_1) = \bar{h} + \varepsilon\omega_1(y;c,\kappa_0^*) + \varepsilon^2\omega_2(y;c,\kappa_0^*,\kappa_1) \\
&\quad + \varepsilon^2 s(y;\varepsilon,c,\kappa_1) + \varepsilon^2 s^{(1)}(0;\varepsilon,c) .
\end{aligned}
$$

Substituting this into (2.32), we have

$$
(2.48)\quad
\begin{cases}
0 = p'' - \varepsilon c(\kappa_0^* + \varepsilon\kappa_1)p' - \varepsilon^{-1}(\kappa_0^* + \varepsilon\kappa_1)^2 F(\phi_0 + \varepsilon\phi_1 + \varepsilon p, \psi_0 + \varepsilon\psi_1 \\
\quad + \varepsilon m_\infty'(\phi_0)p + \varepsilon q + \varepsilon q^{(1)}(0;\varepsilon,c), \bar{n} + \varepsilon\pi_1 + \varepsilon^2\pi_2 + \varepsilon^2 r \\
\quad + \varepsilon^2 r^{(1)}(0;\varepsilon,c), \bar{h} + \varepsilon\omega_1 + \varepsilon^2\omega_2 + \varepsilon^2 s + \varepsilon^2 s^{(1)}(0;\varepsilon,c)) \\
\quad + \varepsilon^{-1}\phi_0'' + \phi_1'' - c(\kappa_0^* + \varepsilon\kappa_1)(\phi_0' + \varepsilon\phi_1') \\
0 = \varepsilon c(m_\infty'(\phi_0)p' + q') + \varepsilon c m_\infty''(\phi_0)\phi_0' p - \varepsilon^{-1}(\kappa_0^* + \varepsilon\kappa_1)\gamma_m(\phi_0 \\
\quad + \varepsilon\phi_1 + \varepsilon p)(m_\infty(\phi_0 + \varepsilon\phi_1 + \varepsilon p) - \psi_0 - \varepsilon\psi_1 - \varepsilon m_\infty'(\phi_0)p - \varepsilon q \\
\quad - \varepsilon q^{(1)}(0;\varepsilon,c)) + c(\psi_0' + \varepsilon\psi_1') \\
0 = cr' + \varepsilon(\kappa_0^* + \varepsilon\kappa_1)\gamma_n(\phi_0 + \varepsilon\phi_1 + \varepsilon p)r + c\pi_2' + \varepsilon^{-1}c\pi_1' \\
\quad - \varepsilon^{-1}(\kappa_0^* + \varepsilon\kappa_1)\gamma_n(\phi_0 + \varepsilon\phi_1 + \varepsilon p)(n_\infty(\phi_0 + \varepsilon\phi_1 + \varepsilon p) \\
\quad - \bar{n} - \varepsilon\pi_1 - \varepsilon^2\pi_2 - \varepsilon^2 r^{(1)}(0;\varepsilon,c)) \\
0 = cs' + \varepsilon(\kappa_0^* + \varepsilon\kappa_1)\gamma_h(\phi_0 + \varepsilon\phi_1 + \varepsilon p)s + c\omega_2' + \varepsilon^{-1}c\omega_1' \\
\quad - \varepsilon^{-1}(\kappa_0^* + \varepsilon\kappa_1)\gamma_h(\phi_0 + \varepsilon\phi_1 + \varepsilon p)(h_\infty(\phi_0 + \varepsilon\phi_1 + \varepsilon p) \\
\quad - \bar{h} - \varepsilon\omega_1 - \varepsilon^2\omega_2 - \varepsilon^2 s^{(1)}(0;\varepsilon,c)) .
\end{cases}
$$

By (2.33), the boundary conditions for (p,q,r,s) become

$$p(-1) = p'(0) = q(-1) = r(-1) = s(-1) = 0 . \tag{2.49}$$

We simply write (2.48), (2.49) as

$$T(t;\varepsilon,c,\kappa_1) = 0 \tag{2.50}$$

for $t = {}^t(p,q,r,s)$. Let T be a mapping from Y_- into Z_-, where

$$Y_- = \overset{\circ}{C}{}^2_-(-1,0) \times \overset{\circ}{C}{}^1_\varepsilon(-1,0) \times \overset{\circ}{C}{}^1_1(-1,0) \times \overset{\circ}{C}{}^1_1(-1,0)$$

and

$$Z_- = C^0(-1,0) \times C^0(-1,0) \times C^0(-1,0) \times C^0(-1,0) .$$

Lemma 6. *For an arbitrarily given constant* κ_1^*, *there are* $\varepsilon_3 >$, $0 < \rho_3$ $(< \rho_1)$ *and* $K > 0$ *such that for any* $\varepsilon \in (0,\varepsilon_3)$ *and* $(c,\kappa_1) \in \Sigma_{\rho_3}$ $\equiv \{(c,\kappa_1) |\ |c - c_*| + |\kappa_1 - \kappa_1^*| \le \rho_3\}$,

(i) $\|T(0;\varepsilon,c,\kappa_1)\|_{Z_-} = O(\varepsilon)$ *uniformly in* (c,κ_1) ;

(ii) *for any* $t_1, t_2 \in Y_-$,

$$\|T_t(t_1;\varepsilon,c,\kappa_1) - T_t(t_2;\varepsilon,c,\kappa_1)\|_{Y_- \to Z_-} \le K \|t_1 - t_2\|_{Y_-} ;$$

(iii) $\|T_t^{-1}(0;\varepsilon,c,\kappa_1)\|_{Z_- \to Y_-} \le K$.

Moreover the results (i) - (iii) *hold for* $\frac{\partial T}{\partial c}$ *and* $\frac{\partial T}{\partial \kappa_1}$ *in place of* T.

This lemma can be proved by an argument similar to Lemma 4, so we omit the proof. It directly leads to

Theorem 2. *Let* c_* *and* κ_1^* *be the same constants as in* Lemmas 4 *and* 6, *respectively. There are* $\varepsilon_4 > 0$ *and* $\rho_4 > 0$ *such that for any* $\varepsilon \in (0,\varepsilon_4)$ *and* $(c,\kappa_1) \in \Sigma_{\rho_4}$, *there exists* $t(\varepsilon,c,\kappa_1) \in Y_-$ *satisfying* (2.50). $t(\varepsilon,c,\kappa_1)$, $\frac{\partial}{\partial c} t(\varepsilon,c,\kappa_1)$ *and* $\frac{\partial}{\partial \kappa_1} t(\varepsilon,c,\kappa_1)$ *are uniformly continuous with respect to* $(\varepsilon,c,\kappa_1) \in (0,\varepsilon_4) \times \Sigma_{\rho_4}$ *in the* Y_- *- topology and satisfy*

$$\begin{cases} \| t(\varepsilon,c,\kappa_1) \|_{Y_-} = O(\varepsilon) \\ \| \frac{\partial t}{\partial c}(\varepsilon,c,\kappa_1) \|_{Y_-} = O(\varepsilon) & \textit{uniformly in } (c,\kappa_1). \\ \| \frac{\partial t}{\partial \kappa_1}(\varepsilon,c,\kappa_1) \|_{Y_-} = O(\varepsilon) \end{cases}$$

Thus, we obtain a solution of (2.1), (2.30) on I_2, which takes the form

$$(2.51) \quad \begin{cases} v(z;\varepsilon,c,\kappa_1) = \phi_0(z/(\varepsilon\kappa);\kappa_0^*) + \varepsilon\phi_1(z/(\varepsilon\kappa);c,\kappa_0^*,\kappa_1) \\ \qquad + \varepsilon p(z/(\varepsilon\kappa);\varepsilon,c,\kappa_1) \\ m(z;\varepsilon,c,\kappa_1) = \psi_0(z/(\varepsilon\kappa);\kappa_0^*) + \varepsilon\psi_1(z/(\varepsilon\kappa);c,\kappa_0^*,\kappa_1) \\ \qquad + \varepsilon m_\infty'(\phi_0(z/(\varepsilon\kappa);\kappa_0^*))p(z/(\varepsilon\kappa);\varepsilon,c,\kappa_1) \\ \qquad + \varepsilon q(z/(\varepsilon\kappa);\varepsilon,c,\kappa_1) + \varepsilon q^{(1)}(0;\varepsilon,c) \\ n(z;\varepsilon,c,\kappa_1) = \bar{n} + \varepsilon\pi_1(z/(\varepsilon\kappa);c,\kappa_0^*) + \varepsilon^2\pi_2(z/(\varepsilon\kappa);c,\kappa_0^*,\kappa_1) \\ \qquad + \varepsilon^2 r(z/(\varepsilon\kappa);\varepsilon,c,\kappa_1) + \varepsilon^2 r^{(1)}(0;\varepsilon,c) \\ h(z;\varepsilon,c,\kappa_1) = \bar{h} + \varepsilon\omega_1(z/(\varepsilon\kappa);c,\kappa_0^*) + \varepsilon^2\omega_2(z/(\varepsilon\kappa);c,\kappa_0^*,\kappa_1) \\ \qquad + \varepsilon^2 s(z/(\varepsilon\kappa);\varepsilon,c,\kappa_1) + \varepsilon^2 s^{(1)}(0;\varepsilon,c) , \end{cases}$$

where $\kappa = \kappa_0^* + \varepsilon\kappa_1$ and p,q,r and s are the remainder terms given in Theorem 2. We write the functions (v,m,n,h), $(\phi_i,\psi_i,\pi_{i+1},\omega_{i+1})$ ($i=0,1$) and (p,q,r,s) constructed above as $(v^{(2)},m^{(2)},n^{(2)},h^{(2)})$, $(\phi_i{}^{(2)},\psi_i{}^{(2)}$, $\pi_{i+1}{}^{(2)},\omega_{i+1}{}^{(2)})$ ($i=0,1$) and $(p^{(2)},q^{(2)},r^{(2)},s^{(2)})$, respectively.

2.3. Construction of solutions on $I_3 = [0,\varepsilon\tau]$

Let $\tau = \tau_0 + \varepsilon\tau_1$, where τ_0 (>0) and τ_1 will be determined later. Consider the system (2.1) on I_3 with the boundary conditions

$$(2.52)\qquad \begin{cases} \frac{d}{dz}v(0) = 0, \quad v(\varepsilon\tau) = \nu_1, \quad m(0) = m^*(\varepsilon) \\ n(0) = n^{(2)}(0;\varepsilon,c,\kappa_1), \quad h(0) = h^{(2)}(0;\varepsilon,c,\kappa_1)\ , \end{cases}$$

where $m^*(\varepsilon) = m_0^* + \varepsilon m_1^* + m_2^*(\varepsilon)$ with $m_2^*(\varepsilon) = o(\varepsilon)$ as $\varepsilon \to 0$. m_0^*, m_1^* and $m_2^*(\varepsilon)$ will be determined later. By $y = z/(\varepsilon\tau)$, (2.1) with (2.52) can be written as

$$(2.53)\qquad \begin{cases} v'' - \varepsilon c\tau v' - \tau^2F(v,m,n,h) = 0 \\ \varepsilon cm' - \tau\gamma_m(v)(m_\infty(v) - m) = 0 \\ cn' - \varepsilon\tau\gamma_n(v)(n_\infty(v) - n) = 0 \\ ch' - \varepsilon\tau\gamma_h(v)(h_\infty(v) - h) = 0 \end{cases} \quad ,\ y \in (0,1)$$

with

$$(2.54)\qquad \begin{cases} v'(0) = 0, \quad v(1) = \nu_1, \quad m(0) = m^*(\varepsilon) \\ n(0) = n^{(2)}(0;\varepsilon,c,\kappa_1), \quad h(0) = h^{(2)}(0;\varepsilon,c,\kappa_1)\ . \end{cases}$$

By an argument similar to that in Subsection 2.2., we construct an approximation to (2.53), (2.54), which is of the form

$$\begin{cases} v(y) = \phi_0(y) + \varepsilon\phi_1(y) \\ m(y) = \psi_0(y) + \varepsilon\psi_1(y) \\ n(y) = \pi_0(y) + \varepsilon\pi_1(y) + \varepsilon^2\pi_2(y) \\ h(y) = \omega_0(y) + \varepsilon\omega_1(y) + \varepsilon^2\omega_2(y) \ . \end{cases}$$

Substituting this into (2.53), (2.54) and equating like powers of ε^0, we have

$$(2.55) \qquad \begin{cases} \phi_0'' - \tau_0^2 F(\phi_0,\psi_0,\pi_0,\omega_0) = 0 & \\ & , \ y \in (0,1) \\ \gamma_m(\phi_0)(m_\infty(\phi_0) - \psi_0) = 0 & \\ \phi_0'(0) = 0, \quad \phi_0(1) = \nu_1, \quad \psi_0(0) = m_0^* & \end{cases}$$

and

$$(2.56) \qquad \begin{cases} c\pi_0' = 0, \quad c\omega_0' = 0 & , \ y \in (0,1) \\ \pi_0(0) = \bar{n}, \quad \omega_0(0) = \bar{h} \ . & \end{cases}$$

(2.56) directly leads to $(\pi_0(y),\omega_0(y)) \equiv (\bar{n},\bar{h})$. Note that if we set $y = -z$ and $\tau_0 = \kappa_0^*$, (2.55) reduces to (2.35) with $\kappa_0 = \kappa_0^*$ in the absence of the boundary condition $\psi_0(0) = m_0^*$. Thus we find that solutions of (2.55) and (2.56) are of the form

$$(2.57) \qquad \begin{cases} \phi_0 = \phi_0^{(2)}(-y;\kappa_0^*) \equiv \phi_0(y) \\ \psi_0 = \psi_0^{(2)}(-y;\kappa_0^*) \equiv \psi_0(y) \\ \pi_0 = \bar{n} \\ \omega_0 = \bar{h} \ . \end{cases}$$

Here we put m_0^* as $m_0^* = m_\infty(\phi_0(0)) = m_\infty(v^*)$, so that ψ_0 and $\psi_0^{(2)}$ are continuous at $y = 0$. Thus, it turns out that the solution $(\phi_0,\psi_0,\pi_0,\omega_0)$ of (2.55) and (2.56) takes the form $(\phi_0(y),\psi_0(y),\bar{n},\bar{h})$.

Using (2.57) and equating like powers of ε in (2.53), (2.54), we have

$$
(2.58)\quad \begin{cases} \phi_1'' - \kappa_0^{*2}(F_v(\phi_0,\psi_0,\bar{n},\bar{h})\phi_1 + F_m(\phi_0,\psi_0,\bar{n},\bar{h})\psi_1) = c\kappa_0^*\,\phi_0' \\ \quad + 2\kappa_0^*\tau_1 F(\phi_0,\psi_0,\bar{n},\bar{h}) + \kappa_0^{*2}(F_n(\phi_0,\psi_0,\bar{n},\bar{h})\pi_1 + F_h(\phi_0,\psi_0,\bar{n},\bar{h})\omega_1) \\ \kappa_0^*\gamma_m(\phi_0)(m_\infty'(\phi_0)\phi_1 - \psi_1) = c\psi_0' \qquad , y \in (0,1) \\ \phi_1'(0) = 0, \quad \phi_1(1) = 0, \quad \psi_1(0) = m_1^* \end{cases}
$$

and

$$
(2.59)\quad \begin{cases} c\pi_1' - \kappa_0^*\gamma_n(\phi_0)(n_\infty(\phi_0) - \bar{n}) = 0 \\ \qquad\qquad\qquad\qquad\qquad , y \in (0,1) \\ c\omega_1' - \kappa_0^*\gamma_h(\phi_0)(h_\infty(\phi_0) - \bar{h}) = 0 \\ \pi_1(0) = \pi_1^{(2)}(0;c,\kappa_0^*), \quad \omega_1(0) = \omega_1^{(2)}(0;c,\kappa_0^*) . \end{cases}
$$

Using (2.43), we obtain a solution of (2.59) which is of the form

$$
\begin{cases} \pi_1 = \dfrac{\kappa_0^*}{c}\displaystyle\int_0^y \gamma_n(\phi_0(\zeta))(n_\infty(\phi_0(\zeta)) - \bar{n})d\zeta + \pi_1^{(2)}(0;c,\kappa_0^*) \\ \quad = \pi_1^{(2)}(-y;c,\kappa_0^*) + \dfrac{2}{c}\kappa_0^*\displaystyle\int_{-y}^0 \gamma_n(\phi_0^{(2)}(\zeta;\kappa_0^*))(n_\infty(\phi_0^{(2)}(\zeta;\kappa_0^*)) \\ \qquad - \bar{n})d\zeta \equiv \pi_1(y;c) \\ \omega_1 = \dfrac{\kappa_0^*}{c}\displaystyle\int_0^y \gamma_h(\phi_0(\zeta))(h_\infty(\phi_0(\zeta)) - \bar{h})d\zeta + \omega_1^{(2)}(0;c,\kappa_0^*) \end{cases}
$$

$$= \omega_1^{(2)}(-y;c,\kappa_0^*) + \frac{2}{c}\kappa_0^* \int_{-y}^{0} \gamma_h(\phi_0^{(2)}(\zeta;\kappa_0^*))(h_\infty(\phi_0^{(2)}(\zeta;\kappa_0^*)) - \bar{h})d\zeta \equiv \omega_1(y;c) .$$

By using Green's function $G(y,z;\kappa_0^*)$ given in (2.45), a solution (ϕ_1,ψ_1) of (2.58) excluding the condition $\psi_1(0) = m_1^*$ can be represented as

(2.60)
$$\begin{cases} \phi_1 = -\int_0^1 G(-y,-z;\kappa_0^*)\{c\kappa_0^*\phi_0' + 2\kappa_0^*\tau_1 F(\phi_0,\psi_0,\bar{n},\bar{h}) \\ \quad + \kappa_0^{*2}(F_n(\phi_0,\psi_0,\bar{n},\bar{h})\pi_1 + F_h(\phi_0,\psi_0,\bar{n},\bar{h})\omega_1) \\ \quad - \kappa_0^* c F_m(\phi_0,\psi_0,\bar{n},\bar{h})\psi_0'/\gamma_m(\phi_0)\}dz \equiv \phi_1(y;c,\tau_1) \\ \psi_1 = m_\infty'(\phi_0(y))\phi_1(y;c,\tau_1) - c\psi_0'(y)/(\kappa_0^*\gamma_m(\phi_0(y))) \equiv \psi_1(y;c,\tau_1) . \end{cases}$$

Here we put m_1^* as $m_1^* = \psi_1(0;c,\tau_1)$ so that (2.60) becomes a solution of (2.58).

Using (2.60) and equating like powers of ε^2 in (2.53), (2.54), we have

(2.61)
$$\begin{cases} c\pi_2' - \kappa_0^*\gamma_n(\phi_0)(n_\infty'(\phi_0)\phi_1 - \pi_1) - \kappa_0^*\gamma_n'(\phi_0)(n_\infty(\phi_0) - \bar{n})\phi_1 \\ \quad - \tau_1\gamma_n(\phi_0)(n_\infty(\phi_0) - \bar{n}) = 0 \\ \qquad\qquad\qquad\qquad , \; y \in (0,1) \\ c\omega_2' - \kappa_0^*\gamma_h(\phi_0)(h_\infty'(\phi_0)\phi_1 - \omega_1) - \kappa_0^*\gamma_h'(\phi_0)(h_\infty(\phi_0) - \bar{h})\phi_1 \\ \quad - \tau_1\gamma_h(\phi_0)(h_\infty(\phi_0) - \bar{h}) = 0 \\ \pi_2(0) = \pi_2^{(2)}(0;c,\kappa_0^*,\kappa_1), \quad \omega_2(0) = \omega_2^{(2)}(0;c,\kappa_0^*,\kappa_1) . \end{cases}$$

From (2.60), we obtain a solution (π_2,ω_2) of (2.61) as $(\pi_2,\omega_2) \equiv (\pi_2(y;c,\kappa_1,\tau_1),\omega_2(y;c,\kappa_1,\tau_1))$.

Using the above approximation, we look for an exact solution (v,m,n,h) of (2.53), (2.54), which takes the form

$$
(2.62)\quad \begin{cases}
v(y;\varepsilon,c,\kappa_1,\tau_1) = \phi_0(y) + \varepsilon\phi_1(y;c,\tau_1) + \varepsilon p(y;\varepsilon,c,\kappa_1,\tau_1) \\
m(y;\varepsilon,c,\kappa_1,\tau_1) = \psi_0(y) + \varepsilon\psi_1(y;c,\tau_1) + \varepsilon m_\infty'(\phi_0(y))p(y;\varepsilon,c,\kappa_1,\tau_1) \\
\qquad + \varepsilon q(y;\varepsilon,c,\kappa_1,\tau_1) + \varepsilon Q(\varepsilon,c,\kappa_1) \\
n(y;\varepsilon,c,\kappa_1,\tau_1) = \bar{n} + \varepsilon\pi_1(y;c) + \varepsilon^2\pi_2(y;c,\kappa_1,\tau_1) \\
\qquad + \varepsilon^2 r(y;\varepsilon,c,\kappa_1,\tau_1) + \varepsilon^2 R(\varepsilon,c,\kappa_1) \\
h(y;\varepsilon,c,\kappa_1,\tau_1) = \bar{h} + \varepsilon\omega_1(y;c) + \varepsilon^2\omega_2(y;c,\kappa_1,\tau_1) \\
\qquad + \varepsilon^2 s(y;\varepsilon,c,\kappa_1,\tau_1) + \varepsilon^2 S(\varepsilon,c,\kappa_1) ,
\end{cases}
$$

where $Q(\varepsilon,c,\kappa_1) = q^{(2)}(0;\varepsilon,c,\kappa_1) + q^{(1)}(0;\varepsilon,c)$, $R(\varepsilon,c,\kappa_1) = r^{(2)}(0;\varepsilon,c,\kappa_1) + r^{(1)}(0;\varepsilon,c)$ and $S(\varepsilon,c,\kappa_1) = s^{(2)}(0;\varepsilon,c,\kappa_1) + s^{(1)}(0;\varepsilon,c)$. Substituting (2.62) into (2.53), we have

$$
(2.63)\quad \begin{cases}
0 = p'' - \varepsilon c(\kappa_0^* + \varepsilon\tau_1)p' - \varepsilon^{-1}(\kappa_0^* + \varepsilon\tau_1)^2 F(\phi_0 + \varepsilon\phi_1 + \varepsilon p,\ \psi_0 + \varepsilon\psi_1 \\
\qquad + \varepsilon m_\infty'(\phi_0) + \varepsilon q + \varepsilon Q(\varepsilon,c,\kappa_1),\ \bar{n} + \varepsilon\pi_1 + \varepsilon^2\pi_2 + \varepsilon^2 r + \varepsilon^2 R(\varepsilon,c,\kappa_1), \\
\qquad \bar{h} + \varepsilon\omega_1 + \varepsilon^2\omega_2 + \varepsilon^2 s + \varepsilon^2 S(\varepsilon,c,\kappa_1)) + \varepsilon^{-1}\phi_0'' + \phi_1'' \\
\qquad - c(\kappa_0^* + \varepsilon\tau_1)(\phi_0' + \varepsilon\phi_1') \\
0 = \varepsilon c\{m_\infty'(\phi_0)p' + q' + m_\infty''(\phi_0)\phi_0' p\} - \varepsilon^{-1}(\kappa_0^* + \varepsilon\tau_1)\gamma_m(\phi_0 + \varepsilon\phi_1 + \varepsilon p) \times \\
\qquad \{m_\infty(\phi_0 + \varepsilon\phi_1 + \varepsilon p) - \psi_0 - \varepsilon\psi_1 - \varepsilon m_\infty'(\phi_0)p - \varepsilon q - \varepsilon Q(\varepsilon,c,\kappa_1)\} \\
\qquad + c(\psi_0' + \varepsilon\psi_1')
\end{cases}
$$

$$\left\{\begin{aligned}
0 &= cr' + \varepsilon(\kappa_0^* + \varepsilon\tau_1)\gamma_n(\phi_0 + \varepsilon\phi_1 + \varepsilon p)r - \varepsilon^{-1}(\kappa_0^* + \varepsilon\tau_1)\gamma_n(\phi_0 + \varepsilon\phi_1 + \varepsilon p) \times \\
&\quad \{n_\infty(\phi_0 + \varepsilon\phi_1 + \varepsilon p) - \bar{n} - \varepsilon\pi_1 - \varepsilon^2\pi_2 - \varepsilon^2 R(\varepsilon,c,\kappa_1)\} + c(\varepsilon^{-1}\pi_1' + \pi_2') \\
0 &= cs' + \varepsilon(\kappa_0^* + \varepsilon\tau_1)\gamma_h(\phi_0 + \varepsilon\phi_1 + \varepsilon p)s - \varepsilon^{-1}(\kappa_0^* + \varepsilon\tau_1)\gamma_h(\phi_0 + \varepsilon\phi_1 + \varepsilon p) \times \\
&\quad \{h_\infty(\phi_0 + \varepsilon\phi_1 + \varepsilon p) - \bar{h} - \varepsilon\omega_1 - \varepsilon^2\omega_2 - \varepsilon^2 S(\varepsilon,c,\kappa_1)\} + c(\varepsilon^{-1}\omega_1' + \omega_2') .
\end{aligned}\right.$$

By (2.54), the boundary conditions for p, r and s become

(2.64) $$p'(0) = p(1) = r(0) = s(0) = 0.$$

We recall that $m_0^* = \psi_0(0)$ and $m_1^* = \psi_1(0;c,\tau_1)$. Here we put $m_2^*(\varepsilon)$ as $m_2^*(\varepsilon) = \varepsilon m_\infty'(\phi_0(0))p(0;\varepsilon,c,\kappa_1,\tau_1) + \varepsilon Q(\varepsilon,c,\kappa_1)$ so as to satisfy

(2.65) $$q(0) = 0 ,$$

which is not determined *a priori*, because $p(0;\varepsilon,c,\kappa_1,\tau_1)$ is not yet known. We simply write (2.63), (2.64), (2.65) as

(2.66) $$T(t;\varepsilon,c,\kappa_1,\tau_1) = 0$$

for $t = {}^t(p,q,r,s)$. Let T be a mapping from Y_+ into Z_+, where

$$Y_+ = \mathring{C}_+^2(0,1) \times \mathring{C}_\varepsilon^1(0,1) \times \mathring{C}_1^1(0,1) \times \mathring{C}_1^1(0,1)$$

and

$$Z_+ = C^0(0,1) \times C^0(0,1) \times C^0(0,1) \times C^0(0,1) .$$

Theorem 3. *For an arbitrarily given constant* τ_1^*, *there are* $\varepsilon_5 > 0$ *and* $\rho_5 > 0$ *such that for any* $\varepsilon \in (0,\varepsilon_5)$ *and* $(c,\kappa_1,\tau_1) \in \Delta_{\rho_5} \equiv \{(c,\kappa_1,\tau_1)|$ $|c - c_*| + |\kappa_1 - \kappa_1^*| + |\tau_1 - \tau_1^*| \le \rho_5\}$, *there exists* $t(\varepsilon,c,\kappa_1,\tau_1) \in Y_+$ *satisfying*

(2.66). $t(\varepsilon,c,\kappa_1,\tau_1)$, $\frac{\partial t}{\partial c}(\varepsilon,c,\kappa_1,\tau_1)$, $\frac{\partial t}{\partial \kappa_1}(\varepsilon,c,\kappa_1,\tau_1)$ *and* $\frac{\partial t}{\partial \tau_1}(\varepsilon,c,\kappa_1,\tau_1)$ *are uniformly continuous with respect to* $(\varepsilon,c,\kappa_1,\tau_1)$ *in the* Y_+ *- topology and satisfy*

$$\begin{cases} \| t(\varepsilon,c,\kappa_1,\tau_1)\|_{Y_+} = O(\varepsilon) \\ \| \frac{\partial t}{\partial c}(\varepsilon,c,\kappa_1,\tau_1)\|_{Y_+} = O(\varepsilon) \\ \| \frac{\partial t}{\partial \kappa_1}(\varepsilon,c,\kappa_1,\tau_1)\|_{Y_+} = O(\varepsilon) \\ \| \frac{\partial t}{\partial \tau_1}(\varepsilon,c,\kappa_1,\tau_1)\|_{Y_+} = O(\varepsilon) \end{cases} \quad \text{uniformly in } (c,\kappa_1,\tau_1)\ .$$

Theorem 3 can be proved in a way similar to that of Theorem 2. So we omit the proof.

Consequently, we obtain a solution of (2.1), (2.52) on I_3, which takes the form

$$(2.67)\quad \begin{cases} v(z;\varepsilon,c,\kappa_1,\tau_1) = \phi_0(z/(\varepsilon\tau)) + \varepsilon\phi_1(z/(\varepsilon\tau);c,\tau_1) + \varepsilon p(z/(\varepsilon\tau);\varepsilon,c,\kappa_1,\tau_1) \\ m(z;\varepsilon,c,\kappa_1,\tau_1) = \psi_0(z/(\varepsilon\tau)) + \varepsilon\psi_1(z/(\varepsilon\tau);c,\tau_1) + \varepsilon m_\infty'(\phi_0(z/(\varepsilon\tau)))\times \\ \qquad\qquad p(z/(\varepsilon\tau);\varepsilon,c,\kappa_1,\tau_1) + \varepsilon q(z/(\varepsilon\tau);\varepsilon,c,\kappa_1,\tau_1) \\ \qquad\qquad + \varepsilon Q(\varepsilon,c,\kappa_1) \\ n(z;\varepsilon,c,\kappa_1,\tau_1) = \bar{n} + \varepsilon\pi_1(z/(\varepsilon\tau);c) + \varepsilon^2\pi_2(z/(\varepsilon\tau);c,\kappa_1,\tau_1) \\ \qquad\qquad + \varepsilon^2 r(z/(\varepsilon\tau);\varepsilon,c,\kappa_1,\tau_1) + \varepsilon^2 R(\varepsilon,c,\kappa_1) \\ h(z;\varepsilon,c,\kappa_1,\tau_1) = \bar{h} + \varepsilon\omega_1(z/(\varepsilon\tau);c) + \varepsilon^2\omega_2(z/(\varepsilon\tau);c,\kappa_1,\tau_1) \\ \qquad\qquad + \varepsilon^2 s(z/(\varepsilon\tau);\varepsilon,c,\kappa_1,\tau_1) + \varepsilon^2 S(\varepsilon,c,\kappa_1)\ , \end{cases}$$

where $\tau = \kappa_0^* + \varepsilon\tau_1$ and p, q, r and s are the remainder terms given in Theorem 3. We write the functions (v,m,n,h), $(\phi_i,\psi_i,\pi_{i+1},\omega_{i+1})$ (i = 0,1) and (p,q,r,s) constructed above as $(v^{(3)},m^{(3)},n^{(3)},h^{(3)})$, $(\phi_i^{(3)},\psi_i^{(3)},\pi_{i+1}^{(3)},\omega_{i+1}^{(3)})$ (i =0,1) and $(p^{(3)},q^{(3)},r^{(3)},s^{(3)})$, respectively.

2.4. Construction of solutions on $I_4 = [\varepsilon\tau,+\infty)$

Finally we consider (2.1) on I_4 with the boundary conditions

$$(2.68)\qquad \begin{cases} v(\varepsilon\tau) = \nu_1, \quad v(+\infty) = 0, \quad m(\varepsilon\tau) = m^{(3)}(\varepsilon\tau;\varepsilon,c,\kappa_1,\tau_1) \\ n(\varepsilon\tau) = n^{(3)}(\varepsilon\tau;\varepsilon,c,\kappa_1,\tau_1), \quad h(\varepsilon\tau) = h^{(3)}(\varepsilon\tau;\varepsilon,c,\kappa_1,\tau_1) . \end{cases}$$

We use the transformation $y = z - \varepsilon\tau$ so that (2.1) with (2.68) becomes

$$(2.69)\qquad \begin{cases} \varepsilon^2 v'' - \varepsilon^2 cv' - F(v,m,n,h) = 0 \\ \varepsilon^2 cm' - \gamma_m(v)(m_\infty(v) - m) = 0 \\ cn' - \gamma_n(v)(n_\infty(v) - n) = 0 \\ ch' - \gamma_h(v)(h_\infty(v) - h) = 0 \end{cases} , \; y \in \mathbb{R}_+$$

with

$$(2.70)\qquad \begin{cases} v(0) = \nu_1, \quad v(+\infty) = 0, \quad m(0) = m^{(3)}(\varepsilon\tau;\varepsilon,c,\kappa_1,\tau_1) \\ n(0) = n^{(3)}(\varepsilon\tau;\varepsilon,c,\kappa_1,\tau_1), \quad h(0) = h^{(3)}(\varepsilon\tau;\varepsilon,c,\kappa_1,\tau_1) . \end{cases}$$

We construct an approximation which is of the form (2.6). Substituting (2.6) into (2.69), (2.70) and equating like powers of ε^0, we obtain

$$(2.71)\qquad \begin{cases} F(v_0,m_0,n_0,h_0) = 0 \\ \gamma_m(v_0)(m_\infty(v_0) - m_0) = 0 \end{cases}$$

and

$$(2.72)\qquad \begin{cases} cn_0' - \gamma_n(v_0)(n_\infty(v_0) - n_0) = 0 \\ ch_0' - \gamma_h(v_0)(h_\infty(v_0) - h_0) = 0 \\ n_0(0) = \bar{n}, \quad h_0(0) = \bar{h} . \end{cases} , \ y \in \mathbb{R}_+$$

Since (2.71) is reduced to $F(v_0, m_\infty(v_0), n_0, h_0) = 0$, we must take the smallest root $v_0 = \omega(n_0, h_0)$ of $F(v_0, m_\infty(v_0), n_0, h_0) = 0$, noting (A-4) and $v_0(+\infty) = 0$. Therefore, (2.72) is rewritten as

$$(2.73)\qquad \begin{cases} cn_0' - \gamma_n(\omega(n_0,h_0))(n_\infty(\omega(n_0,h_0)) - n_0) = 0 \\ ch_0' - \gamma_h(\omega(n_0,h_0))(h_\infty(\omega(n_0,h_0)) - h_0) = 0 \\ n_0(0) = \bar{n}, \quad h_0(0) = \bar{h} . \end{cases} , \ y \in \mathbb{R}_+$$

It follows from (A-4) that (2.73) has an equilibrium point $(n_0, h_0) = (\bar{n}, \bar{h})$. Thus, we have $(v_0, m_0, n_0, h_0) = (0, \bar{m}, \bar{n}, \bar{h})$, as a solution of (2.71) and (2.72). Equating like powers of ε in (2.69), (2.70), we have

$$(2.74)\qquad \begin{cases} F_v(0,\bar{m},\bar{n},\bar{h})v_1 + F_m(0,\bar{m},\bar{n},\bar{h})m_1 + F_n(0,\bar{m},\bar{n},\bar{h})n_1 + F_h(0,\bar{m},\bar{n},\bar{h})h_1 = 0 \\ \gamma_m(0)(m_\infty'(0)v_1 - m_1) = 0 \end{cases}$$

and

$$(2.75)\qquad \begin{cases} cn_1' - \gamma_n(0)(n_\infty'(0)v_1 - n_1) = 0 \\ ch_1' - \gamma_h(0)(h_\infty'(0)v_1 - h_1) = 0 \end{cases} , \ y \in \mathbb{R}_+ ,$$

where the boundary conditions for n_1 and h_1 at $y = 0$ will be given later. By using (2.74), (2.75) is reduced to the linear differential equations with respect to n_1 and h_1 :

$$(2.76)\qquad c\begin{pmatrix} n_1' \\ h_1' \end{pmatrix} = -\begin{pmatrix} \gamma_n(0)(1+n_\infty'(0)F_n^0) & \gamma_n(0)n_\infty'(0)F_h^0 \\ \gamma_h(0)h_\infty'(0)F_n^0 & \gamma_h(0)(1+h_\infty'(0)F_h^0) \end{pmatrix}\begin{pmatrix} n_1 \\ h_1 \end{pmatrix}, \quad y \in \mathbb{R}_+,$$

where F_n^0 and F_h^0 are the functions given in (2.12). Since the characteristic equation corresponding to the matrix in the right hand side of (2.76) has two different negative roots, say α_1 and α_2, a general solution (n_1,h_1) of (2.76) can be represented as

$$(2.77)\qquad \begin{cases} n_1(y;c) = k_1\, e^{\alpha_1 y/c} + k_2\, e^{\alpha_2 y/c} \\ h_1(y;c) = k_3\, e^{\alpha_1 y/c} + k_4\, e^{\alpha_2 y/c} \end{cases},$$

where k_1 and k_2 are arbitrary constants and k_3 and k_4 satisfy the relations

$$\begin{cases} k_3 = -\left(\dfrac{F_n(0,\bar{m},\bar{n},\bar{h})}{F_h(0,\bar{m},\bar{n},\bar{h})} + \dfrac{\alpha_1 + \gamma_n(0)}{\gamma_n(0)n_\infty'(0)F_h^0}\right) k_1 \\ k_4 = -\left(\dfrac{F_n(0,\bar{m},\bar{n},\bar{h})}{F_h(0,\bar{m},\bar{n},\bar{h})} + \dfrac{\alpha_2 + \gamma_n(0)}{\gamma_n(0)n_\infty'(0)F_h^0}\right) k_2 \end{cases}.$$

Thus, we find that a solution (v_1,m_1,n_1,h_1) of (2.74) and (2.75) takes the form

$$\begin{cases} v_1 = -F_n^0\, n_1(y;c) - F_h^0\, h_1(y;c) \equiv v_1(y;c) \\ m_1 = m_\infty'(0)v_1(y;c) \equiv m_1(y;c) \\ n_1 = n_1(y;c) \end{cases}$$

$$h_1 = h_1(y;c) ,$$

where

$$v_1(+\infty;c) = m_1(+\infty;c) = n_1(+\infty;c) = h_1(+\infty;c) = 0 .$$

Since the approximation up to order ε, $\varepsilon v_1(y;c)$, does not satisfy the boundary condition at $y = 0$, we must construct an approximation in a neighborhood of $y = 0$ which is of the form

$$(2.78)\quad \begin{cases} v(y) = \varepsilon v_1(y;c) + \phi_0(y/\varepsilon) + \varepsilon\phi_1(y/\varepsilon) \\ m(y) = \overline{m} + \varepsilon m_1(y;c) + \psi_0(y/\varepsilon) + \varepsilon\psi_1(y/\varepsilon) \\ n(y) = \overline{n} + \varepsilon n_1(y;c) + \pi_0(y/\varepsilon) + \varepsilon\pi_1(y/\varepsilon) + \varepsilon^2\pi_2(y/\varepsilon) \\ h(y) = \overline{h} + \varepsilon h_1(y;c) + \omega_0(y/\varepsilon) + \varepsilon\omega_1(y/\varepsilon) + \varepsilon^2\omega_2(y/\varepsilon) . \end{cases}$$

Using $\xi = y/\varepsilon$, we rewrite (2.69) as

$$(2.79)\quad \begin{cases} v^{\cdot\cdot} - \varepsilon cv^{\cdot} - F(v,m,n,h) = 0 \\ \varepsilon cm^{\cdot} - \gamma_m(v)(m_\infty(v) - m) = 0 \\ cn^{\cdot} - \varepsilon\gamma_n(v)(n_\infty(v) - n) = 0 \\ ch^{\cdot} - \varepsilon\gamma_h(v)(h_\infty(v) - h) = 0 \end{cases} , \ \xi \in \mathbb{R}_+ .$$

Substituting (2.78) into (2.79) with (2.70) and equating like powers of ε^0, we have

$$(2.80)\quad \begin{cases} \phi_0^{\cdot\cdot} - F(\phi_0,\overline{m}+\psi_0,\overline{n}+\pi_0,\overline{h}+\omega_0) = 0 \\ \gamma_m(\phi_0)(m_\infty(\phi_0) - \overline{m} - \psi_0) = 0 \\ \phi_0(0) = \nu_1, \ \ \phi_0(+\infty) = 0, \ \ \psi_0(0) = \psi_0^{(3)}(1) - \overline{m} \end{cases} , \ \xi \in \mathbb{R}_+$$

and

$$(2.81)\qquad \begin{cases} c\pi_0^{\cdot} = 0, \quad c\omega_0^{\cdot} = 0 & , \ \xi \in \mathbb{R}_+ \\ \pi_0(0) = 0, \quad \omega_0(0) = 0 \ , \end{cases}$$

which leads to $(\pi_0(\xi),\omega_0(\xi)) \equiv (0,0)$. Noting that $\psi_0(0) = \psi_0^{(3)}(1) - \bar{m} = \psi_0^{(1)}(0)$ and replacing ξ by $-\xi$, we find that (2.80) with $(\pi_0(\xi),\omega_0(\xi)) \equiv (0,0)$ reduces to (2.18). Therefore, a solution of (2.80) is represented as

$$(2.82)\qquad \phi_0(\xi) = \phi_0^{(1)}(-\xi), \quad \psi_0(\xi) = \psi_0^{(1)}(-\xi) \ .$$

Using (2.82) and equating like powers of ε in (2.79), (2.70), we have

$$(2.83)\qquad \begin{cases} \phi_1^{\cdot\cdot} - F_v(\phi_0,\bar{m}+\psi_0,\bar{n},\bar{h})\phi_1 - F_m(\phi_0,\bar{m}+\psi_0,\bar{n},\bar{h})\psi_1 = c\phi_0^{\cdot} \\ \quad + F_v(\phi_0,\bar{m}+\psi_0,\bar{n},\bar{h})v_1(0) + F_n(\phi_0,\bar{m}+\psi_0,\bar{n},\bar{h})(n_1(0)+\pi_1) \\ \quad + F_h(\phi_0,\bar{m}+\psi_0,\bar{n},\bar{h})(h_1(0)+\omega_1) + F_m(\phi_0,\bar{m}+\psi_0,\bar{n},\bar{h})m_1(0) \\ & , \ \xi \in \mathbb{R}_+ \\ c\psi_0^{\cdot} - \gamma_m(\phi_0)(m_\infty'(\phi_0)(v_1(0)+\phi_1) - m_1(0) - \psi_1) = 0 \\ \phi_1(0) = -v_1(0;c), \quad \phi_1(+\infty) = 0, \quad \psi_1(0) = \psi_1^{(3)}(1;c,\tau_1) - m_1(0;c) \end{cases}$$

and

$$(2.84)\qquad \begin{cases} c\pi_1^{\cdot} - \gamma_n(\phi_0)(n_\infty(\phi_0) - \bar{n}) = 0 \\ & , \ \xi \in \mathbb{R}_+ \\ c\omega_1^{\cdot} - \gamma_h(\phi_0)(h_\infty(\phi_0) - \bar{h}) = 0 \\ \pi_1(0) = \pi_1^{(3)}(1;c) - n_1(0;c), \quad \omega_1(0) = \omega_1^{(3)}(1;c) - h_1(0;c) \ . \end{cases}$$

In place of the boundary conditions in (2.84), we impose the conditions

$\pi_1(+\infty) = \omega_1(+\infty) = 0$. Substituting $\phi_0(\xi)$ into (2.84), we directly have

$$\begin{cases} \pi_1 = \dfrac{1}{c}\displaystyle\int_\xi^{+\infty} \gamma_n(\phi_0(\zeta))(n_\infty(\phi_0(\zeta)) - \bar{n})d\zeta \equiv \pi_1(\xi;c) \\ \omega_1 = \dfrac{1}{c}\displaystyle\int_\xi^{+\infty} \gamma_h(\phi_0(\zeta))(h_\infty(\phi_0(\zeta)) - \bar{h})d\zeta \equiv \omega_1(\xi;c) . \end{cases}$$

By using (2.22), it turns out that $\pi_1(\xi;c) = - \pi_1^{(1)}(-\xi;c)$ and $\omega_1(\xi;c) = - \omega_1^{(1)}(-\xi;c)$. Thus the boundary conditions in (2.84) are rewritten as

$$n_1(0;c) = \pi_1^{(1)}(0;c) + \pi_1^{(3)}(1;c), \quad h_1(0;c) = \omega_1^{(1)}(0;c) + \omega_1^{(3)}(1;c),$$

which gives the boundary conditions at $y = 0$ to (2.75). Thus (2.77) leads to

$$\begin{cases} k_1 + k_2 = \pi_1^{(1)}(0;c) + \pi_1^{(3)}(1;c) \\ k_3 + k_4 = \omega_1^{(1)}(0;c) + \omega_1^{(3)}(1;c) . \end{cases}$$

Since $\alpha_1 \neq \alpha_2$, k_1 and k_2 (and then k_3 and k_4) are uniquely determined as functions of c. By (2.83), we have the problem for ϕ_1 only :

$$(2.85) \quad \begin{cases} \ddot{\phi_1} - F_3(\xi)\phi_1 = G_3(\xi;c) \quad , \ \xi \in \mathbb{R}_+ \\ \phi_1(0) = - v_1(0;c), \quad \phi_1(+\infty) = 0 , \end{cases}$$

where

$$F_3(\xi) = F_v(\phi_0,\bar{m}+\psi_0,\bar{n},\bar{h}) + m_\infty'(\phi_0)F_m(\phi_0,\bar{m}+\psi_0,\bar{n},\bar{h})$$

and

$$G_3(\xi;c) = c\dot{\phi_0} + F_v(\phi_0,\bar{m}+\psi_0,\bar{n},\bar{h})v_1(0) + F_n(\phi_0,\bar{m}+\psi_0,\bar{n},\bar{h})(n_1(0)+\pi_1)$$
$$+ F_h(\phi_0,\bar{m}+\psi_0,\bar{n},\bar{h})(h_1(0)+\omega_1) + F_m(\phi_0,\bar{m}+\psi_0,\bar{n},\bar{h}) \times$$

$$(m_\infty'(\phi_0)v_1(0) - c\psi_0^{\boldsymbol\cdot}/\gamma_m(\phi_0)) \quad .$$

Since $\phi_0^{\boldsymbol\cdot}(\xi)$ is a negative solution of $\phi^{\boldsymbol{\cdot\cdot}} - F_3(\xi;c)\phi = 0$ from Lemma 3 and (2.82), a solution ϕ_1 of (2.85) is explicitly represented as

$$\phi_1(\xi;c) = \phi_0^{\boldsymbol\cdot}(\xi)(- v_1(0;c)\phi_0^{\boldsymbol\cdot}(0)^{-1} - \int_0^\xi (\phi_0^{\boldsymbol\cdot}(\eta))^{-2} \int_\eta^{+\infty} \phi_0^{\boldsymbol\cdot}(\zeta)G_3(\zeta;c)d\zeta d\eta) \, .$$

Thus, we have a solution $(\phi_1,\psi_1,\pi_1,\omega_1)$ of (2.83) and (2.84) which takes the form

$$(2.86) \quad \begin{cases} \phi_1 = \phi_1(\xi;c) \\ \psi_1 = m_\infty'(\phi_0(\xi))(v_1(0;c) + \phi_1(\xi;c)) - m_1(0;c) - c\psi_0^{\boldsymbol\cdot}(\xi)/\gamma_m(\phi_0(\xi)) \\ \quad \equiv \psi_1(\xi;c) \\ \pi_1 = \pi_1(\xi;c) \\ \omega_1 = \omega_1(\xi;c) \, . \end{cases}$$

Equating like powers of ε^2 in (2.79), we have

$$(2.87) \quad \begin{cases} c\pi_2^{\boldsymbol\cdot} = \gamma_n'(\phi_0)(v_1(0) + \phi_1)(n_\infty(\phi_0) - \overline{n}) + \gamma_n(\phi_0)\{n_\infty'(\phi_0)(v_1(0) \\ \quad + \phi_1) - n_1(0) - \pi_1\} - cn_1'(0) \\ c\omega_2^{\boldsymbol\cdot} = \gamma_h'(\phi_0)(v_1(0) + \phi_1)(h_\infty(\phi_0) - \overline{h}) + \gamma_h(\phi_0)\{h_\infty'(\phi_0)(v_1(0) \\ \quad + \phi_1) - h_1(0) - \omega_1\} - ch_1'(0) \, . \end{cases}$$

By directly solving (2.87) under the boundary conditions $\pi_2(+\infty) = \omega_2(+\infty)$

$= 0$, we obtain a solution $(\pi_2,\omega_2) \equiv (\pi_2(\xi;c),\omega_2(\xi;c))$. Here we note that $(\phi_1(\xi;c),\psi_1(\xi;c),\ \pi_2(\xi;c),\omega_2(\xi;c)) \in X^2_{\sigma_-,1}(\mathbb{R}_+) \times (X^1_{\sigma_-,1}(\mathbb{R}_+))^3$.

We now look for an exact solution (v,m,n,h) of (2.69), (2.70) which takes the form

$$
(2.88)\quad
\begin{cases}
v(y;\varepsilon,c,\kappa_1,\tau_1) = \varepsilon v_1(y;c) + \phi_0(y/\varepsilon) + \varepsilon\phi_1(y/\varepsilon;c) + \varepsilon p(y;\varepsilon,c,\kappa_1,\tau_1) \\
\qquad\qquad - \varepsilon e^{-\sigma y}(F^0_n\, r(y;\varepsilon,c,\kappa_1,\tau_1) + F^0_h\, s(y;\varepsilon,c,\kappa_1,\tau_1)) \\
m(y;\varepsilon,c,\kappa_1,\tau_1) = \overline{m} + \varepsilon m_1(y;c) + \psi_0(y/\varepsilon) + \varepsilon\psi_1(y/\varepsilon;c) \\
\qquad\qquad + \varepsilon m_\infty'(\phi_0)p(y;\varepsilon,c,\kappa_1,\tau_1) + \varepsilon e^{-\sigma y}q(y;\varepsilon,c,\kappa_1,\tau_1) \\
\qquad\qquad - \varepsilon e^{-\sigma y}m_\infty'(\phi_0)(F^0_n\, r(y;\varepsilon,c,\kappa_1,\tau_1) \\
\qquad\qquad + F^0_h\, s(y;\varepsilon,c,\kappa_1,\tau_1)) + \varepsilon e^{-\sigma y}M(\varepsilon,c,\kappa_1,\tau_1) \\
n(y;\varepsilon,c,\kappa_1,\tau_1) = \overline{n} + \varepsilon n_1(y;c) + \varepsilon\pi_1(y/\varepsilon;c) + \varepsilon^2(\pi_2(y/\varepsilon;c) \\
\qquad\qquad - e^{-\sigma y}\pi_2(0;c)) + \varepsilon e^{-\sigma y}r(y;\varepsilon,c,\kappa_1,\tau_1) \\
\qquad\qquad + \varepsilon^2 e^{-\sigma y}N(\varepsilon,c,\kappa_1,\tau_1) \\
h(y;\varepsilon,c,\kappa_1,\tau_1) = \overline{h} + \varepsilon h_1(y;c) + \varepsilon\omega_1(y/\varepsilon;c) + \varepsilon^2(\omega_2(y/\varepsilon;c) \\
\qquad\qquad - e^{-\sigma y}\omega_2(0;c)) + \varepsilon e^{-\sigma y}s(y;\varepsilon,c,\kappa_1,\tau_1) \\
\qquad\qquad + \varepsilon^2 e^{-\sigma y}H(\varepsilon,c,\kappa_1,\tau_1)
\end{cases}
$$

where $\sigma > 0$ is any fixed number satisfying $\max(\alpha_1,\alpha_2) < -\sigma$ and $M = q^{(3)}(1;\varepsilon,c,\kappa_1,\tau_1) + q^{(2)}(0;\varepsilon,c,\kappa_1) + q^{(1)}(0;\varepsilon,c)$, $N = \pi_2^{(3)}(1;c,\kappa_1,\tau_1) + r^{(3)}(1;\varepsilon,c,\kappa_1,\tau_1) + r^{(2)}(0;\varepsilon,c,\kappa_1) + r^{(1)}(0;\varepsilon,c)$ and $H = \omega_2^{(3)}(1;c,\kappa_1,\tau_1)$

$+ s^{(3)}(1;\varepsilon,c,\kappa_1,\tau_1) + s^{(2)}(0;\varepsilon,c,\kappa_1) + s^{(1)}(0;\varepsilon,c)$. Substituting (2.88) into (2.69), we have

$$
(2.89)\quad \left\{
\begin{aligned}
0 =\ & \varepsilon^2 p'' - \varepsilon^2 cp' - \varepsilon^{-1} F(\varepsilon v_1 + \phi_0 + \varepsilon\phi_1 + \varepsilon p - \varepsilon e^{-\sigma y}(F_n^0 r + F_h^0 s), \bar{m} + \varepsilon m_1 \\
& + \psi_0 + \varepsilon\psi_1 + \varepsilon m_\infty'(\phi_0)p + \varepsilon e^{-\sigma y} q - \varepsilon e^{-\sigma y} m_\infty'(\phi_0)(F_n^0 r + F_h^0 s) + \varepsilon e^{-\sigma y} M, \\
& \bar{n} + \varepsilon n_1 + \varepsilon\pi_1 + \varepsilon^2(\pi_2 - e^{-\sigma y}\pi_2(0)) + \varepsilon e^{-\sigma y} r + \varepsilon^2 e^{-\sigma y} N, \bar{h} + \varepsilon h_1 + \varepsilon\omega_1 \\
& + \varepsilon^2(\omega_2 - e^{-\sigma y}\omega_2(0)) + \varepsilon e^{-\sigma y} s + \varepsilon^2 e^{-\sigma y} H) + \varepsilon^2 v_1'' + \varepsilon^{-1}\ddot{\phi}_0 + \ddot{\phi}_1 \\
& - \varepsilon^2 e^{-\sigma y} F_n^0 (r'' - 2\sigma r' + \sigma^2 r) - \varepsilon^2 e^{-\sigma y} F_h^0 (s'' - 2\sigma s' + \sigma^2 s) \\
& - \varepsilon c(\varepsilon v_1' + \varepsilon^{-1}\dot{\phi}_0 + \dot{\phi}_1 + \varepsilon e^{-\sigma y} F_n^0(\sigma r - r') + \varepsilon e^{-\sigma y} F_h^0(\sigma s - s')) \\
0 =\ & \varepsilon c e^{\sigma y}(\varepsilon m_\infty'(\phi_0)p' + m_\infty''(\phi_0)\dot{\phi}_0 p) + \varepsilon^2 c(q' - \sigma q) + \varepsilon c\{-\varepsilon m_\infty'(\phi_0) \times \\
& (F_n^0 r' + F_h^0 s') + (\sigma\varepsilon m_\infty'(\phi_0) - m_\infty''(\phi_0)\dot{\phi}_0)(F_n^0 r + F_h^0 s)\} \\
& - \varepsilon^{-1} e^{\sigma y}\gamma_m(\varepsilon v_1 + \phi_0 + \varepsilon\phi_1 + \varepsilon p - \varepsilon e^{-\sigma y}(F_n^0 r + F_h^0 s))(m_\infty(\varepsilon v_1 + \phi_0 \\
& + \varepsilon\phi_1 + \varepsilon p - \varepsilon e^{-\sigma y}(F_n^0 r + F_h^0 s)) - \bar{m} - \varepsilon m_1 - \psi_0 - \varepsilon\psi_1 - \varepsilon m_\infty'(\phi_0)p \\
& - \varepsilon e^{-\sigma y} q + \varepsilon e^{-\sigma y} m_\infty'(\phi_0)(F_n^0 r + F_h^0 s) - \varepsilon e^{-\sigma y} M) \\
& + \varepsilon c e^{\sigma y}(\varepsilon m_1' + \varepsilon^{-1}\dot{\psi}_0 + \dot{\psi}_1) - \varepsilon^2\sigma c M \\
0 =\ & cr' - \sigma cr - \varepsilon^{-1} e^{\sigma y}\gamma_n(\varepsilon v_1 + \phi_0 + \varepsilon\phi_1 + \varepsilon p - \varepsilon e^{-\sigma y}(F_n^0 r + F_h^0 s))(n_\infty(\varepsilon v_1 \\
& + \phi_0 + \varepsilon\phi_1 + \varepsilon p - \varepsilon e^{-\sigma y}(F_n^0 r + F_h^0 s)) - \bar{n} - \varepsilon n_1 - \varepsilon\pi_1 - \varepsilon^2(\pi_2 - e^{-\sigma y}\pi_2(0)) \\
& - \varepsilon e^{-\sigma y} r - \varepsilon^2 e^{-\sigma y} N) + c e^{\sigma y}(n_1' + \varepsilon^{-1}\dot{\pi}_1 + \dot{\pi}_2) + \varepsilon\sigma c\pi_2(0) - \varepsilon\sigma c N \\
0 =\ & cs' - \sigma cs - \varepsilon^{-1} e^{\sigma y}\gamma_h(\varepsilon v_1 + \phi_0 + \varepsilon\phi_1 + \varepsilon p - \varepsilon e^{-\sigma y}(F_n^0 r + F_h^0 s))(h_\infty(\varepsilon v_1
\end{aligned}
\right.
$$

$$\left| \begin{array}{l} + \phi_0 + \varepsilon\phi_1 + \varepsilon p - \varepsilon e^{-\sigma y}(F_n^0 r + F_h^0 s)) - \bar{h} - \varepsilon h_1 - \varepsilon\omega_1 - \varepsilon^2(\omega_2 - e^{-\sigma y}\omega_2(0)) \\ - \varepsilon e^{-\sigma y}s - \varepsilon^2 e^{-\sigma y}H) + ce^{\sigma y}(h_1' + \varepsilon^{-1}\omega_1^{\cdot} + \omega_2^{\cdot}) + \varepsilon\sigma c\omega_2(0) - \varepsilon\sigma cH \ . \end{array} \right.$$

The boundary conditions for (p,q,r,s) become

$$(2.90) \qquad p(0) = p(+\infty) = q(0) = r(0) = s(0) = 0 \ .$$

We write (2.89), (2.90) as

$$(2.91) \qquad T(t;\varepsilon,c,\kappa_1,\tau_1) = 0 \ .$$

Let T be a mapping from $\mathring{Y}_{\sigma,\varepsilon}$ into $Z_{\sigma,\varepsilon}$, where

$$\mathring{Y}_{\sigma,\varepsilon} = \mathring{X}^2_{\sigma,\varepsilon}(\mathbb{R}_+) \times \mathring{X}^1_{\sigma,\varepsilon^2}(\mathbb{R}_+) \times \mathring{E}^2_\varepsilon(\mathbb{R}_+) \times \mathring{E}^2_\varepsilon(\mathbb{R}_+)$$

and

$$Z_{\sigma,\varepsilon} = X^0_{\sigma,1}(\mathbb{R}_+) \times C^0(\mathbb{R}_+) \times X^1_{0,\varepsilon}(\mathbb{R}_+) \times X^1_{0,\varepsilon}(\mathbb{R}_+) \ .$$

Lemma 7. *Let* $\sigma > 0$ *be fixed sufficiently small. Then there are* $\varepsilon_6 > 0$, $\rho_6 > 0$ *and* $K > 0$ *such that for any* $\varepsilon \in (0,\varepsilon_6)$, $(c,\kappa_1,\tau_1) \in \Delta_{\rho_6}$,

(i) $\|T(0;\varepsilon,c,\kappa_1,\tau_1)\|_{Z_{\sigma,\varepsilon}} = O(\varepsilon)$ *uniformly in* (c,κ_1,τ_1) ;

(ii) *for any* $t_1, t_2 \in \mathring{Y}_{\sigma,\varepsilon}$,

$$\|T_t(t_1;\varepsilon,c,\kappa_1,\tau_1) - T_t(t_2;\varepsilon,c,\kappa_1,\tau_1)\|_{\mathring{Y}_{\sigma,\varepsilon} \to Z_{\sigma,\varepsilon}} \le K\|t_1 - t_2\|_{\mathring{Y}_{\sigma,\varepsilon}} \ ;$$

(iii) $\|T_t^{-1}(0;\varepsilon,c,\kappa_1,\tau_1)\|_{Z_{\sigma,\varepsilon} \to \mathring{Y}_{\sigma,\varepsilon}} \le K$.

Moreover the results (i) - (iii) *hold for* $\frac{\partial T}{\partial c}$, $\frac{\partial T}{\partial \kappa_1}$ *and* $\frac{\partial T}{\partial \tau_1}$ *in place of* T.

The proof is stated in the appendix.

By the above lemma, we have

Theorem 4. *Let* $\sigma > 0$ *be fixed sufficiently small. Then there exist* $\varepsilon_7 > 0$, $\rho_7 > 0$ *such that for any* $\varepsilon \in (0,\varepsilon_7)$ *and* $(c,\kappa_1,\tau_1) \in \Delta_{\rho_7}$ *, there exists* $t(\varepsilon,c,\kappa_1,\tau_1) \in \mathring{Y}_{\sigma,\varepsilon}$ *satisfying* (2.91). $t(\varepsilon,c,\kappa_1,\tau_1)$, $\frac{\partial t}{\partial c}(\varepsilon,c,\kappa_1,\tau_1)$, $\frac{\partial t}{\partial \kappa_1}(\varepsilon,c,\kappa_1,\tau_1)$ *and* $\frac{\partial t}{\partial \tau_1}(\varepsilon,c,\kappa_1,\tau_1)$ *are uniformly continuous with respect to* $(\varepsilon,c,\kappa_1,\tau_1)$ *in the* $\mathring{Y}_{\sigma,\varepsilon}$ *- topology and satisfy*

$$\left\{\begin{aligned} &\|t(\varepsilon,c,\kappa_1,\tau_1)\|_{\mathring{Y}_{\sigma,\varepsilon}} = O(\varepsilon) \\ &\left\|\frac{\partial t}{\partial c}(\varepsilon,c,\kappa_1,\tau_1)\right\|_{\mathring{Y}_{\sigma,\varepsilon}} = O(\varepsilon) \\ &\left\|\frac{\partial t}{\partial \kappa_1}(\varepsilon,c,\kappa_1,\tau_1)\right\|_{\mathring{Y}_{\sigma,\varepsilon}} = O(\varepsilon) \\ &\left\|\frac{\partial t}{\partial \tau_1}(\varepsilon,c,\kappa_1,\tau_1)\right\|_{\mathring{Y}_{\sigma,\varepsilon}} = O(\varepsilon) \end{aligned}\right. \qquad \textit{uniformly in } (c,\kappa_1,\tau_1).$$

Thus, we obtain a solution of (2.1) with (2.68) on I_4, which takes the form

$$\left\{\begin{aligned} v(z;\varepsilon,c,\kappa_1,\tau_1) &= \varepsilon v_1(z-\varepsilon\tau;c) + \phi_0(z/\varepsilon-\tau) + \varepsilon\phi_1(z/\varepsilon-\tau;c) \\ &\quad + \varepsilon p(z-\varepsilon\tau;\varepsilon,c,\kappa_1,\tau_1) - \varepsilon e^{-\sigma(z-\varepsilon\tau)}F_n^0 \times \\ &\quad r(z-\varepsilon\tau;\varepsilon,c,\kappa_1,\tau_1) - \varepsilon e^{-\sigma(z-\varepsilon\tau)}F_h^0 \times \\ &\quad s(z-\varepsilon\tau;\varepsilon,c,\kappa_1,\tau_1) \\ m(z;\varepsilon,c,\kappa_1,\tau_1) &= \bar{m} + \varepsilon m_1(z-\varepsilon\tau;c) + \psi_0(z/\varepsilon-\tau) + \varepsilon\psi_1(z/\varepsilon-\tau;c) \\ &\quad + \varepsilon m_\infty'(\phi_0)p(z-\varepsilon\tau;\varepsilon,c,\kappa_1,\tau_1) \end{aligned}\right.$$

$$
\left\{
\begin{aligned}
& + \varepsilon e^{-\sigma(z-\varepsilon\tau)} q(z-\varepsilon\tau;\varepsilon,c,\kappa_1,\tau_1) \\
& - \varepsilon e^{-\sigma(z-\varepsilon\tau)} m_\infty'(\phi_0)(F_n^0 r(z-\varepsilon\tau;\varepsilon,c,\kappa_1,\tau_1) \\
& + F_h^0 s(z-\varepsilon\tau;\varepsilon,c,\kappa_1,\tau_1)) + \varepsilon e^{-\sigma(z-\varepsilon\tau)} M(\varepsilon,c,\kappa_1,\tau_1) \\
n(z;\varepsilon,c,\kappa_1,\tau_1) &= \bar{n} + \varepsilon n_1(z-\varepsilon\tau;c) + \varepsilon\pi_1(z/\varepsilon-\tau;c) + \varepsilon^2(\pi_2(z/\varepsilon-\tau;c) \\
& - e^{-\sigma(z-\varepsilon\tau)}\pi_2(0;c)) + \varepsilon e^{-\sigma(z-\varepsilon\tau)} r(z-\varepsilon\tau;\varepsilon,c,\kappa_1,\tau_1) \\
& + \varepsilon^2 e^{-\sigma(z-\varepsilon\tau)} N(\varepsilon,c,\kappa_1,\tau_1) \\
h(z;\varepsilon,c,\kappa_1,\tau_1) &= \bar{h} + \varepsilon h_1(z-\varepsilon\tau;c) + \varepsilon\omega_1(z/\varepsilon-\tau;c) + \varepsilon^2(\omega_2(z/\varepsilon-\tau;c) \\
& - e^{-\sigma(z-\varepsilon\tau)}\omega_2(0;c)) + \varepsilon e^{-\sigma(z-\varepsilon\tau)} s(z-\varepsilon\tau;\varepsilon,c,\kappa_1,\tau_1) \\
& + \varepsilon^2 e^{-\sigma(z-\varepsilon\tau)} H(\varepsilon,c,\kappa_1,\tau_1)
\end{aligned}
\right.
$$

where $\tau = \kappa_0^* + \varepsilon\tau_1$ and p, q, r and s are the remainder terms given in Theorem 4. We write the functions (v,m,n,h), $(\phi_i,\psi_i,\pi_{i+1},\omega_{i+1})$ ($i=0,1$) and (p,q,r,s) constructed above as $(v^{(4)},m^{(4)},n^{(4)},h^{(4)})$, $(\phi_i{}^{(4)},\psi_i{}^{(4)},\pi_{i+1}{}^{(4)},\omega_{i+1}{}^{(4)})$ ($i = 0,1$) and $(p^{(4)},q^{(4)},r^{(4)},s^{(4)})$, respectively. It is obvious that

$$
\left\{
\begin{aligned}
& v^{(4)}(+\infty;\varepsilon,c,\kappa_1,\tau_1) = 0, \quad m^{(4)}(+\infty;\varepsilon,c,\kappa_1,\tau_1) = \bar{m} \\
& n^{(4)}(+\infty;\varepsilon,c,\kappa_1,\tau_1) = \bar{n}, \quad h^{(4)}(+\infty;\varepsilon,c,\kappa_1,\tau_1) = \bar{h}\,.
\end{aligned}
\right.
$$

2.5. Construction of a solution on $\mathbb{R}$

In this subsection, we determine c, κ_1 and τ_1 as functions of ε such that $v^{(i)}$ ($i=1,2,3,4$) are matched in C^1 - sense and $(m^{(i)},n^{(i)},h^{(i)})$ ($i=1,2,3,4$) are matched in C^0 - sense at $z = -\varepsilon\kappa$, 0 and $\varepsilon\tau$.

By the construction of the solution $(v^{(i)}, m^{(i)}, n^{(i)}, h^{(i)})$ on I_i (i=1,2,3,4), we already know that $n^{(i)}$ and $h^{(i)}$ are continuous at $z = -\varepsilon\kappa$, 0, $\varepsilon\tau$, and $v^{(i)}$ and $m^{(i)}$ continuous at $z = -\varepsilon\kappa$, $\varepsilon\tau$, and $\frac{d}{dz}v^{(2)} = \frac{d}{dz}v^{(3)}$ at $z = 0$. By using (2.51),(2.67) and $\phi_0{}^{(2)}(0) = \phi_0{}^{(3)}(0)$, we note that

$$m^{(2)}(0;\varepsilon,c,\kappa_1) - m^{(3)}(0;\varepsilon,c,\kappa_1,\tau_1)$$
$$= m_\infty{}'(\phi_0{}^{(2)}(0))(v^{(2)}(0;\varepsilon,c,\kappa_1) - v^{(3)}(0;\varepsilon,c,\kappa_1,\tau_1)) .$$

Thus, if $v^{(2)}(0;\varepsilon,c,\kappa_1) = v^{(3)}(0;\varepsilon,c,\kappa_1,\tau_1)$, then $m^{(2)}(0;\varepsilon,c,\kappa_1) = m^{(3)}(0;\varepsilon,c,\kappa_1,\tau_1)$ holds. Therefore, it is sufficient to determine c, κ_1 and τ_1 such that $v^{(2)} = v^{(3)}$ at $z = 0$, $\frac{d}{dz}v^{(1)} = \frac{d}{dz}v^{(2)}$ at $z = -\varepsilon\kappa$ and $\frac{d}{dz}v^{(3)} = \frac{d}{dz}v^{(4)}$ at $z = \varepsilon\tau$. We recall that

$$\begin{cases} v^{(2)}(0;\varepsilon,c,\kappa_1) - v^{(3)}(0;\varepsilon,c,\kappa_1,\tau_1) \\ \quad \equiv \varepsilon A_1(c,\kappa_1,\tau_1) + \varepsilon A_2(\varepsilon,c,\kappa_1,\tau_1) \\ \varepsilon\kappa\frac{d}{dz}v^{(1)}(-\varepsilon\kappa;\varepsilon,c) - \varepsilon\kappa\frac{d}{dz}v^{(2)}(-\varepsilon\kappa;\varepsilon,c,\kappa_1) \\ \quad \equiv B_0 + \varepsilon B_1(c,\kappa_1) + \varepsilon B_2(\varepsilon,c,\kappa_1) \\ \varepsilon\tau\frac{d}{dz}v^{(3)}(\varepsilon\tau;\varepsilon,c,\kappa_1,\tau_1) - \varepsilon\tau\frac{d}{dz}v^{(4)}(\varepsilon\tau;\varepsilon,c,\kappa_1,\tau_1) \\ \quad \equiv C_0 + \varepsilon C_1(c,\tau_1) + \varepsilon C_2(\varepsilon,c,\kappa_1,\tau_1) , \end{cases}$$

where

$$A_1(c,\kappa_1,\tau_1) = \phi_1{}^{(2)}(0;c,\kappa_0^*,\kappa_1) - \phi_1{}^{(3)}(0;c,\tau_1) ,$$

$$A_2(\varepsilon,c,\kappa_1,\tau_1) = p^{(2)}(0;\varepsilon,c,\kappa_1) - p^{(3)}(0;\varepsilon,c,\kappa_1,\tau_1) ,$$

$$B_0 = \kappa_0^*\phi_0{}^{(1)\cdot}(0) - \phi_0{}^{(2)\prime}(-1;\kappa_0^*) ,$$

$$B_1(c,\kappa_1) = \kappa_1\phi_0^{(1)\cdot}(0) + \kappa_0^*\phi_1^{(1)\cdot}(0;c) - \phi_1^{(2)\prime}(-1;c,\kappa_0^*,\kappa_1) ,$$

$$B_2(\varepsilon,c,\kappa_1) = \varepsilon\kappa_1\phi_1^{(1)\cdot}(0;c) + (\kappa_0^*+\varepsilon\kappa_1)p^{(1)\cdot}(0;\varepsilon,c) - p^{(2)\prime}(-1;\varepsilon,c,\kappa_1) ,$$

$$C_0 = \phi_0^{(3)\prime}(1) - \kappa_0^*\phi_0^{(4)\cdot}(0) ,$$

$$C_1(c,\tau_1) = \phi_1^{(3)\prime}(1;c,\tau_1) - \tau_1\phi_0^{(4)\cdot}(0) - \kappa_0^*\phi_1^{(4)\cdot}(0;c) ,$$

$$\begin{aligned} C_2(\varepsilon,c,\kappa_1,\tau_1) = {} & p^{(3)\prime}(1;\varepsilon,c,\kappa_1,\tau_1) - \varepsilon\tau_1\phi_1^{(4)\cdot}(0;c) \\ & - \varepsilon(\kappa_0^*+\varepsilon\tau_1)\{v_1^{(4)\prime}(0;c) + p^{(4)\prime}(0;\varepsilon,c,\kappa_1,\tau_1) \\ & - (F_n^0 r^{(4)\prime}(0;\varepsilon,c,\kappa_1,\tau_1) + F_h^0 s^{(4)\prime}(0;\varepsilon,c,\kappa_1,\tau_1))\} . \end{aligned}$$

By Lemmas 3 and 5 and the definition of v^*, we find that

$$B_0 = \kappa_0^*\Big(\sqrt{2\int_0^{\nu_1} F(v,m_\infty(v),\bar{n},\bar{h})dv} - \sqrt{2\int_{v^*}^{\nu_1} F(v,m_\infty(v),\bar{n},\bar{h})dv}\ \Big) = 0.$$

Similarly $C_0 = 0$ is found. Therefore, we determine c, κ_1 and τ_1 as functions of ε so as to satisfy

$$(2.92)\quad \begin{cases} A(\varepsilon,c,\kappa_1,\tau_1) \equiv A_1(c,\kappa_1,\tau_1) + A_2(\varepsilon,c,\kappa_1,\tau_1) = 0 \\ B(\varepsilon,c,\kappa_1) \equiv B_1(c,\kappa_1) + B_2(\varepsilon,c,\kappa_1) = 0 \\ C(\varepsilon,c,\kappa_1,\tau_1) \equiv C_1(c,\tau_1) + C_2(\varepsilon,c,\kappa_1,\tau_1) = 0 . \end{cases}$$

Lemma 8. *There uniquely exist constants* $c_* > 0$, κ_1^* and τ_1^* *such that*

$$(2.93)\quad \begin{cases} A(0,c_*,\kappa_1^*,\tau_1^*) = 0 \\ B(0,c_*,\kappa_1^*) = 0 \end{cases}$$

$$\left\{ C(0,c_*,\kappa_1^*,\tau_1^*) = 0 \right.$$

and

$$(2.94) \qquad \left| \frac{\partial(A,B,C)}{\partial(c,\kappa_1,\tau_1)} \right|_{\varepsilon=0,c=c_*,\kappa_1=\kappa_1^*,\tau_1=\tau_1^*} \neq 0 .$$

The proof is stated in the appendix.

Thus, we can apply the usual Implicit Function Theorem to (2.92) and find that there is $\varepsilon_0 > 0$ such that there exist continuous functions $c(\varepsilon)$, $\kappa_1(\varepsilon)$ and $\tau_1(\varepsilon)$ defined for $\varepsilon \in [0,\varepsilon_0)$ satisfying $\lim_{\varepsilon\to 0} c(\varepsilon) = c_*$, $\lim_{\varepsilon\to 0} \kappa_1(\varepsilon) = \kappa_1^*$ and $\lim_{\varepsilon\to 0} \tau_1(\varepsilon) = \tau_1^*$. Thus, we complete the proof of Theorem A.

3. Instability of the slow traveling wave solution

In the previous section, we have constructed the presumably slow traveling wave solution $\mathbf{V}(x+\varepsilon c(\varepsilon)t;\varepsilon) \equiv (v(x+\varepsilon c(\varepsilon)t), m(x+\varepsilon c(\varepsilon)t), n(x+\varepsilon c(\varepsilon)t), h(x+\varepsilon c(\varepsilon)t))$ with the velocity $\varepsilon c(\varepsilon) = \varepsilon(c_* + o(1))$ for sufficiently small ε. In this section, by using Evans' stability criterion [4], [5], [6] and [7] we prove that this solution is unstable.

Let us introduce the traveling coordinate system $(z,t) = (x+\varepsilon ct,t)$ so that (1.3) takes the form

$$(3.1) \qquad \begin{cases} \dfrac{\partial v}{\partial t} = \dfrac{\partial^2 v}{\partial z^2} - \varepsilon c \dfrac{\partial v}{\partial z} - F(v,m,n,h) \\[2ex] \dfrac{\partial m}{\partial t} = -\varepsilon c \dfrac{\partial m}{\partial z} + \gamma_m(v)(m_\infty(v) - m) \\[2ex] \dfrac{\partial n}{\partial t} = -\varepsilon c \dfrac{\partial n}{\partial z} + \varepsilon^2 \gamma_n(v)(n_\infty(v) - n) \end{cases}$$

$$\frac{\partial h}{\partial t} = -\varepsilon c \frac{\partial h}{\partial z} + \varepsilon^2 \gamma_h(v)(h_\infty(v) - h) .$$

The stationary problem of (3.1) is thus written as

$$(3.2) \quad \begin{cases} 0 = \dfrac{d^2 v}{dz^2} - \varepsilon c \dfrac{dv}{dz} - F(v,m,n,h) \\ 0 = -\varepsilon c \dfrac{dm}{dz} + \gamma_m(v)(m_\infty(v) - m) \\ 0 = -\varepsilon c \dfrac{dn}{dz} + \varepsilon^2 \gamma_n(v)(n_\infty(v) - n) \\ 0 = -\varepsilon c \dfrac{dh}{dz} + \varepsilon^2 \gamma_h(v)(h_\infty(v) - h) \end{cases}$$

or by putting $\frac{dv}{dz} = u$,

$$(3.3) \qquad \frac{d}{dz} \mathbf{U} = \mathbf{F}(\mathbf{U}, c, \varepsilon) ,$$

where $\mathbf{U} = {}^t(v,u,m,n,h)$ and

$$\mathbf{F}(\mathbf{U},c,\varepsilon) = \begin{pmatrix} u \\ \varepsilon c u + F(v,m,n,h) \\ \dfrac{1}{\varepsilon c} \gamma_m(v)(m_\infty(v) - m) \\ \dfrac{\varepsilon}{c} \gamma_n(v)(n_\infty(v) - n) \\ \dfrac{\varepsilon}{c} \gamma_h(v)(h_\infty(v) - h) \end{pmatrix} .$$

Let $A(c,\varepsilon)$ be the linearized matrix of $\mathbf{F}$ about the resting state $\pi = {}^t(0,0,\bar{m},\bar{n},\bar{h})$. Evans [5] and Hastings [10] showed that $A(c,\varepsilon)$ has one positive eigenvalue and four eigenvalues with negative real part for all $c > 0$ and sufficiently small $\varepsilon > 0$. Let $\nu(c,\varepsilon)$ and $\mathbf{Y}(c,\varepsilon)$ be respectively the positive eigenvalue of $A(c,\varepsilon)$ and the corresponding eigenvector. Then there is a unique solution of (3.3), say $\boldsymbol{\phi}_u(z;c,\varepsilon)$, which has the asymptotic form

$$\boldsymbol{\phi}_u(z;c,\varepsilon) - \boldsymbol{\pi} - e^{\nu(c,\varepsilon)z}\boldsymbol{\gamma}(c,\varepsilon) = O(\ e^{(\nu(c,\varepsilon)+\delta)z}\ ) \quad \text{as} \quad z \to -\infty$$

for some $\delta > 0$. Let $\boldsymbol{\phi}(z;\varepsilon) = \mathbf{U}(z;c(\varepsilon),\varepsilon)$ be the traveling wave solution of (3.3) constructed in Section 2, and $\overline{A}(z;\varepsilon)$ be the linearized matrix of $\mathbf{F}$ about $\boldsymbol{\phi}(z;\varepsilon)$. Since $\overline{A}(\pm\infty;\varepsilon) = A(c(\varepsilon),\varepsilon)$, $-\overline{A}(\pm\infty;\varepsilon)^*$ ($*$ means the transpose) has one negative eigenvalue $-\nu(c(\varepsilon),\varepsilon)$ and four eigenvalues with positive real part. The eigenvector corresponding to $-\nu(c(\varepsilon),\varepsilon)$ is described by

$$\boldsymbol{\gamma}^*(\varepsilon) = {}^t(\ \nu(\varepsilon)-\varepsilon c(\varepsilon), 1, F_m(0,\overline{m},\overline{n},\overline{h})/(\nu(\varepsilon)+\frac{\gamma_m(0)}{\varepsilon c(\varepsilon)}),$$
$$F_n(0,\overline{m},\overline{n},\overline{h})/(\nu(\varepsilon)+\frac{\varepsilon}{c(\varepsilon)}\gamma_n(0)), F_h(0,\overline{m},\overline{n},\overline{h})/(\nu(\varepsilon)+\frac{\varepsilon}{c(\varepsilon)}\gamma_h(0))),$$

where $\nu(\varepsilon) = \nu(c(\varepsilon),\varepsilon)$. Let us consider

$$\frac{d}{dz}\boldsymbol{\beta}(z;\varepsilon) = -\overline{A}(z;\varepsilon)^*\boldsymbol{\beta}(z;\varepsilon).$$

Then, there is a unique solution $\boldsymbol{\beta}(z;\varepsilon)$ satisfying

$$\text{(3.4)} \qquad \boldsymbol{\beta}(z;\varepsilon) - e^{-\nu(\varepsilon)z}\,\boldsymbol{\gamma}^*(\varepsilon) = O(\ e^{-(\nu(\varepsilon)+\delta)z}\ ) \quad \text{as} \quad z \to +\infty$$

for some $\delta > 0$. Evans' instability criterion for the traveling wave solution $\boldsymbol{\phi}(z;\varepsilon)$ can be stated as follows :

Theorem 5 (Evans [7]). *If*

$$\text{(3.5)} \qquad \lim_{z\to+\infty} e^{-\nu(\varepsilon)z}\boldsymbol{\gamma}^*(\varepsilon)\cdot\frac{\partial\boldsymbol{\phi}_u}{\partial c}(z;c(\varepsilon),\varepsilon) < 0,$$

then the solution $\boldsymbol{\phi}(z;\varepsilon)$ *is unstable.*

We now prove (3.5). Define $\boldsymbol{\phi}_s(z;c,\varepsilon)$ by a solution of (3.3) which has the asymptotic form

$$\boldsymbol{\phi}_s(z;c,\varepsilon) \longrightarrow \boldsymbol{\pi} \quad \text{as} \quad z \to +\infty$$

and

$$\boldsymbol{\phi}_s(z;c(\varepsilon),\varepsilon) = \boldsymbol{\phi}_u(z;c(\varepsilon),\varepsilon) \quad \text{for any} \quad z \in \mathbb{R} \ .$$

That is, there is $\bar{z}$ such that

$$\boldsymbol{\phi}_s(z;c(\varepsilon),\varepsilon) = \boldsymbol{\phi}_u(z;c(\varepsilon),\varepsilon) = \boldsymbol{\phi}(z-\bar{z};\varepsilon) \quad \text{for any} \quad z \in \mathbf{R} \ .$$

Lemma 9. *Let* $g(z;\varepsilon)$ *be*

$$g(z;\varepsilon) = [\ \frac{\partial \boldsymbol{\phi}_u}{\partial c}(z;c(\varepsilon),\varepsilon) - \frac{\partial \boldsymbol{\phi}_s}{\partial c}(z;c(\varepsilon),\varepsilon) \cdot \boldsymbol{\beta}(z-\bar{z};\varepsilon) \ .$$

Then the following assertion holds :

(i) $g(z;\varepsilon)$ *is a constant independent of* z.

(ii) $$\lim_{z\to+\infty} g(z;\varepsilon) = \lim_{z\to+\infty} e^{-\nu(\varepsilon)z}\boldsymbol{\gamma}^*(\varepsilon)\cdot\frac{\partial \boldsymbol{\phi}_u}{\partial c}(z;c(\varepsilon),\varepsilon) \ .$$

Proof. Appending $\frac{dc}{dz} = 0$ to (3.3), we obtain the following system in $\mathbf{R}^6$ - space :

$$\text{(3.6)} \quad \begin{cases} \dfrac{d}{dz}\mathbf{U} = \mathbf{F}(\mathbf{U},c,\varepsilon) \\[2ex] \dfrac{dc}{dz} = 0 \ . \end{cases}$$

The linearized system of (3.6) about ${}^t(\ \boldsymbol{\phi}(z-\bar{z};\varepsilon), c(\varepsilon)\ )$ can be written as

$$\text{(3.7)} \qquad \frac{d}{dz}\mathbf{P}(z;\varepsilon) = E(z;\varepsilon)\,\mathbf{P}(z;\varepsilon)\ ,$$

where

$$E(z;\varepsilon) = \left(\begin{array}{c:c} \overline{A}(z-\overline{z};\varepsilon) & \begin{matrix} 0 \\ \varepsilon u(z-\overline{z}) \\ -\frac{1}{c(\varepsilon)}\frac{d}{dz}m(z-\overline{z}) \\ -\frac{1}{c(\varepsilon)}\frac{d}{dz}n(z-\overline{z}) \\ -\frac{1}{c(\varepsilon)}\frac{d}{dz}h(z-\overline{z}) \end{matrix} \\ \hdashline \mathbf{0} & 0 \end{array}\right) .$$

We note here that

$$\mathbf{P}_1(z;\varepsilon) = {}^t\!\left(\frac{\partial \boldsymbol{\phi}_u}{\partial c}(z;c(\varepsilon),\varepsilon),\ 1\right)$$

and

$$\mathbf{P}_2(z;\varepsilon) = {}^t\!\left(\frac{\partial \boldsymbol{\phi}_s}{\partial c}(z;c(\varepsilon),\varepsilon),\ 1\right)$$

satisfy (3.7). Let us consider the adjoint system of (3.7) :

$$\text{(3.8)} \qquad \frac{d}{dz}\mathbf{P}(z;\varepsilon)^* = -\,E(z;\varepsilon)^*\,\mathbf{P}(z;\varepsilon)^*\ .$$

Let $\beta_i(z;\varepsilon)$ ($i=1,2,3,4,5$) be the i-th component of $\boldsymbol{\beta}(z;\varepsilon)$ and define $\gamma(z;\varepsilon)$ by a solution of

$$\frac{d\gamma}{dz} = -\varepsilon u(z)\beta_2(z;\varepsilon) + \frac{1}{c(\varepsilon)}\frac{dm}{dz}(z)\beta_3(z;\varepsilon) + \frac{1}{c(\varepsilon)}\frac{dn}{dz}(z)\beta_4(z;\varepsilon) + \frac{1}{c(\varepsilon)}\frac{dh}{dz}(z)\beta_5(z;\varepsilon)$$

with $\gamma(z;\varepsilon) \to 0$ as $z \to +\infty$. Then the function

$$\mathbf{P}_3(z;\varepsilon) = {}^t(\,\boldsymbol{\beta}(z-\bar{z};\varepsilon),\ \gamma(z-\bar{z};\varepsilon)\,)$$

is a solution of (3.8) and decays to $\mathbf{0}$ as $z \to +\infty$. Since $\mathbf{P}_1$ and $\mathbf{P}_2$ satisfy (3.7) and $\mathbf{P}_3$ satisfies (3.8), $\mathbf{P}_1\cdot\mathbf{P}_3$ and $\mathbf{P}_2\cdot\mathbf{P}_3$ are independent of z. This implies that

$$g(z;\varepsilon) = (\,\mathbf{P}_1 - \mathbf{P}_2\,)\cdot\mathbf{P}_3$$

is independent of z. Thus (i) is proved.

Next, we show (ii). Since $\boldsymbol{\phi}_s(z;c,\varepsilon)$ is a solution of (3.3), $\frac{\partial}{\partial c}\boldsymbol{\phi}_s(z;c,\varepsilon)$ satisfies

$$\begin{cases} \dfrac{d}{dz}\dfrac{\partial\boldsymbol{\phi}_s}{\partial c} = (\,\dfrac{\partial\mathbf{F}}{\partial\mathbf{U}}\,)(\boldsymbol{\phi}_s,c,\varepsilon)\,\dfrac{\partial\boldsymbol{\phi}_s}{\partial c} + (\,\dfrac{\partial\mathbf{F}}{\partial c}\,)(\boldsymbol{\phi}_s,c,\varepsilon)\,, \\ \lim\limits_{z\to+\infty}\dfrac{\partial\boldsymbol{\phi}_s}{\partial c}(z;c,\varepsilon) \ \text{ is bounded}\,. \end{cases}$$

Thus, $\lim\limits_{z\to+\infty}\dfrac{\partial\boldsymbol{\phi}_s}{\partial c}(z;c(\varepsilon),\varepsilon) = 0$ follows so that, by (3.4), (ii) can be shown.

From Theorem 5 and Lemma 9, we find that the instability of $\boldsymbol{\phi}(z;\varepsilon)$ can be proved by showing $g < 0$ at one appropriate point $z^* \in \mathbb{R}$. To do it, we explicitly construct $\boldsymbol{\phi}_u(z;c,\varepsilon)$ for $z \in (-\infty,z^*]$ and $\boldsymbol{\phi}_s(z;c,\varepsilon)$ for $z \in [z^*,+\infty)$ by the singular perturbation method used in Section 2. Using the solution $(v^{(i)},m^{(i)},n^{(i)},h^{(i)})$ obtained in Section 2 on each subinterval I_i ($i=1,2,3,4$) ; let $\mathbf{U}_i(z;\varepsilon,c,\kappa_1,\tau_1)$ be defined by

$$\mathbf{U}_i(z;\varepsilon,c,\kappa_1,\tau_1) = {}^t(v^{(i)},\frac{d}{dz}v^{(i)},m^{(i)},n^{(i)},h^{(i)})(\varepsilon z;\varepsilon,c,\kappa_1,\tau_1).$$

Then by the first and the second equations of (2.92), $\kappa_1 = \kappa_1(c,\varepsilon)$ and $\tau_1 = \tau_1(c,\varepsilon)$ are uniquely determined as functions of c and ε.

Therefore by putting $z^* = \bar{z} + \kappa_0^* + \varepsilon\tau_1(c,\varepsilon)$, $\boldsymbol{\phi}_u(z;c,\varepsilon)$ and $\boldsymbol{\phi}_s(z;c,\varepsilon)$ are respectively represented as

$$\boldsymbol{\phi}_u(z;c,\varepsilon) = \begin{cases} \mathbf{U}_1(z-\bar{z};\varepsilon,c,\kappa_1(c,\varepsilon),\tau_1(c,\varepsilon)), & z \in (-\infty,\bar{z}-\kappa_0^*-\varepsilon\kappa_1(c,\varepsilon)] \\ \mathbf{U}_2(z-\bar{z};\varepsilon,c,\kappa_1(c,\varepsilon),\tau_1(c,\varepsilon)), & z \in [\bar{z}-\kappa_0^*-\varepsilon\kappa_1(c,\varepsilon),\bar{z}] \\ \mathbf{U}_3(z-\bar{z};\varepsilon,c,\kappa_1(c,\varepsilon),\tau_1(c,\varepsilon)), & z \in [\bar{z},z^*] \end{cases}$$

and

$$\boldsymbol{\phi}_s(z;c,\varepsilon) = \mathbf{U}_4(z-\bar{z};\varepsilon,c,\kappa_1(c,\varepsilon),\tau_1(c,\varepsilon)), \quad z \in [z^*,+\infty) .$$

Hence it follows that for sufficiently small $\varepsilon > 0$,

$$(3.9) \qquad \frac{\partial \boldsymbol{\phi}_u}{\partial c}(z^*;c(\varepsilon),\varepsilon) - \frac{\partial \boldsymbol{\phi}_s}{\partial c}(z^*;c(\varepsilon),\varepsilon)$$

$$= \frac{\partial}{\partial c}[\,\mathbf{U}_3 - \mathbf{U}_4\,](\kappa_0^*+\varepsilon\tau_1(c(\varepsilon),\varepsilon);\varepsilon,c(\varepsilon),\kappa_1(c(\varepsilon),\varepsilon),\tau_1(c(\varepsilon),\varepsilon))$$

$$= {}^t(\,0,\,\rho,\,0,\,0,\,0\,)$$

where

$$\rho = \frac{\varepsilon}{\kappa_0^*}\Big[\Big(\frac{\partial}{\partial c}\phi_1^{(3)\prime}(1) - \kappa_0^*\frac{\partial}{\partial c}\phi_1^{(4)\cdot}(0)\Big) + \Big(\frac{\partial}{\partial \tau_1}\phi_1^{(3)\prime}(1) - \phi_0^{(4)\cdot}(0)\Big)\frac{\partial \tau_1}{\partial c}\Big]$$

$$+ 0(\,\varepsilon^2\,)$$

$$= \frac{\varepsilon}{\kappa_0^*}\Big[\,\frac{\partial C_1}{\partial c} + \frac{\partial C_1}{\partial \tau_1}\,\frac{\partial \tau_1}{\partial c}\,\Big] + 0(\,\varepsilon^2\,)$$

$$= -4\varepsilon\Big(\frac{g_1(0;\kappa_0^*)}{g_1(0;\kappa_0^*)'}\Big)^2 \frac{(\phi_0^{(2)\prime\prime}(0;\kappa_0^*))^2}{\phi_0^{(1)\cdot}(0)}\Big[\int_{-\infty}^{0}(\phi_0^{(1)\cdot}(z))^2$$

$$\times (1 - F_m(\phi_0^{(1)}(z),\bar{m}+\psi_0^{(1)}(z),\bar{n},\bar{h})\,\frac{m_\infty{}'(\phi_0^{(1)}(z))}{\gamma_m(\phi_0^{(1)}(z))}\,)dz$$

$$+ \frac{1}{\kappa_0^*} \int_{-1}^{0} (\phi_0^{(2)\prime}(z;\kappa_0^*))^2 (1 - F_m(\phi_0^{(2)}(z;\kappa_0^*), \psi_0^{(2)}(z;\kappa_0^*), \bar{n}, \bar{h})$$

$$\times \frac{m_\infty'(\phi_0^{(2)}(z;\kappa_0^*))}{\gamma_m(\phi_0^{(2)}(z;\kappa_0^*))})dz \;] + O(\varepsilon^2)$$

$$< 0 .$$

Here we used the relations $\phi_0^{(1)\cdot}(0) > 0$, $F_m < 0$, $m_\infty' > 0$ and $\gamma_m > 0$. On the other hand, since $\boldsymbol{\beta}(z^*;\varepsilon)$ is normal to the four dimensional stable manifold at $\boldsymbol{\phi}(z^*;\varepsilon)$, it can be also explicitly constructed by using the singular perturbation technique as follows :

$$(3.10) \qquad \boldsymbol{\beta}(z^*;\varepsilon) = \left(\begin{pmatrix} -\phi_0^{(4)\cdot\cdot}(0)/\phi_0^{(4)\cdot}(0) \\ 1 \\ 0 \\ -\int_0^{\nu_1} F_n(v, m_\infty(v), \bar{n}, \bar{h})dv/\phi_0^{(4)\cdot}(0) \\ -\int_0^{\nu_1} F_h(v, m_\infty(v), \bar{n}, \bar{h})dv/\phi_0^{(4)\cdot}(0) \end{pmatrix} + o(1) \right) e^{-\nu(\varepsilon)z^*}$$

as $\varepsilon \to 0$. This formula is shown in the appendix. Therefore (3.9) and (3.10) immediately lead to

$$g(z^*;\varepsilon) < 0 ,$$

which completes the proof of Theorem B.

Appendix

In this section, we prove Lemmas 4, 7, 8 and (3.10).

Proof of Lemma 4.

(i) and (ii) are obvious. We only show (iii). To do so, it is sufficient to show that for any $g = {}^t(g^{(p)}, g^{(q)}, g^{(r)}, g^{(s)}) \in Z_\sigma$, there uniquely exists $t \in \mathring{Y}_{\sigma,\varepsilon}$ satisfying

$$T_t(0;\varepsilon,c)t = g \tag{A.1}$$

such that

$$\|t\|_{\mathring{Y}_{\sigma,\varepsilon}} \le K \|g\|_{Z_\sigma}$$

for a positive constant K independent of ε and c, where $T_t(0;\varepsilon,c)$ is of the form

$$T_t(0;\varepsilon,c) = \begin{pmatrix} T_p^{(p)} & T_q^{(p)} & T_r^{(p)} & T_s^{(p)} \\ T_p^{(q)} & T_q^{(q)} & 0 & 0 \\ T_p^{(r)} & 0 & T_r^{(r)} & 0 \\ T_p^{(s)} & 0 & 0 & T_s^{(s)} \end{pmatrix} .$$

Here

$$T_p^{(p)} = \frac{d^2}{d\xi^2} - \varepsilon c \frac{d}{d\xi} - F_v(\Phi,\Psi,\Pi,\Omega) - m_\infty{}'(\phi_0)F_m(\Phi,\Psi,\Pi,\Omega) ,$$

$$T_q^{(p)} = -F_m(\Phi,\Psi,\Pi,\Omega) ,$$

$$T_r^{(p)} = -\varepsilon F_n(\Phi,\Psi,\Pi,\Omega) ,$$

$$T_s^{(p)} = -\varepsilon F_h(\Phi,\Psi,\Pi,\Omega) ,$$

$$T_p^{(q)} = \varepsilon c m_\infty'(\phi_0)\frac{d}{d\xi} + \varepsilon c m_\infty''(\phi_0)\dot{\phi}_0 - \gamma_m'(\Phi)(m_\infty(\Phi) - \Psi)$$

$$- \gamma_m(\Phi)(m_\infty'(\Phi) - m_\infty'(\phi_0)) ,$$

$$T_q^{(q)} = \varepsilon c \frac{d}{d\xi} + \gamma_m(\Phi) ,$$

$$T_p^{(r)} = -\gamma_n'(\Phi)(n_\infty(\Phi) - \Pi) - \gamma_n(\Phi)n_\infty'(\Phi) ,$$

$$T_r^{(r)} = c\frac{d}{d\xi} + \varepsilon\gamma_n(\Phi) ,$$

$$T_p^{(s)} = -\gamma_h'(\Phi)(h_\infty(\Phi) - \Omega) - \gamma_h(\Phi)h_\infty'(\Phi) ,$$

and

$$T_s^{(s)} = c\frac{d}{d\xi} + \varepsilon\gamma_h(\Phi) ,$$

where

$$\Phi = \phi_0 + \varepsilon\phi_1,\ \Psi = \bar{m} + \psi_0 + \varepsilon\psi_1,\ \Pi = \bar{n} + \varepsilon\pi_1 + \varepsilon^2\pi_2 \text{ and } \Omega = \bar{h} + \varepsilon\omega_1 + \varepsilon^2\omega_2.$$

It is easily verified that

$$\text{(A.2)}\quad \begin{cases} \| T_q^{(p)} \|_{X^1_{\sigma,\varepsilon}(\mathbb{R}_-) \to X^0_{\sigma,1}(\mathbb{R}_-)} = O(1) \\ \| T_r^{(p)} \|_{X^1_{\sigma,1}(\mathbb{R}_-) \to X^0_{\sigma,1}(\mathbb{R}_-)} = O(\varepsilon) \\ \| T_s^{(p)} \|_{X^1_{\sigma,1}(\mathbb{R}_-) \to X^0_{\sigma,1}(\mathbb{R}_-)} = O(\varepsilon) \text{ , uniformly in } c \\ \| T_p^{(q)} \|_{\mathring{X}^2_{\sigma,1}(\mathbb{R}_-) \to X^0_{\sigma,1}(\mathbb{R}_-)} = O(\varepsilon) \\ \| T_p^{(r)} \|_{\mathring{X}^2_{\sigma,1}(\mathbb{R}_-) \to X^0_{\sigma,1}(\mathbb{R}_-)} = O(1) \end{cases}$$

$$\| T_p^{(s)} \|_{\overset{\circ}{X}{}^2_{\sigma,1}(\mathbb{R}_-) \to X^0_{\sigma,1}(\mathbb{R}_-)} = 0(1)$$

and that $T_q^{(q)}$, $T_r^{(r)}$ and $T_s^{(s)}$ are uniformly invertible in (ε,c). Suppose that $T_p^{(p)}(0;\varepsilon,c)$ has a uniformly bounded inverse from $X^0_{\sigma,1}(\mathbb{R}_-)$ into $\overset{\circ}{X}{}^2_{\sigma,1}(\mathbb{R}_-)$ in (ε,c). Then (A.1) can be written as

$$\text{(A.3)}\quad \begin{cases} p = T_p^{(p)^{-1}}(T_1 p - (T_q^{(p)} T_q^{(q)^{-1}} g^{(q)} + T_r^{(p)} T_r^{(r)^{-1}} g^{(r)} \\ \qquad + T_s^{(p)} T_s^{(s)^{-1}} g^{(s)}) + g^{(p)}) \\ q = -T_q^{(q)^{-1}}(T_p^{(q)} p - g^{(q)}) \\ r = -T_r^{(r)^{-1}}(T_p^{(r)} p - g^{(r)}) \\ s = -T_s^{(s)^{-1}}(T_p^{(s)} p - g^{(s)}) , \end{cases}$$

where $T_1 = T_q^{(p)} T_q^{(q)^{-1}} T_p^{(q)} + T_r^{(p)} T_r^{(r)^{-1}} T_p^{(r)} + T_s^{(p)} T_s^{(s)^{-1}} T_p^{(s)}$. It follows from (A.2) that $\| T_p^{(p)^{-1}} T_1 \|_{X^0_{\sigma,1} \to X^0_{\sigma,1}} < 1$ as $\varepsilon \to 0$, so that (A.3) has a unique solution (p,q,r,s) in $\overset{\circ}{Y}_{\sigma,\varepsilon}$. Thus it is sufficient to show the uniform invertibility of $T_p^{(p)}(0;\varepsilon,c)$. From (2.24) we know that $T_p^{(p)}(0;0,c) \equiv \frac{d^2}{d\xi^2} - F_1(\xi)$ has a bounded inverse from $X^0_{\sigma,1}(\mathbb{R}_-)$ into $\overset{\circ}{X}{}^2_{\sigma,1}(\mathbb{R}_-)$, which is uniform in c. Furthermore, noting $\| T_p^{(p)}(0;\varepsilon,c) - T_p^{(p)}(0;0,c) \|_{\overset{\circ}{X}{}^2_{\sigma,1} \to X^0_{\sigma,1}} = 0(\varepsilon)$, we find that $T_p^{(p)}(0;\varepsilon,c)$ is uniformly invertible. By an argument similar to that of T, we know that (i) - (iii) also hold for $\frac{\partial T}{\partial c}$, which completes the proof.

Proof of Lemma 7.

Since (i) and (ii) are obvious, we only consider (iii). Note that $T_t(0;\varepsilon,c,\kappa_1,\tau_1)$ is of the form

$$T_t(0;\varepsilon,c,\kappa_1,\tau_1) = \begin{pmatrix} T_p^{(p)} & T_q^{(p)} & T_r^{(p)} & T_s^{(p)} \\ T_p^{(q)} & T_q^{(q)} & T_r^{(q)} & T_s^{(q)} \\ T_p^{(r)} & 0 & T_r^{(r)} & T_s^{(r)} \\ T_p^{(s)} & 0 & T_r^{(s)} & T_s^{(s)} \end{pmatrix} .$$

Here

$$T_p^{(p)} = \varepsilon^2 \frac{d^2}{dy^2} - \varepsilon^2 c \frac{d}{dy} - F_v(\Phi,\Psi,\Pi,\Omega) - m_\infty'(\phi_0)F_m(\Phi,\Psi,\Pi,\Omega) ,$$

$$T_q^{(p)} = -e^{-\sigma y}F_m(\Phi,\Psi,\Pi,\Omega) ,$$

$$T_r^{(p)} = -\varepsilon^2 e^{-\sigma y}F_n^0\left(\frac{d^2}{dy^2} - 2\sigma \frac{d}{dy} - c \frac{d}{dy} + \sigma^2 + \sigma c\right)$$
$$+ e^{-\sigma y}\left\{ \frac{F_v(\Phi,\Psi,\Pi,\Omega) + m_\infty'(\phi_0)F_m(\Phi,\Psi,\Pi,\Omega)}{F_v(0,\bar{m},\bar{n},\bar{h}) + m_\infty'(0)F_m(0,\bar{m},\bar{n},\bar{h})} F_n(0,\bar{m},\bar{n},\bar{h}) - F_n(\Phi,\Psi,\Pi,\Omega)\right\},$$

$$T_s^{(p)} = -\varepsilon^2 e^{-\sigma y}F_h^0\left(\frac{d^2}{dy^2} - 2\sigma \frac{d}{dy} - c \frac{d}{dy} + \sigma^2 + \sigma c\right)$$
$$+ e^{-\sigma y}\left\{ \frac{F_v(\Phi,\Psi,\Pi,\Omega) + m_\infty'(\phi_0)F_m(\Phi,\Psi,\Pi,\Omega)}{F_v(0,\bar{m},\bar{n},\bar{h}) + m_\infty'(0)F_m(0,\bar{m},\bar{n},\bar{h})} F_h(0,\bar{m},\bar{n},\bar{h}) - F_h(\Phi,\Psi,\Pi,\Omega)\right\},$$

$$T_p^{(q)} = \varepsilon c e^{\sigma y}\left(\varepsilon m_\infty'(\phi_0) \frac{d}{dy} + m_\infty''(\phi_0)\phi_0^{\cdot}\right) - e^{\sigma y}\gamma_m'(\Phi)(m_\infty(\Phi) - \Psi)$$
$$- e^{\sigma y}\gamma_m(\Phi)(m_\infty'(\Phi) - m_\infty'(\phi_0)) ,$$

$$T_q^{(q)} = \varepsilon^2 c\left(\frac{d}{dy} - \sigma\right) + \gamma_m(\Phi) ,$$

$$T_r^{(q)} = (\varepsilon c(-\varepsilon m_\infty'(\phi_0)\frac{d}{dy} + (\varepsilon\sigma m_\infty'(\phi_0) - m_\infty''(\phi_0)\phi_0^{\cdot})) + \gamma_m'(\Phi)(m_\infty(\Phi) - \Psi)$$

$$+ \gamma_m(\Phi)(m_\infty'(\Phi) - m_\infty'(\phi_0)))F_n^0 ,$$

$$T_s^{(q)} = (\varepsilon c(-\varepsilon m_\infty'(\phi_0)\frac{d}{dy} + (\varepsilon\sigma m_\infty'(\phi_0) - m_\infty''(\phi_0)\phi_0^{\cdot})) + \gamma_m'(\Phi)(m_\infty(\Phi) - \Psi)$$

$$+ \gamma_m(\Phi)(m_\infty'(\Phi) - m_\infty'(\phi_0)))F_h^0 ,$$

$$T_p^{(r)} = -e^{\sigma y}(\gamma_n'(\Phi)(n_\infty(\Phi) - \Pi) + \gamma_n(\Phi)n_\infty'(\Phi)) ,$$

$$T_r^{(r)} = c\frac{d}{dy} - \sigma c + \gamma_n'(\Phi)(n_\infty(\Phi) - \Pi)F_n^0 + \gamma_n(\Phi)(n_\infty'(\Phi)F_n^0 + 1) ,$$

$$T_s^{(r)} = (\gamma_n'(\Phi)(n_\infty(\Phi) - \Pi) + \gamma_n(\Phi)n_\infty'(\Phi))F_h^0 ,$$

$$T_p^{(s)} = -e^{\sigma y}(\gamma_h'(\Phi)(h_\infty(\Phi) - \Omega) + \gamma_h(\Phi)h_\infty'(\Phi)) ,$$

$$T_r^{(s)} = (\gamma_h'(\Phi)(h_\infty(\Phi) - \Omega) + \gamma_h(\Phi)h_\infty'(\Phi))F_n^0 ,$$

$$T_s^{(s)} = c\frac{d}{dy} - \sigma c + \gamma_h'(\Phi)(h_\infty(\Phi) - \Omega)F_h^0 + \gamma_h(\Phi)(h_\infty'(\Phi)F_h^0 + 1) ,$$

where $\Phi = \varepsilon v_1 + \phi_0 + \varepsilon\phi_1$, $\Psi = \bar{m} + \varepsilon m_1 + \psi_0 + \varepsilon\psi_1 + \varepsilon e^{-\sigma y}M$, $\Pi = \bar{n} + \varepsilon n_1 + \varepsilon\pi_1 + \varepsilon^2(\pi_2 - e^{-\sigma y}\pi_2(0)) + \varepsilon^2 e^{-\sigma y}N$ and $\Omega = \bar{h} + \varepsilon h_1 + \varepsilon\omega_1 + \varepsilon^2(\omega_2 - e^{-\sigma y}\omega_2(0)) + \varepsilon^2 e^{-\sigma y}H$. It is easy to show that

$$\left\{\begin{array}{l}
\| T_q^{(p)} \|_{\mathring{X}^1_{\sigma,\varepsilon^2}(\mathbb{R}_+) \to X^0_{\sigma,1}(\mathbb{R}_+)} = O(1) \\
\| T_r^{(p)} \|_{\mathring{E}^2_\varepsilon(\mathbb{R}_+) \to X^0_{\sigma,1}(\mathbb{R}_+)} = O(\varepsilon) \\
\| T_s^{(p)} \|_{\mathring{E}^2_\varepsilon(\mathbb{R}_+) \to X^0_{\sigma,1}(\mathbb{R}_+)} = O(\varepsilon) \\
\| T_p^{(q)} \|_{\mathring{X}^2_{\sigma,\varepsilon}(\mathbb{R}_+) \to C^0(\mathbb{R}_+)} = O(\varepsilon) \\
\| T_r^{(q)} \|_{\mathring{E}^2_\varepsilon(\mathbb{R}_+) \to C^0(\mathbb{R}_+)} = O(\varepsilon) \qquad \text{uniformly in } (c,\kappa_1,\tau_1). \\
\| T_s^{(q)} \|_{\mathring{E}^2_\varepsilon(\mathbb{R}_+) \to C^0(\mathbb{R}_+)} = O(\varepsilon) \\
\| T_p^{(r)} \|_{\mathring{X}^2_{\sigma,\varepsilon}(\mathbb{R}_+) \to X^1_{0,\varepsilon}(\mathbb{R}_+)} = O(1) \\
\| T_p^{(s)} \|_{\mathring{X}^2_{\sigma,\varepsilon}(\mathbb{R}_+) \to X^1_{0,\varepsilon}(\mathbb{R}_+)} = O(1) \\
\| T_q^{(q)^{-1}} \|_{C^0(\mathbb{R}_+) \to \mathring{X}^1_{\sigma,\varepsilon^2}(\mathbb{R}_+)} = O(1)
\end{array}\right.$$

By an argument similar to that in the proof of Lemma 4, we know that $T_p^{(p)}$ has a uniformly bounded inverse in $(\varepsilon,c,\kappa_1,\tau_1)$. In order to prove (iii), it is sufficient to show that $T_2 = \begin{pmatrix} T_r^{(r)} & T_s^{(r)} \\ T_r^{(s)} & T_s^{(s)} \end{pmatrix}$ has a uniformly bounded inverse in $(\varepsilon,c,\kappa_1,\tau_1)$. To do it, we prove that for any $g \in X^1_{0,\varepsilon}(\mathbb{R}_+) \times X^1_{0,\varepsilon}(\mathbb{R}_+)$, $T_2 u = g$ has a unique solution $u \in \mathring{E}^2_\varepsilon(\mathbb{R}_+) \times \mathring{E}^2_\varepsilon(\mathbb{R}_+)$ satisfying

$$\|u\|_{\mathring{E}^2_\varepsilon(\mathbb{R}_+) \times \mathring{E}^2_\varepsilon(\mathbb{R}_+)} \le K \|g\|_{X^1_{0,\varepsilon}(\mathbb{R}_+) \times X^1_{0,\varepsilon}(\mathbb{R}_+)}$$

for a positive constant K independent of ε, c, κ_1 and τ_1. First we can rewrite $T_2u = g$ as a convinient form

$$u' = D(+\infty)u + (D(y) - D(+\infty))u + g(y)/c, \quad u(0) = 0 ,$$

where

$$D(y) = \begin{pmatrix} \sigma - \frac{1}{c}\gamma_n'(\Phi)(n_\infty(\Phi) - \Pi)F_n^0 - \frac{1}{c}\gamma_n(\Phi)(n_\infty'(\Phi)F_n^0 + 1) & -\frac{1}{c}(\gamma_n'(\Phi)(n_\infty(\Phi) - \Pi) + \gamma_n(\Phi)n_\infty'(\Phi))F_h^0 \\ -\frac{1}{c}(\gamma_h'(\Phi)(h_\infty(\Phi) - \Omega) + \gamma_h(\Phi)h_\infty'(\Phi))F_n^0 & \sigma - \frac{1}{c}\gamma_h'(\Phi)(h_\infty(\Phi) - \Omega)F_h^0 - \frac{1}{c}\gamma_h(\Phi)(h_\infty'(\Phi)F_h^0 + 1) \end{pmatrix}$$

and

$$D(+\infty) = \begin{pmatrix} \sigma - \frac{1}{c}\gamma_n(0)(n_\infty'(0)F_n^0 + 1) & -\frac{1}{c}\gamma_n(0)n_\infty'(0)F_h^0 \\ -\frac{1}{c}\gamma_h(0)h_\infty'(0)F_n^0 & \sigma - \frac{1}{c}\gamma_h(0)(h_\infty'(0)F_h^0 + 1) \end{pmatrix}.$$

When $\sigma > 0$ is chosen sufficiently small, $D(+\infty)$ has two eigenvalues with negative real part. Therefore, there exist $d > 0$ and $L > 0$ independent of ε, c, κ_1 and τ_1 such that $|e^{D(+\infty)y}| \le Le^{-dy}$ for $y \in \mathbb{R}_+$. On the other hand, there exists $y_0 > 0$ such that $|(D(y) - D(+\infty))u| \le d|u|/2L$ for any $y \ge y_0$. It follows that there exists a positive constant K independent of ε, c, κ_1 and τ_1 such that $\|u\|_{C^0(\mathbb{R}_+) \times C^0(\mathbb{R}_+)} \le K\|g\|_{C^0(\mathbb{R}_+) \times C^0(\mathbb{R}_+)}$ (see Coddington and Levinson [Chapter 13:2]). By an argument similar to that of T, we know that (i) - (iii) also hold for $\frac{\partial T}{\partial c}$, $\frac{\partial T}{\partial \kappa_1}$ and $\frac{\partial T}{\partial \tau_1}$. Thus, the proof of Lemma 7 is completed.

Proof of Lemma 8.

Note that A_2, B_2 and C_2 are of order $O(\varepsilon)$ uniformly in (c,κ_1,τ_1). Then when ε tends to zero, (2.93) leads to

$$\text{(A.4)} \qquad A_1(c,\kappa_1,\tau_1) = \phi_1{}^{(2)}(0;c,\kappa_0^*,\kappa_1) - \phi_1{}^{(3)}(0;c,\tau_1) = 0$$

$$\text{(A.5)} \qquad B_1(c,\kappa_1) = \kappa_1\phi_0{}^{(1)\cdot}(0) + \kappa_0^*\phi_1{}^{(1)\cdot}(0;c) - \phi_1{}^{(2)}{}'(-1;c,\kappa_0^*,\kappa_1) = 0$$

$$\text{(A.6)} \qquad C_1(c,\tau_1) = \phi_1{}^{(3)}{}'(1;c,\tau_1) - \tau_1\phi_0{}^{(4)\cdot}(0) - \kappa_0^*\phi_1{}^{(4)\cdot}(0;c) = 0\ .$$

By (A.5) and (A.6), we have

$$\text{(A.7)} \qquad \phi_1{}^{(2)}{}'(-1;c,\kappa_0^*,\kappa_1) + \phi_1{}^{(3)}{}'(1;c,\tau_1) = \kappa_1\phi_0{}^{(1)\cdot}(0) + \tau_1\phi_0{}^{(4)\cdot}(0)$$
$$+ \kappa_0^*(\phi_1{}^{(1)\cdot}(0;c) + \phi_1{}^{(4)\cdot}(0;c))\ .$$

On the other hand, by using (2.39), (2.46), (2.60) and (A.4), we have

$$\text{(A.8)} \qquad \phi_1{}^{(2)}{}'(-1;c,\kappa_0^*,\kappa_1) + \phi_1{}^{(3)}{}'(1;c,\tau_1)$$
$$= 2g_1{}'(-1;\kappa_0^*)\{\kappa_0^*(\tau_1 - \kappa_1)\int_{-1}^{0}\phi_0{}^{(2)}{}'(z;\kappa_0^*)$$
$$\times F(\phi_0{}^{(2)}(z;\kappa_0^*),\psi_0{}^{(2)}(z;\kappa_0^*),\bar{n},\bar{h})dz + \int_{-1}^{0}\phi_0{}^{(2)}{}'(z;\kappa_0^*)L_1(z;c)dz\}$$

$$= 2\{(\tau_1 - \kappa_1)\int_{\nu_1}^{v^*} F(v, m_\infty(v), \bar{n}, \bar{h})dv +$$

$$+ \int_{-1}^{0} \phi_0^{(2)\prime}(z;\kappa_0^*)L_1(z;c)dz\}/\phi_0^{(1)\cdot}(0)$$

$$= (\kappa_1 - \tau_1)(\phi_0^{(2)\prime}(-1;\kappa_0^*))^2/(\kappa_0^{*2}\phi_0^{(1)\cdot}(0))$$

$$+ 2\int_{-1}^{0} \phi_0^{(2)\prime}(z;\kappa_0^*)L_1(z;c)dz/\phi_0^{(1)\cdot}(0)$$

$$= (\kappa_1 - \tau_1)\phi_0^{(1)\cdot}(0) + 2\int_{-1}^{0} \phi_0^{(2)\prime}(z;\kappa_0^*)L_1(z;c)dz/\phi_0^{(1)\cdot}(0) ,$$

where

$$L_1(z;c) = -c\kappa_0^*\phi_0^{(2)\prime}(z;\kappa_0^*) + \kappa_0^{*3}F_n(\phi_0^{(2)}(z;\kappa_0^*), \psi_0^{(2)}(z;\kappa_0^*), \bar{n}, \bar{h})$$

$$\times \int_z^0 \gamma_n(\phi_0^{(2)}(\xi;\kappa_0^*))\{n_\infty(\phi_0^{(2)}(\xi;\kappa_0^*)) - \bar{n}\}d\xi/c$$

$$+ \kappa_0^{*3}F_h(\phi_0^{(2)}(z;\kappa_0^*), \psi_0^{(2)}(z;\kappa_0^*), \bar{n}, \bar{h})$$

$$\times \int_z^0 \gamma_h(\phi_0^{(2)}(\xi;\kappa_0^*))\{h_\infty(\phi_0^{(2)}(\xi;\kappa_0^*)) - \bar{h}\}d\xi/c$$

$$+ \kappa_0^* c\, F_m(\phi_0^{(2)}(z;\kappa_0^*), \psi_0^{(2)}(z;\kappa_0^*), \bar{n}, \bar{h})\psi_0^{(2)\prime}(z;\kappa_0^*)$$

$$/\gamma_m(\phi_0^{(2)}(z;\kappa_0^*)) .$$

In the same way, we obtain

(A.9) $$\phi_1^{(1)\cdot}(0;c) + \phi_1^{(4)\cdot}(0;c) = 2\kappa_0^* \int_{-\infty}^{0} \phi_0^{(1)\cdot}(z)[c\phi_0^{(1)\cdot}(z)$$

$$\times (1 - F_m(\phi_0^{(1)}(z), \bar{m} + \psi_0^{(1)}(z), \bar{n}, \bar{h})\,\frac{m_\infty'(\phi_0^{(1)}(z))}{\gamma_m(\phi_0^{(1)}(z))})$$

$$+ F_n(\phi_0^{(1)}(z),\bar{m}+\psi_0^{(1)}(z),\bar{n},\bar{h})(\pi_1^{(1)}(z;c) - n_1^{(4)}(0;c)/2)$$

$$+ F_h(\phi_0^{(1)}(z),\bar{m}+\psi_0^{(1)}(z),\bar{n},\bar{h})(\omega_1^{(1)}(z;c) - h_1^{(4)}(0;c)/2)]dz$$

$$/\phi_0^{(1)\cdot}(0) .$$

Thus, (A.7), (A.8) and (A.9) lead to

$$c_*^2 L_2 = L_{1n} + L_{1h} + \kappa_0^*(L_{2n} + L_{2h})$$

where

$$L_2 = \int_{-\infty}^{0}(\phi_0^{(1)\cdot}(z))^2\{1 - F_m(\phi_0^{(1)}(z),\bar{m}+\psi_0^{(1)}(z),\bar{n},\bar{h})\,\frac{m_\infty'(\phi_0^{(1)}(z))}{\gamma_m(\phi_0^{(1)}(z))}\}\,dz$$

$$+ \frac{1}{\kappa_0^*}\int_{-1}^{0}(\phi_0^{(2)\prime}(z;\kappa_0^*))^2\{1 - F_m(\phi_0^{(2)}(z;\kappa_0^*),\psi_0^{(2)}(z;\kappa_0^*),\bar{n},\bar{h})$$

$$\times \frac{m_\infty'(\phi_0^{(2)}(z;\kappa_0^*))}{\gamma_m(\phi_0^{(2)}(z;\kappa_0^*))}\}\,dz ,$$

$$L_{1n} = \int_0^{\nu_1}F_n(v,m_\infty(v),\bar{n},\bar{h})dv\int_{-\infty}^{0}\gamma_n(\phi_0^{(1)}(z))(n_\infty(\phi_0^{(1)}(z)) - \bar{n})dz$$

$$- \int_{-\infty}^{0}\phi_0^{(1)\cdot}(z)F_n(\phi_0^{(1)}(z),\bar{m}+\psi_0^{(1)}(z),\bar{n},\bar{h})\int_{-\infty}^{z}\gamma_n(\phi_0^{(1)}(\xi))$$

$$\times (n_\infty(\phi_0^{(1)}(\xi)) - \bar{n})d\xi dz ,$$

$$L_{1h} = \int_0^{\nu_1}F_h(v,m_\infty(v),\bar{n},\bar{h})dv\int_{-\infty}^{0}\gamma_h(\phi_0^{(1)}(z))(h_\infty(\phi_0^{(1)}(z)) - \bar{h})dz$$

$$- \int_{-\infty}^{0}\phi_0^{(1)\cdot}(z)F_h(\phi_0^{(1)}(z),\bar{m}+\psi_0^{(1)}(z),\bar{n},\bar{h})\int_{-\infty}^{z}\gamma_h(\phi_0^{(1)}(\xi))$$

$$\times (h_\infty(\phi_0^{(1)}(\xi)) - \bar{h})d\xi dz ,$$

$$L_{2n} = \int_0^{v_1} F_n(v,m_\infty(v),\bar{n},\bar{h})dv \int_{-1}^{0} \gamma_n(\phi_0^{(2)}(z;\kappa_0^*))(n_\infty(\phi_0^{(2)}(z;\kappa_0^*)) - \bar{n})dz$$

$$+ \int_{-1}^{0} \phi_0^{(2)\prime}(z;\kappa_0^*)F_n(\phi_0^{(2)}(z;\kappa_0^*),\psi_0^{(2)}(z;\kappa_0^*),\bar{n},\bar{h}) \int_z^0 \gamma_n(\phi_0^{(2)}(\xi;\kappa_0^*))$$

$$\times (n_\infty(\phi_0^{(2)}(\xi;\kappa_0^*)) - \bar{n})d\xi dz ,$$

$$L_{2h} = \int_0^{v_1} F_h(v,m_\infty(v),\bar{n},\bar{h})dv \int_{-1}^{0} \gamma_h(\phi_0^{(2)}(z;\kappa_0^*))(h_\infty(\phi_0^{(2)}(z;\kappa_0^*)) - \bar{h})dz$$

$$+ \int_{-1}^{0} \phi_0^{(2)\prime}(z;\kappa_0^*)F_h(\phi_0^{(2)}(z;\kappa_0^*),\psi_0^{(2)}(z;\kappa_0^*),\bar{n},\bar{h}) \int_z^0 \gamma_h(\phi_0^{(2)}(\xi;\kappa_0^*))$$

$$\times (h_\infty(\phi_0^{(2)}(\xi;\kappa_0^*)) - \bar{h})d\xi dz .$$

Since L_2, L_{in}, L_{ih} $(i=1,2)$ are all positive constants, we can determine c_* as

$$c_* = \sqrt{(L_{1n} + L_{1h} + \kappa_0^*(L_{2n} + L_{2h}))/L_2} .$$

We next determine κ_1^* and τ_1^*. It follows from (A.5) and (A.6) that

$$\text{(A.10)} \quad \kappa_1^* L_3 = -[\kappa_0^*\phi_1^{(1)\cdot}(0;c_*) + \int_{-1}^{0} G_y(-1,z;\kappa_0^*)(c_*\kappa_0^*\phi_0^{(2)\prime}(z;\kappa_0^*)$$

$$+ \kappa_0^{*2}F_n(\phi_0^{(2)}(z;\kappa_0^*),\psi_0^{(2)}(z;\kappa_0^*),\bar{n},\bar{h})\pi_1^{(2)}(z;c_*,\kappa_0^*)$$

$$+ \kappa_0^{*2}F_h(\phi_0^{(2)}(z;\kappa_0^*),\psi_0^{(2)}(z;\kappa_0^*),\bar{n},\bar{h})\omega_1^{(2)}(z;c_*,\kappa_0^*)$$

$$- \kappa_0^* c_* F_m(\phi_0^{(2)}(z;\kappa_0^*),\psi_0^{(2)}(z;\kappa_0^*),\bar{n},\bar{h}) \frac{\psi_0^{(2)\prime}(z;\kappa_0^*)}{\gamma_m(\phi_0^{(2)}(z;\kappa_0^*))})dz]$$

and

$$(A.11)\qquad \tau_1^* L_4 = -[\kappa_0^*\phi_1^{(4)\cdot}(0;c_*) - \int_0^1 G_y(-1,-z;\kappa_0^*)(c_*\kappa_0^*\phi_0^{(3)\prime}(z)$$
$$+ \kappa_0^{*2}F_n(\phi_0^{(3)}(z),\psi_0^{(3)}(z),\bar{n},\bar{h})\pi_1^{(3)}(z;c_*)$$
$$+ \kappa_0^{*2}F_h(\phi_0^{(3)}(z),\psi_0^{(3)}(z),\bar{n},\bar{h})\omega_1^{(3)}(z;c_*)$$
$$- \kappa_0^* c_* F_m(\phi_0^{(3)}(z),\psi_0^{(3)}(z),\bar{n},\bar{h})\ \frac{\psi_0^{(3)\prime}(z)}{\gamma_m(\phi_0^{(3)}(z))}\ )dz\ ] ,$$

where

$$L_3 = - L_4$$
$$= \phi_0^{(1)\cdot}(0) + 2\kappa_0^*\int_{-1}^0 G_y(-1,z;\kappa_0^*)F(\phi_0^{(2)}(z;\kappa_0^*),\psi_0^{(2)}(z;\kappa_0^*),\bar{n},\bar{h})dz\ .$$

Let us show $L_3 \neq 0$. We rewrite L_3 as

$$L_3 = -2\kappa_0^*\phi_0^{(2)\prime\prime}(0;\kappa_0^*)\ \frac{g_1'(-1;\kappa_0^*)}{g_1'(0;\kappa_0^*)}\ \int_{-1}^0 \phi_0^{(2)\prime}(z;\kappa_0^*)$$
$$\times\ F(\phi_0^{(2)}(z;\kappa_0^*),\psi_0^{(2)}(z;\kappa_0^*),\bar{n},\bar{h})\ \int_{-1}^z (\phi_0^{(2)\prime}(\xi;\kappa_0^*))^{-2}d\xi dz\ .$$

Since ν_1 is arbitrarily fixed to satisfy $\nu_1 \in (\mu(\bar{n},\bar{h}),v^*)$, it holds that $\mu(\bar{n},\bar{h}) < \phi_0^{(2)}(z;\kappa_0^*) \le v^*$ for $-1 \le z \le 0$ and hence $F(\phi_0^{(2)}(z;\kappa_0^*),\psi_0^{(2)}(z;\kappa_0^*),\bar{n},\bar{h}) < 0$ for $-1 \le z \le 0$. Thus $L_3 \neq 0$ so that κ_1^* and τ_1^* are uniquely determined from (A.10) and (A.11), respectively.

Finally we show (2.94). Since the derivatives of A_2, B_2 and C_2 with respect to c, κ_1 and τ_1 are $O(\varepsilon)$ uniformly in (c,κ_1,τ_1), (2.94) can be rewritten as

$$\left|\frac{\partial(A,B,C)}{\partial(c,\kappa_1,\tau_1)}\right|_{\varepsilon=0,c=c_*,\kappa_1=\kappa_1^*,\tau_1=\tau_1^*} = \left|\frac{\partial(A_1,B_1,C_1)}{\partial(c,\kappa_1,\tau_1)}\right|_{c=c_*,\kappa_1=\kappa_1^*,\tau_1=\tau_1^*}$$

$$
= \left| \begin{array}{ccc} \dfrac{\partial A_1}{\partial c} & \dfrac{\partial A_1}{\partial \kappa_1} & \dfrac{\partial A_1}{\partial \tau_1} \\ \dfrac{\partial B_1}{\partial c} & \dfrac{\partial B_1}{\partial \kappa_1} & 0 \\ \dfrac{\partial C_1}{\partial c} & 0 & \dfrac{\partial C_1}{\partial \tau_1} \end{array} \right|_{c=c_\star,\kappa_1=\kappa_1^\star,\ \tau_1=\tau_1^\star}
$$

Each element of the above determinant is represented as

$$
\frac{\partial A_1}{\partial c} = -2\kappa_0^\star g_2(0;\kappa_0^\star) \int_{-1}^{0} g_1(z;\kappa_0^\star)\{\phi_0^{(2)\prime}(z;\kappa_0^\star) + \frac{\kappa_0^{\star 2}}{c_\star^2} F_n(\phi_0^{(2)}(z;\kappa_0^\star),\psi_0^{(2)}(z;\kappa_0^\star),
$$

$$
\bar{n},\bar{h})\int_z^0 \gamma_n(\phi_0^{(2)}(\xi;\kappa_0^\star))(n_\infty(\phi_0^{(2)}(\xi;\kappa_0^\star)) - \bar{n})d\xi + \frac{\kappa_0^{\star 2}}{c_\star^2} F_h(\phi_0^{(2)}(z;\kappa_0^\star),
$$

$$
\psi_0^{(2)}(z;\kappa_0^\star),\bar{n},\bar{h})\int_z^0 \gamma_h(\phi_0^{(2)}(\xi;\kappa_0^\star))(h_\infty(\phi_0^{(2)}(\xi;\kappa_0^\star)) - \bar{h})d\xi
$$

$$
- F_m(\phi_0^{(2)}(z;\kappa_0^\star),\psi_0^{(2)}(z;\kappa_0^\star),\bar{n},\bar{h}) \frac{m_\infty'(\phi_0^{(2)}(z;\kappa_0^\star))}{\gamma_m(\phi_0^{(2)}(z;\kappa_0^\star))} \phi_0^{(2)\prime}(z;\kappa_0^\star)\}dz ,
$$

$$
\frac{\partial A_1}{\partial \kappa_1} = - \frac{\partial A_1}{\partial \tau_1} = -2\kappa_0^\star g_2(0;\kappa_0^\star) \int_{-1}^{0} g_1(z;\kappa_0^\star)F(\phi_0^{(2)}(z;\kappa_0^\star),\psi_0^{(2)}(z;\kappa_0^\star),\bar{n},\bar{h})dz ,
$$

$$
\frac{\partial B_1}{\partial c} = \kappa_0^\star\{\int_{-\infty}^{0} (\phi_0^{(1)\cdot}(z))^2(1 - F_m(\phi_0^{(1)}(z),\bar{m}+\psi_0^{(1)}(z),\bar{n},\bar{h}) \frac{m_\infty'(\phi_0^{(1)}(z))}{\gamma_m(\phi_0^{(1)}(z))})dz
$$

$$
- \frac{1}{c_\star^2} \int_{-\infty}^{0} \phi_0^{(1)\cdot}(z)F_n(\phi_0^{(1)}(z),\bar{m}+\psi_0^{(1)}(z),\bar{n},\bar{h}) \int_{-\infty}^{z} \gamma_n(\phi_0^{(1)}(\xi))
$$

$$
\times (n_\infty(\phi_0^{(1)}(\xi)) - \bar{n})d\xi dz - \frac{1}{c_\star^2} \int_{-\infty}^{0} \phi_0^{(1)\cdot}(z)F_h(\phi_0^{(1)}(z),\bar{m}+\psi_0^{(1)}(z),\bar{n},\bar{h})
$$

$$
\times \int_{-\infty}^{z} \gamma_h(\phi_0^{(1)}(\xi))(h_\infty(\phi_0^{(1)}(\xi)) - \bar{h})d\xi dz\}/\phi_0^{(1)\cdot}(0)
$$

$$
- \frac{\partial}{\partial c}\phi_1^{(2)\prime}(-1;c_\star,\kappa_0^\star,\kappa_1^\star) ,
$$

$$\frac{\partial B_1}{\partial \kappa_1} = -2\,\frac{\phi_0^{(2)}{}''(0;\kappa_0^*)}{g_1{}'(0;\kappa_0^*)}\int_{-1}^{0} g_1(z;\kappa_0^*)F(\phi_0^{(2)}(z;\kappa_0^*),\psi_0^{(2)}(z;\kappa_0^*),\bar{n},\bar{h})dz/\phi_0^{(1)}{}^{\cdot}(0)\ ,$$

$$\frac{\partial C_1}{\partial c} = -\frac{\partial}{\partial c}\phi_1^{(2)}{}'(-1;c_*,\kappa_0^*,\kappa_1^*) - 2\{\int_{-1}^{0}(\phi_0^{(2)}{}'(z;\kappa_0^*))^2(1-F_m(\phi_0^{(2)}(z;\kappa_0^*),$$

$$\psi_0^{(2)}(z;\kappa_0^*),\bar{n},\bar{h})\frac{m_\infty{}'(\phi_0^{(2)}(z;\kappa_0^*))}{\gamma_m(\phi_0^{(2)}(z;\kappa_0^*))})dz + \frac{\kappa_0^{*2}}{c_*^2}\int_{-1}^{0}\phi_0^{(2)}{}'(z;\kappa_0^*)$$

$$\times F_n(\phi_0^{(2)}(z;\kappa_0^*),\psi_0^{(2)}(z;\kappa_0^*),\bar{n},\bar{h})\int_z^0\gamma_n(\phi_0^{(2)}(\xi;\kappa_0^*))(n_\infty(\phi_0^{(2)}(\xi;\kappa_0^*)-\bar{n})d\xi dz$$

$$+\frac{\kappa_0^{*2}}{c_*^2}\int_{-1}^{0}\phi_0^{(2)}{}'(z;\kappa_0^*)F_h(\phi_0^{(2)}(z;\kappa_0^*),\psi_0^{(2)}(z;\kappa_0^*),\bar{n},\bar{h})\int_z^0\gamma_h(\phi_0^{(2)}(\xi;\kappa_0^*))$$

$$\times (h_\infty(\phi_0^{(2)}(\xi;\kappa_0^*))-\bar{h})d\xi dz\}/\phi_0^{(1)}{}^{\cdot}(0) - \kappa_0^*\{\int_{-\infty}^{0}(\phi_0^{(1)}{}^{\cdot}(z))^2$$

$$\times (1-F_m(\phi_0^{(1)}(z),\bar{m}+\psi_0^{(1)}(z),\bar{n},\bar{h})\ \frac{m_\infty{}'(\phi_0^{(1)}(z))}{\gamma_m(\phi_0^{(1)}(z))})dz$$

$$+\frac{2}{c_*^2}\int_{-\infty}^{0}\phi_0^{(1)}{}^{\cdot}(z)F_n(\phi_0^{(1)}(z),\bar{m}+\psi_0^{(1)}(z),\bar{n},\bar{h})dz\{\int_{-\infty}^{0}\gamma_n(\phi_0^{(1)}(z))$$

$$\times (n_\infty(\phi_0^{(1)}(z))-\bar{n})dz + \kappa_0^*\int_{-1}^{0}\gamma_n(\phi_0^{(2)}(z;\kappa_0^*))(n_\infty(\phi_0^{(2)}(z;\kappa_0^*))-\bar{n})dz\}$$

$$+\frac{2}{c_*^2}\int_{-\infty}^{0}\phi_0^{(1)}{}^{\cdot}(z)F_h(\phi_0^{(1)}(z),\bar{m}+\psi_0^{(1)}(z),\bar{n},\bar{h})dz\{\int_{-\infty}^{0}\gamma_h(\phi_0^{(1)}(z))$$

$$\times (h_\infty(\phi_0^{(1)}(z))-\bar{h})dz + \kappa_0^*\int_{-1}^{0}\gamma_h(\phi_0^{(2)}(z;\kappa_0^*))(h_\infty(\phi_0^{(2)}(z;\kappa_0^*))-\bar{h})dz\}$$

$$- \frac{1}{c_*^2} \int_{-\infty}^{0} \phi_0^{(1)\cdot}(z) F_n(\phi_0^{(1)}(z), \bar{m}+\psi_0^{(1)}(z), \bar{n}, \bar{h}) \int_{-\infty}^{z} \gamma_n(\phi_0^{(1)}(\xi))(n_\infty(\phi_0^{(1)}(\xi))$$

$$- \bar{n}) d\xi dz - \frac{1}{c_*^2} \int_{-\infty}^{0} \phi_0^{(1)\cdot}(z) F_h(\phi_0^{(1)}(z), \bar{m}+\psi_0^{(1)}(z), \bar{n}, \bar{h}) \int_{-\infty}^{z} \gamma_h(\phi_0^{(1)}(\xi))$$

$$\times (h_\infty(\phi_0^{(1)}(\xi)) - \bar{h}) d\xi dz + \frac{g_1'(-1;\kappa_0^*)}{g_1(0;\kappa_0^*)} \frac{\partial}{\partial c} A_1(c_*, \kappa_1^*, \tau_1^*)$$

and

$$\frac{\partial C_1}{\partial \tau_1} = -2 \frac{\phi_0^{(2)''}(0;\kappa_0^*)}{g_1'(0;\kappa_0^*)} \int_{-1}^{0} g_1(z;\kappa_0^*) F(\phi_0^{(2)}(z;\kappa_0^*), \psi_0^{(2)}(z;\kappa_0^*), \bar{n}, \bar{h}) dz / \phi_0^{(1)\cdot}(0) .$$

By easy computations, it is shown that for $c = c_*$, $\kappa_1 = \kappa_1^*$ and $\tau_1 = \tau_1^*$

$$\left| \frac{\partial(A_1, B_1, C_1)}{\partial(c, \kappa_1, \tau_1)} \right| = \frac{\partial A_1}{\partial c} \frac{\partial B_1}{\partial \kappa_1} \frac{\partial C_1}{\partial \tau_1} - \frac{\partial A_1}{\partial \tau_1} \frac{\partial B_1}{\partial \kappa_1} \frac{\partial C_1}{\partial c} - \frac{\partial A_1}{\partial \kappa_1} \frac{\partial B_1}{\partial c} \frac{\partial C_1}{\partial \tau_1}$$

$$= 16 \kappa_0^{*2} g_1(0;\kappa_0^*) \left\{ \frac{\phi_0^{(2)''}(0;\kappa_0^*)}{g_1'(0;\kappa_0^*) \phi_0^{(1)\cdot}(0)} \right\}^2$$

$$\times \left\{ \int_{-1}^{0} g_1(z;\kappa_0^*) F(\phi_0^{(2)}(z;\kappa_0^*), \psi_0^{(2)}(z;\kappa_0^*), \bar{n}, \bar{h}) \right\}^2 \left[\int_{-\infty}^{0} (\phi_0^{(1)\cdot}(z))^2 \right.$$

$$\times (1 - F_m(\phi_0^{(1)}(z), \bar{m}+\psi_0^{(1)}(z), \bar{n}, \bar{h}) \frac{m_\infty'(\phi_0^{(1)}(z))}{\gamma_m(\phi_0^{(1)}(z))}) dz$$

$$+ \frac{1}{\kappa_0^*} \int_{-1}^{0} (\phi_0^{(2)'}(z;\kappa_0^*))^2 (1 - F_m(\phi_0^{(2)}(z;\kappa_0^*), \psi_0^{(2)}(z;\kappa_0^*), \bar{n}, \bar{h})$$

$$\left. \times \frac{m_\infty'(\phi_0^{(2)}(z;\kappa_0^*))}{\gamma_m(\phi_0^{(2)}(z;\kappa_0^*))}) dz \right] .$$

Since $F_m < 0$, $\gamma_m > 0$ and $m_\infty{}' > 0$, we find that

$$\left| \frac{\partial(A_1, B_1, C_1)}{\partial(c, \kappa_1, \tau_1)} \right|_{c=c_*, \kappa_1=\kappa_1^*, \tau_1=\tau_1^*} \neq 0.$$

Thus, Lemma 8 is proved.

Proof of (3.10)

Since $A(c(\varepsilon),\varepsilon)$ has one positive eigenvalue and four eigenvalues with negative real part, there is a four dimensional surface of trajectories called the stable manifold which tends to $\boldsymbol{\pi}$ as $z \to +\infty$. Since $\boldsymbol{\beta}(z;\varepsilon)$ is normal to the stable manifold at $\boldsymbol{\phi}(z;\varepsilon)$ for each z, we intend to construct the normal vector. In order to do so, we have to construct the stable manifold and its tangent vector. Let us consider the system (3.2) with $c = c(\varepsilon)$ in $[\tau(\varepsilon),+\infty)$ subject to the boundary conditions

$$\text{(A.12)} \qquad \begin{cases} v(\tau(\varepsilon)) = \nu_1, \quad v(+\infty) = 0, \quad m(\tau(\varepsilon)) = \psi_0{}^{(3)}(1) + \varepsilon m_0 \\ n(\tau(\varepsilon)) = \overline{n} + \varepsilon n_0, \quad h(\tau(\varepsilon)) = \overline{h} + \varepsilon h_0 \ , \end{cases}$$

where $\tau(\varepsilon) = \kappa_0^* + \varepsilon\tau_1(c(\varepsilon),\varepsilon)$ and m_0, n_0, h_0 are parameters. Let $\tilde{m}_0$, $\tilde{n}_0$ and $\tilde{h}_0$ be

$$\tilde{m}_0 = (m^{(3)}(\varepsilon\tau(\varepsilon)) - \psi_0{}^{(3)}(1))/\varepsilon \ ,$$

$$\tilde{n}_0 = (n^{(3)}(\varepsilon\tau(\varepsilon)) - \overline{n})/\varepsilon$$

and

$$\tilde{h}_0 = (h^{(3)}(\varepsilon\tau(\varepsilon)) - \overline{h})/\varepsilon \ ,$$

respectively and take the parameter (m_0,n_0,h_0) in some neighborhood J of

$(\tilde{m}_0,\tilde{n}_0,\tilde{h}_0)$. By using the method in Subsection 2.4., we can construct the solution ${}^t(v,m,n,h)(z;\varepsilon,m_0,n_0,h_0)$ of (3.2), (A.12) with $c = c(\varepsilon)$. Therefore letting

$$\overline{\mathbf{U}}(z;\varepsilon,m_0,n_0,h_0) = {}^t(v,\frac{dv}{dz},m,n,h)(z-\bar{z};\varepsilon,m_0,n_0,h_0) ,$$

the four dimensional stable manifold around the traveling wave solution $\boldsymbol{\phi}(z;\varepsilon)$ is given by

$$\{ \overline{\mathbf{U}}(z;\varepsilon,m_0,n_0,h_0) \mid z \geq z^*, \quad (m_0,n_0,h_0) \in J\} .$$

Define $\mathbf{P}_i(z;\varepsilon)$ ($i=1,2,3,4$) by

$$\mathbf{P}_1(z;\varepsilon) = \frac{d}{dz}\overline{\mathbf{U}}(z;\varepsilon,\tilde{m}_0,\tilde{n}_0,\tilde{h}_0), \quad \mathbf{P}_2(z;\varepsilon) = \frac{\partial}{\partial m_0}\overline{\mathbf{U}}(z;\varepsilon,\tilde{m}_0,\tilde{n}_0,\tilde{h}_0),$$

$$\mathbf{P}_3(z;\varepsilon) = \frac{\partial}{\partial n_0}\overline{\mathbf{U}}(z;\varepsilon,\tilde{m}_0,\tilde{n}_0,\tilde{h}_0) \quad \text{and} \quad \mathbf{P}_4(z;\varepsilon) = \frac{\partial}{\partial h_0}\overline{\mathbf{U}}(z;\varepsilon,\tilde{m}_0,\tilde{n}_0,\tilde{h}_0) .$$

Then these are linearly independent tangent vectors of the stable manifold at $\boldsymbol{\phi}(z-\bar{z};\varepsilon)$, by which the normal vector $\boldsymbol{\beta}(z;\varepsilon)$ is represented as

$$\boldsymbol{\beta}(z;\varepsilon) = \left(K \begin{bmatrix} -\phi_0^{(4)\cdot\cdot}(z-z^*)/\phi_0^{(4)\cdot}(z-z^*) \\ 1 \\ 0 \\ -\displaystyle\int_0^{\phi_0^{(4)}(z-z^*)} F_n(v,m_\infty(v),\bar{n},\bar{h})dv/\phi_0^{(4)\cdot}(z-z^*) \\ -\displaystyle\int_0^{\phi_0^{(4)}(z-z^*)} F_h(v,m_\infty(v),\bar{n},\bar{h})dv/\phi_0^{(4)\cdot}(z-z^*) \end{bmatrix} + o(1) \right) e^{-\nu(\varepsilon)}$$

uniformly in $z \in [z^*,+\infty)$ as $\varepsilon \to 0$, where K is some constant. Since

$$e^{\nu(\varepsilon)z}\boldsymbol{\beta}(z;\varepsilon) \longrightarrow K \begin{pmatrix} \nu(0) \\ 1 \\ 0 \\ F_n(0,\overline{m},\overline{n},\overline{h})/\nu(0) \\ F_h(0,\overline{m},\overline{n},\overline{h})/\nu(0) \end{pmatrix} + o(1) \quad \text{as} \quad z \to +\infty ,$$

it follows from (3.4) and the definition of $\mathbf{Y}^*(\varepsilon)$ that $K = 1$, which implies (3.10).

References

[1] G. A. Carpenter, A geometric approach to singular perturbation problems with applications to nerve impulse equations, J. Differential Equations, 23 (1977), 335-367.

[2] E. A. Coddington and N. Levinson, Theory of the ordinary differential equations, McGraw-Hill Book Company, Inc., New York (1955).

[3] J. W. Cooley and F. A. Dodge, Jr., Digital computer solutions for excitation and propagation of the nerve impulse, Biophys. J. 6 (1966), 583-599.

[4] J. W. Evans, Nerve axon equations, I: Linear approximations, Indiana Univ. Math. J. 21 (1972), 877-885.

[5] J. W. Evans, Nerve axon equations, II: Stability at rest, Indiana Univ. Math. J. 22 (1972), 75-90.

[6] J. W. Evans, Nerve axon equations, III: Stability of the nerve impulse, Indiana Univ. Math. J. 22 (1972), 577-593.

[7] J. W. Evans, Nerve axon equations, IV: The stable and the unstable

impulse, Indiana Univ. Math. J. 24 (1975), 1169-1190.

[8] J. W. Evans and J. A. Feroe, Local stability theory of the nerve impulse, Math. Biosci. 37 (1977), 23-50.

[9] P. C. Fife, Semilinear elliptic boundary value problems with small parameters, Arch. Rational Mech. Anal. 52 (1973), 205-232.

[10] S. P. Hastings, On travelling wave solutions of the Hodgkin - Huxley equations, Arch. Rational Mech. Anal. 60 (1976), 229-257.

[11] L. A. Hodgkin and A. F. Huxley, A quantitative description of membrane current and its application to conduction and excitation in nerve, J. Physiol. 117 (1952), 500-544.

[12] A. F. Huxley, Ion movements during nerve activity, Ann. N. Y. Acad. Sci. 81 (1959), 221-246.

[13] A. F. Huxley, Can a nerve propagate subthreshold disturbance ?, J. Physiol. 148 (1959), 80-81 P.

[14] K. Maginu, A geometrical condition for the instability of solitary travelling wave solutions in reaction - diffusion equations, J. Differential Equations, to appear.

[15] R. N. Miller and J. Rinzel, The dependence of impulse propagation speed on firing frequency, dispersion, for the Hodgkin - Huxley model, Biophys. J. 34 (1981), 227-259.

Recent Topics in Nonlinear PDE III, Tokyo, 1986
Lecture Notes in Num. Appl. Anal., 9, 75–104 (1987)

Traveling Train Solutions of FitzHugh-Nagumo Systems

Masayuki ITO

Department of Mathematics and Computer Sciences
Tokushima University
Minamijosanjima 1-1, Tokushima 770, Japan

1. Introduction.

Signals propagating along a nerve axon are modeled by traveling wave solutions of the Hodgkin-Huxley(HH) or FitzHugh-Nagumo(FHN) systems. The existence and the stability problems of the traveling wave solutions have been studied by many authors in various ways. Rinzel and Keller [15] have shown numerically that there exist two branches of traveling *train* solutions of FHN system (parametrised by the length of their periods) with different propagating velocities, namely, fast solutions and slow solutions. For the HH system, the the similar results have been obtained by Miller and Rinzel[14]. The two branches connect each other at the minimal period. Traveling pulse solutions can be regarded as traveling train

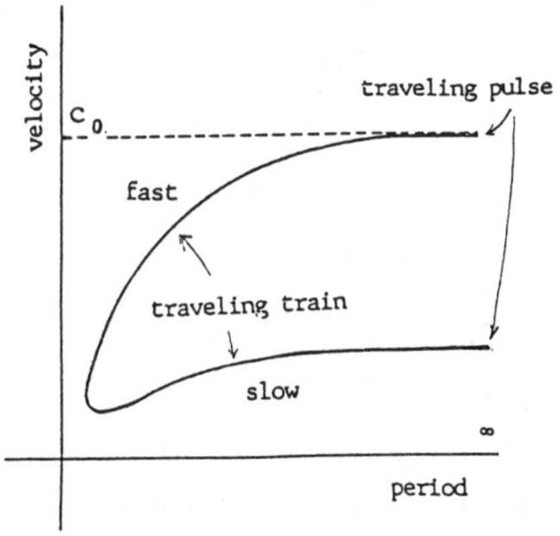

Fig. 1. The relation between period and velocity for traveling train solutions.

solutions with the infinite period (see Fig. 1 or refer to Fig. 8 in [15] and Fig. 2 in [14]). Jones[11] and Yanagida[16] have shown rigorously the stability of the fast traveling pulse solutions of FHN systems whose existence was shown by Langer[12]. Ikeda, Mimura and Tsujikawa [9] [10] have also constructed traveling pulse solutions of HH systems and shown the stability of the fast solutions as well as the instability of the slow solutions. Their proofs are based on the result, shown by Evans ([2]~[4]), that the linearized stabilty of a traveling pulse solution implies its stability. Here, the linearized stability means that the eigenvalue 0 is simple and that the spectrum (other than 0) of the linearized operator about the traveling pulse sollution lies on the left half plane $\{\lambda\in\mathbb{C}:\mathrm{Re}\lambda\leq-\delta\}$ $(\delta>0)$. The main cntributions given by Jonse, Yanagida and Ikeda et al. are the study of the negativity or positivity of eigenvalues in a neighborhood of 0.

On the other hand, for the traveling train solutions, Maginu[13] has shown by the topological methods the instability of the slow solutions and the fast solutions, whose periods are close to the minimal period, for FHN systems. However, a completely rigorous proof of the stability or the instability of the fast traveling train solutions, whose period are not close to the minimal period, has not been given yet. Also the distribution of spectrum of the linearized operator has been not known.

In this note, we study the distribution of the spectrum of the linearized operator about the fast traveling train solutions of FHN system. The existence of such solutions has been shown by many authors(for instance, Carpenter[1] and Hastings[8], [9]). However, their reults and methods of proof do not seem to give us fully detailed properties of the solutions to know the distribution of the spectrum. We construct the fast traveling train solutions by another method, namely, the method of matched asymptotic expansion. By using the obtaind asymptotic expansions of the solutions, we study the distribution of the spectrum in a neighborhood of the origin.

The FHN system to be studied here is of the form:

$$(1.1)\quad \begin{cases} \dfrac{\partial u}{\partial t} = \dfrac{\partial^2 u}{\partial z^2} + f(u) - w, \\[2ex] \dfrac{\partial w}{\partial t} = \varepsilon(u - \gamma w), \end{cases}$$

where t is time, z is the spatial variable, $f(u) = u(u - a)(1 - u)$ $(0 < a < 1/2)$, and ε, γ are small positive constants. The traveling wave solutions $(u(z,t), v(z,t))$ of (1. 1) with verocity c are of the form $(u(y), w(y))$ with $y = z + ct$, which are given by solutions of

$$(1.2)\quad \begin{cases} 0 = \dfrac{d^2 u}{dy^2} - c\dfrac{du}{dy} + f(u) - w, \\[2ex] 0 = \qquad - c\dfrac{dw}{dy} + \varepsilon(u - \gamma w). \end{cases} \qquad y \in \mathbb{R},$$

Traveling train solutions of (1. 1) are defined by periodic solutions of (1. 2). We shall show that, for any $0 < c < c_0$, there exists an ε-family of priodic solutions $(u^\varepsilon, w^\varepsilon)$ of (1. 2) with period $Y^\varepsilon = O(1/\varepsilon)$, where c_0 is the fast verocity of traveling pulse solutions in the limit $\varepsilon \downarrow 0$ whose stabilty was shown by Jones[ ] and Yanagida[16].

We next study the distribution problem of eigenvalues μ for

$$\begin{cases} \mu p = \dfrac{d^2 p}{dy^2} - c\dfrac{dp}{dy} + f'(u^\varepsilon)p - q, \end{cases}$$

$$(1.\ 3)\left\{\begin{array}{l} \\ \mu q = \quad - c\dfrac{dq}{dy} + \varepsilon(p - \gamma q)\ , \end{array}\right.$$

where u^ε is the first component of the solution of (1. 2) obtaind before, and f' is the derivative of f. Of course, there is the eigenvalue 0 corresponding to the eigenvector $(\frac{d}{dy}u^\varepsilon\ ,\ \frac{d}{dy}w^\varepsilon\ )$. We shall show that (1.3) has a family of eigenvallues $\mu(\varepsilon,\theta)$ with parameters ε and θ such that

$$(1.\ 4)\qquad \lim_{\varepsilon\downarrow 0}\mu(\varepsilon,\theta)/\varepsilon = i\sigma_1\theta + \sigma_2\theta^2 + O(\theta^3)\ ,$$

for small $|\theta|$ ($\theta \in \mathbb{R}$), where σ_1 and σ_2 are real constants. Moreover, if c is closed to 0 or c_0, then σ_2 is negative.

The above result shows an striking feature of the distribution of the spectrum of the linearized operator about traveling train solutions. Indeed, in the case of traveling pulse sollutions, only discrete eigenvalues exist in some ε-neighborhood of the origin. The continuous existence of spectra (1. 4) seems to be interested. Signal waves propagating along a nerve axon are expected to have two properties: 1) the peak number of the waves passing any point per unit time is maintained in the propagating process, but 2) that must change immedeately if the firing number per unit time (or the frequency of repetitve stimulation) changes at the starting point of the signal. Thus, if we regard traveling train solutions as models of signals, they are also expected to have some properties corresponding to 1) and 2), and to be stable in a weaker sense than the usual sense. The distribution of the spectrum (1. 4) seems to be related to the above properties, say, the nonpositivity of $\mu_0(\theta) \equiv \lim_{\varepsilon\downarrow 0}\ \mu(\varepsilon,\theta)$ is to 1) and the continuous existence is to 2). But this is still open. In the next section, we state our results more precisely. In Section 3, we seek asymptotic expansions to the solutions of (1. 2) for small ε. The algorithm used to obtain coefficients of the expansions plays the key role in not only the construction of solutions of (1. 2) but also in the analysis of the distribution problem of the spectrum. We give the outline of the proof of the existence theorem (Theorem 1 in the next section) in Section 4, and study the distribution problem of the spectum in Section 5.

2. Theorems.

In the limit case of $\varepsilon \downarrow 0$, a traveling train solution can be obtained in the following heuristic way. Introducing the variable $x = \varepsilon y$, we write (1.2) in the form:

$$(2.\ 1)\quad \begin{cases} \varepsilon^2 u_{xx} - \varepsilon c u_x + f(u) - w = 0, \\ \qquad\qquad\qquad\qquad\qquad\qquad\qquad -\infty < x < +\infty, \\ - c w_x + u - \gamma w = 0, \end{cases}$$

where we denote simply du/dx by u_x. We seek the limit form of a periodic soluton of (2. 1) with period of $O(1)$ as $\varepsilon \downarrow 0$. When $\varepsilon = 0$, the first equation of (2. 1) is reduced to $f(u) - w = 0$. This has three solution branchs $u = h_-(w), h_0(w), h_+(w)$ $(h_-(u) < h_0(u) < h_+(u))$ for $\underline{w} \equiv \inf_{0<u<1} f(u) < w < \bar{w} \equiv \sup_{0<u<1} f(u)$ (see Fig. 2). Thus, the second equation implies

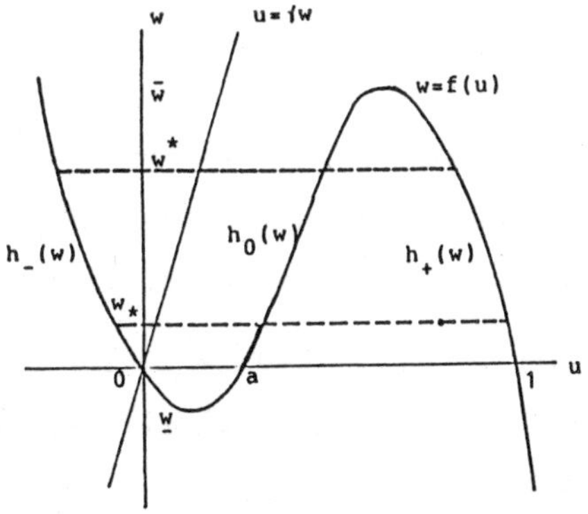

Fig. 2. uw-plane

$$(2.\ 2) \qquad -cw_x + h(w) - w = 0\ , \qquad h = h_-\ ,\ h_0 \ \text{ or } \ h_+\ .$$

On the other hand, using a stretched variable $\xi = (x - x_0)/\varepsilon$ for any fixed x_0, we rewrite (2. 1) into

$$(2.\ 3) \quad \begin{cases} u_{\xi\xi} - cu_\xi + f(u) - w = 0\ , \\ \qquad\qquad\qquad\qquad -\infty < \xi < +\infty\ , \\ -cw_\xi + \varepsilon(u - \gamma w) = 0\ . \end{cases}$$

When $\varepsilon = 0$, the second equation of (2. 3) yields w = constant. Consider the following problems:

$$(2.\ 4) \quad \begin{cases} u_{\xi\xi} - cu_\xi + f(u) - w = 0\ , \qquad -\infty < \xi < +\infty\ , \\ u(-\infty) = h_-(w)\ , \quad u(+\infty) = h_+(w)\ . \end{cases}$$

$$(2.\ 5) \quad \begin{cases} u_{\xi\xi} - cu_\xi + f(u) - w = 0\ , \qquad -\infty < \xi < +\infty\ , \\ u(-\infty) = h_+(w)\ , \quad u(+\infty) = h_-(w)\ . \end{cases}$$

It is known that there exists $c_0 > 0$ such that (2. 4) with $w = 0$ has a unique monotone solution when $c = c_0$. Moreover, by using the results in [6], we can easily show the following lemma.

Lemma 2. 1. For any $0 < c < c_0$, there exists uniquely $w_* = w_*(c)$ (or $w^* = w^*(c)$) such that (2. 4) (or (2. 5) resp.) has a unique (except for translation) monotone solution. Moreover,

$$0 < w_*(c)\ f((1+a)/3) < w^*(c) < 2f((1+a)/3),$$
$$\lim_{c\downarrow 0} w_*(c) = 0\ , \quad \lim_{c\uparrow c_0} w_*(c) = f((1+a)/3),$$
$$\lim_{c\downarrow 0} w^*(c) = 2f((1+a)/3)\ , \quad \lim_{c\uparrow c_0} w^*(c) = f((1+a)/3).$$

Denote by $T(\xi)$ the soluton of (2. 4) with $w = w_*$ and $u(0)$

$= (h_-(w_*)+h_+(w_*))/2$, and by $S(\xi)$ the solution of (2. 5) with $w = w^*$ and $u(0) = (h_-(w^*)+h_+(w^*))/2$. Returning (2. 2), we consider the probrem;

(2. 6) $\quad - cw_x + h_-(w) - w = 0 \quad$ for $x > 0$, $\quad w(0) = w^*$.

Since $h_-(w) - \gamma w < 0$ for $w > 0$, (2. 6) has a monotone decreasing solution $w = \bar{W}^I(x)$, so that there exists uniquely x_* satisfying $w_* = \bar{W}^I(x_*)$. The next problem,

(2. 7) $\quad - cw_x + h_+(w) - \gamma w = 0 \quad$ for $x > x_*$, $\quad w(x_*) = w_*$,

has a unique monotone increasing solution $w = \bar{W}^{II}(x)$ since $h_+(w) - \gamma w > 0$. The equation $\bar{W}^{II}(x) = w^*$ has a unique solution $x = x^*$. Let $I = (0, x_*)$, $II = (x_*, x^*)$ and

$$(U(x), W(x)) = \begin{cases} (h_-(\bar{W}^I(x-nx^*)), \bar{W}^I(x-nx^*)) & \text{for } x-nx^* \in I, \\ (h_+(\bar{W}^{II}(x-nx^*)), \bar{W}^{II}(x-nx^*)) & \text{for } x-nx^* \in II, \end{cases}$$

for any integer n . This is a periodic solution of (2. 1) in the limt case $\varepsilon \downarrow 0$ (Fig. 3). The discontinuity of U at $x = nx^*$ and $nx^* + x_*$ can be regard as the result of the limit process for the sharp transitions $S((x-nx^*)/\varepsilon)$ and $T((x^*-nx_*-x)/\varepsilon)$. Indeed, we shall show the following theorem.

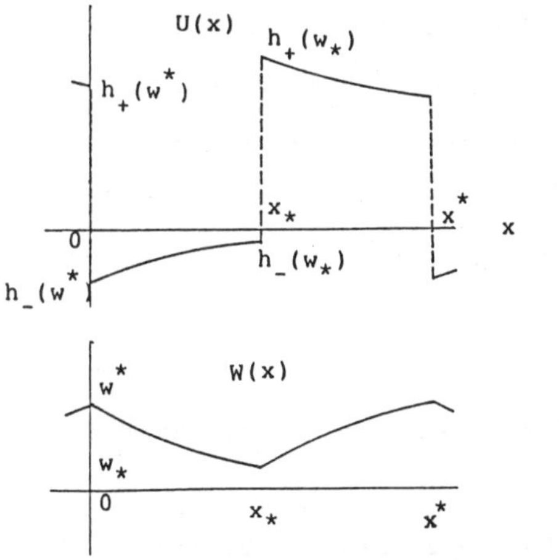

Fig. 3. The limit form of the traveling train solutions

Theorem 1. Let $0 < c < c_0$, and ε_0 be sufficiently small. Then, for $0 < \varepsilon < \varepsilon_0$, there exists a periodic solution $(u^\varepsilon, w^\varepsilon)$ of (2. 1) with period $\ell^\varepsilon x^*$ such that, as $\varepsilon \downarrow 0$,

$$\ell^\varepsilon \to 1,$$
$$u^\varepsilon(\ell^\varepsilon x) \to U(x) \quad \text{uniformly in any compact in } I \cup II,$$
$$w^\varepsilon(\ell^\varepsilon x) \to W(x) \quad \text{uniformly in } I \cup II .$$

Next we consider the distribution problem of the spectrum of the linearized operator about the above solutions $(u^\varepsilon, w^\varepsilon)$. Here, we restrict our attention to eigenvalues $\mu = O(\varepsilon)$. Denote μ/ε by λ. By using the variable $x = \varepsilon y$, we write (1. 3) in the form;

$$\text{(2. 8)} \quad \begin{cases} \varepsilon^2 p_{xx} - \varepsilon c p_x + f'(u^\varepsilon)p - q = \varepsilon\lambda p , \\ & -\infty < x < +\infty , \\ - c q_x + p - \gamma q = \lambda q . \end{cases}$$

We define eigenvalues of (2. 8) as follows.

Definition 2. 1. $\lambda \in \mathbb{C}$ is said to be an eigenvalue of (2. 8) associating with an eigenvector (p, q) if 1) p is a complex valued, bounded and twice differentiable function whose derivatives of order up to 2 are bounded; 2) q is a complex valued, bounded and differentiable function whose derivative is bounded; and 3) p, q and λ satisfy (2. 8).

Our reaults on the eigenvalue problem (2. 8) are as follows.

Theorem 2. Let ε be small. Then there exists a family of eigenvalues $\lambda(\varepsilon, \theta) = \lambda_0(\theta) + O(\varepsilon)$ $0 < \theta < 2\pi$ such that $\lambda_0(\theta)$ is a solution of

(2. 9) $$\theta(\lambda)\exp(-\lambda x^*/c) = \theta(0)e^{i\theta} ,$$

where $\theta(\lambda) = (1 - \frac{1}{\alpha c\lambda + A})(1 - \frac{1}{\beta c\lambda + B})$,

$$\alpha = \int_{-\infty}^{+\infty} T_\xi(\xi)^2 e^{-c\xi} d\xi \left(\int_{-\infty}^{+\infty} T_\xi(\xi)e^{-c\xi}d\xi \right)^{-1} ,$$

$$\beta = \int_{-\infty}^{+\infty} S_\xi(\xi)^2 e^{-c\xi} d\xi \left(\int_{-\infty}^{+\infty} S_\xi(\xi)e^{-c\xi}d\xi \right)^{-1} ,$$

$$A = -(h_-(w_*) - \gamma w_*)/(h_+(w_*) - h_-(w_*)),$$

$$B = -(h_+(w^*) - \gamma w^*)/(h_-(w^*) - h_+(w^*)).$$

Corollary 3. Let c be closed enough to 0 or c_0 . Then

(2. 10) $$\lambda_0(\theta) = i\sigma_1\theta + \sigma_2\theta^2 + O(\varepsilon^3)$$

for small θ , where σ_1 and σ_2 are negative real numbers (Fig. 4).

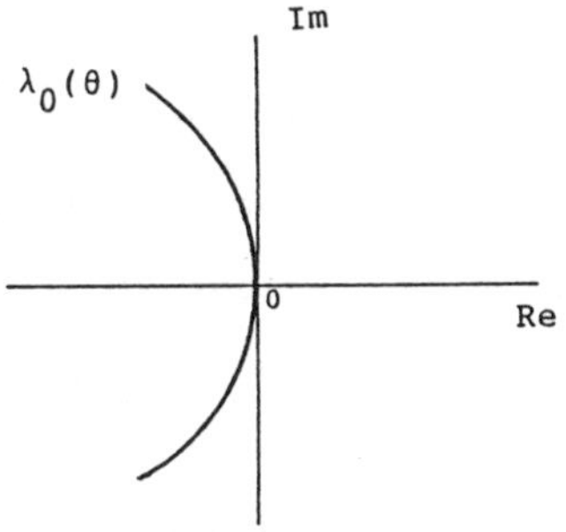

Fig. 4. $\lambda_0(\theta)$ on $\mathbb{C}$-plane for small $|\theta|$.

3. Asymptotic expansions to traveling trains.

In this section, assuming the existence of periodic solutions of (2. 1) , we seek singularly perturbed expansions to the periodic solutions by the method of matched expansion. The method used here is like the one derived by van Harten and Vader-Burger [7] to show the existence of stationary solutions of reaction-diffusion systems on bounded intervals. We shall see that the algorithm determining the coefficients of the expansions is also used in the justification of the expansions and the proof of Theorem 2.

Assuming that the periodic solution of (2. 1) has period $\ell^\varepsilon x^*$ and introducing the variable $x' = x/\ell^\varepsilon$, we write (2. 1) into the form;

$$(3.\ 1)\quad \begin{cases} \varepsilon^2 u_{x'x'} - \varepsilon c \ell^{\varepsilon} u_{x'} + (\ell^{\varepsilon})^2 (f(u) - w) = 0\ , \\ \qquad\qquad\qquad\qquad\qquad\qquad\qquad -\infty < x' < +\infty\ , \\ -cw_{x'} + \ell^{\varepsilon}(u - \gamma w) = 0\ . \end{cases}$$

Thus, we seek asymptotic expansions of periodic solutions of (3. 1) with period x^* as well as ℓ^{ε}. We assume that ℓ^{ε} can be expanded in the form $\ell^{\varepsilon} = 1 + \varepsilon\ell_1 + \varepsilon^2\ell_2 + \cdots$, where ℓ_1, ℓ_2, $\cdots$, are constants to be determined later.

3-1. Outer expansions.

We assume that the solution (u, w) of (3. 1) has the asymptotic forms in the regions I , II and $III \equiv (x^*, x^* + x_*)$:

$$(3.\ 2;\ I)\quad \begin{cases} u \sim H^I u \equiv U_0^I(x) + \varepsilon U_1^I(x) + \varepsilon^2 U_2^I(x) + \cdots\ , \\ \qquad\qquad\qquad\qquad\qquad\qquad x \in I\ , \\ w \sim H^I w \equiv W_0^I(x) + \varepsilon W_1^I(x) + \varepsilon^2 W_2^I(x) + \cdots\ , \end{cases}$$

$$(3.\ 2;\ II)\quad \begin{cases} u \sim H^{II} u \equiv U_0^{II}(x) + \varepsilon U_1^{II}(x) + \varepsilon^2 U_2^{II}(x) + \cdots\ , \\ \qquad\qquad\qquad\qquad\qquad\qquad x \in II\ , \\ w \sim H^{II} w \equiv W_0^{II}(x) + \varepsilon W_1^{II}(x) + \varepsilon^2 W_2^{II}(x) + \cdots\ , \end{cases}$$

$$(3.\ 2;\ III)\quad \begin{cases} u \sim H^{III} u \equiv U_0^{III}(x) + \varepsilon U_1^{III}(x) + \varepsilon^2 U_2^{III}(x) + \cdots\ , \\ \qquad\qquad\qquad\qquad\qquad\qquad x \in III, \\ w \sim H^{III} w \equiv W_0^{III}(x) + \varepsilon W_1^{III}(x) + \varepsilon^2 W_2^{III}(x) + \cdots\ . \end{cases}$$

Substituting (3. 2) into (3. 1) and equating the terms of like powers of ε, we have

$$(3.\ 3;\ 0)\quad \begin{cases} f(U_0^J) - W_0^J = 0\ , \\ \qquad\qquad\qquad\qquad\qquad\qquad x \in J\ , \\ -cW_{0\,x}^J + U_0^J - \gamma W_0^J = 0\ , \end{cases}$$

$$f'(U_0^J)U_i^J - W_i^J = F_i^J\ ,$$

$$(3.\ 3;\ i)\quad \begin{cases} & x \in J, \quad i \geq 1, \\ -cW^J_{i\,x} + U^J_i - \gamma W^J_i + \ell_i (U^J_0 - \gamma W^J_0) = G^J_i , & \end{cases}$$

where $J = I$, II or III , and F^J_i , G^J_i depend only on U^J_0 , W^J_0 , $\cdots$, U^J_{i-1} , W^J_{i-1} , and ℓ_1 , $\cdots$, ℓ_{i-1} .

Set

$$(3.\ 4)\quad \begin{cases} (U^I_0(x),\ W^I_0(x)) = (h_-(\bar{W}^I_0(x)),\ \bar{W}^I_0(x)) & x \in I , \\ (U^{II}_0(x),\ W^{II}_0(x)) = (h_+(\bar{W}^{II}_0(x)),\ \bar{W}^{II}_0(x)) & x \in II , \\ (U^{III}_0(x),\ W^{III}_0(x)) = (h_-(\bar{W}^I_0(x-x^*)),\ \bar{W}^I_0(x-x^*)) & x \in III , \end{cases}$$

Where $\bar{W}^I_0$ and $\bar{W}^{II}_0$ are as in Section 2. Then U^J_0 and W^J_0 ($J = I$, II, III) satisfy (3. 3; 0), and the solutions of (3. 3; i) can be written in the form;

$$(3.\ 5)\quad \begin{cases} W^I_i(x) = W^I_i(0)A^I(x) + c^{-1}\ell_i\int_0^x A^I(x-y)(U^I_0 - \gamma W^I_0)(y)dy \\ \qquad + c^{-1}\int_0^x A^I(x-y)\{G^I_i + F^I_i / f'(U^I_0)\}(y)dy \\ \qquad\qquad \text{for } x \in I, \\ W^{II}_i(x) = W^{II}_i(x_*)A^{II}(x) + c^{-1}\ell_i\int_{x_*}^x A^{II}(x-y)(U^{II}_0 - \gamma W^{II}_0)(y)dy \\ \qquad + c^{-1}\int_{x_*}^x A^{II}(x-y)\{G^{II}_i + F^{II}_i / f'(U^{II}_0)\}(y)dy , \\ \qquad\qquad \text{for } x \in II , \\ W^{III}_i(x) = W^{III}_i(x^*)A^{III}(x) + c^{-1}\ell_i\int_{x*}^x A^{III}(x-y)(U^{III}_0 - \gamma W^{III}_0)(y)dy \\ \qquad + c^{-1}\int_{x*}^x A^{III}(x-y)\{G^{III}_i + F^{III}_i / f'(U^{III}_0)\}(y)dy \\ \qquad\qquad \text{for } x \in III, \\ U^J_i(x) = (W^J_i(x) - F^J_i(x)) / f'(U^J_0(x)) \\ \qquad\qquad \text{for } x \in I, II, III, \end{cases}$$

where

$$A^{I}(x) = \exp\left(c^{-1} \int_0^x \{[f'(U_0^{I})]^{-1} - \gamma\}(y)dy \right),$$

$$A^{II}(x) = \exp\left(c^{-1} \int_{x_*}^x \{[f'(U_0^{II})]^{-1} - \gamma\}(y)dy \right),$$

$$A^{III}(x) = \exp\left(c^{-1} \int_{x*}^x \{[f'(U_0^{III})]^{-1} - \gamma\}(y)dy \right).$$

Note that $f'(U_0^J) < 0$ and $0 < A^J(x) < 1$ for $x \in J = I$, II and III.

3-2. Inner expansion at $x \sim x_*$.

In a neighborhood of x_*, we assume that the solution (u, w) of (3. 1) can be repesented by the following series.

$$(3.\ 6)\quad \begin{cases} u \sim (1-t(\xi))(U_0^I(x)+\varepsilon U_1^I(x)+\cdots) + t(\xi)(U_0^{II}(x)+\varepsilon U_1^{II}(x)+\cdots) \\ \qquad + \varepsilon\hat{u}_1(\xi) + \varepsilon^2 \hat{u}_2(\xi) + \varepsilon^3 \hat{u}_3(\xi) + \cdots, \\ w \sim (1-t(\xi))(W_0^I(x)+\varepsilon W_1^I(x)+\cdots) + t(\xi)(W_0^{II}(x)+\varepsilon W_1^{II}(x)+\cdots) \\ \qquad + \varepsilon\hat{w}_1(\xi) + \varepsilon^2 \hat{w}_2(\xi) + \varepsilon^3 \hat{w}_3(\xi) + \cdots, \end{cases}$$

where $\xi = (x - x_*)/\varepsilon$, $t(\xi) = (T(\xi)-T(-\infty))/(T(+\infty)-T(-\infty))$ and $T(\xi)$ is as in Section 2. The right-hand side of (3. 6) can be rewritten into the form:

$$(3.\ 7)\quad \begin{cases} E_*u \equiv T(\xi) + \varepsilon(u_1(\xi)+\hat{u}_1(\xi)) + \varepsilon^2(u_2(\xi) + \hat{u}_2(\xi)) + \cdots, \\ E_*w \equiv w_* + \varepsilon(w_1(\xi)+\hat{w}_1(\xi)) + \varepsilon^2(w_2(\xi) + \hat{w}_2(\xi)) + \cdots, \end{cases}$$

where

$$(3.\ 8)\quad \begin{cases} u_i(\xi) = (1-t(\xi)) \Sigma_{k=0}^i \xi^k(d^kU_{i-k}^I/dx^k)(x_*) / i! \\ \qquad + t(\xi) \Sigma_{k=0}^i \xi^k(d^kU_{i-k}^{II}/dx^k)(x_*) / i!, \\ w_i(\xi) = (1-t(\xi)) \Sigma_{k=0}^i \xi^k(d^kW_{i-k}^I/dx^k)(x_*) / i! \\ \qquad + t(\xi) \Sigma_{k=0}^i \xi^k(d^kW_{i-k}^{II}/dx^k)(x_*) / i!. \end{cases} \qquad i \geq 1,$$

Substituting (3. 7) into (3. 1) and equating the terms of like power of ε , we have

$$(3.\ 9;\ 0)\begin{cases} T_{\xi\xi} - cT_{\xi} + f(T) - w_* = 0 , \\ & -\infty < \xi < +\infty , \\ - c\, w_{*\xi} = 0 , \end{cases}$$

$$(3.\ 9;\ i)\begin{cases} L\hat{u}_i \equiv \hat{u}_{i\xi\xi} - c\hat{u}_{i\xi} + f'(T)\hat{u}_i \\ \quad = -Lu_i + w_i + \hat{w}_i + c\ell_i T_{\xi} - 2\ell_i(f(T) - w_*) + \hat{F}_i , \\ & -\infty < \xi < +\infty , \\ - c\,\hat{w}_{i\xi} = c\, w_{i\xi} - \hat{G}_i , & i \geq 1 , \end{cases}$$

where $\hat{F}_i$ and $\hat{G}_i$ are functions determined only by u_k , $\hat{u}_k$, w_k , $\hat{w}_k$ and ℓ_k $(k \leq i-1)$, in particuler, $\hat{F}_1 = 0$, $\hat{G}_1 = T - \gamma w_*$. By the definition of T , we know that (3. 9; 0) holds. In order to match the inner expansions with the outer ones, we impose the conditions:

(3.10; i) $\hat{u}_i(\xi) \to 0$, $\hat{w}_i(\xi) \to 0$, as $|\xi| \to +\infty$, $i \geq 1$.

Solvability conditions of (3. 9; i) with (3.10; i) can be obtained in the following way.

By the second equation of (3. 9; i), we have

$$(3.11) \qquad \hat{w}_i(\xi) = \hat{\pi}_i - w_i(\xi) - c^{-1}\int_0^{\xi} \hat{G}_i(\bar{\xi})\, d\bar{\xi} ,$$

where $\hat{\pi}_i$ is a constant of integration. By using (3. 8), we can write (3.11) in the form:

$$(3.12) \qquad \hat{w}_i(\xi) = \hat{\pi}_i - (1 - t(\xi))W_i^{I}(x_*) - t(\xi)W_i^{II}(x_*) + \hat{g}_i(\xi) ,$$

where $\hat{g}_i$ is a function detemined only by $\hat{u}_k$, $\hat{w}_k$, U_k^J , W_k^J and ℓ_k $(k \leq i-1,\ J = I\ ,\ II)$. The matching conditions $\hat{w}_i(\xi) \to 0$ $(|\xi| \to +\infty)$ imply

$$(3.13) \qquad 0 = \hat{\pi}_i - W_i^{II}(x_*) + \hat{g}_i(+\infty) , \quad 0 = \hat{\pi}_i - W_i^{I}(x_*) + \hat{g}_i(-\infty) .$$

Thus, the solvability condition for $\hat{w}_i$ is

(3.14) $\quad W_i^{II}(x_*) - W_i^I(x_*) = \hat{f}_i \equiv \hat{g}_i(+\infty) - \hat{g}_i(-\infty)$.

Indeed, if (3.14) is satisfied,

(3.15) $\quad \hat{w}_i(\xi) = \hat{g}_i(\xi) - t(\xi)\hat{g}_i(+\infty) - (1-t(\xi))\hat{g}_i(-\infty)$

is a unique solution of the second equation of (3. 9; i) with the matching condition. (3.15) shows that $\hat{w}_i$ can be determined only by $\hat{u}_k$, $\hat{w}_k$, U_k^J , W_k^J and ℓ_k $(k \leq i - 1, J = I , II)$.

Next, we consider the solvability condition for $\hat{u}_i$. Note that $LT_\xi = 0$ and $\hat{z}(\xi) \equiv T_\xi(\xi)e^{-c\xi}$ satisfies

$$L^\dagger \hat{z} \equiv \hat{z}_{\xi\xi} + c\hat{z}_\xi + f'(T)\hat{z} = 0 .$$

Thus, multiplying the first equation of (3. 9; i) by $\hat{z}$ and integrating it on $-\infty < \xi < +\infty$, we have

$$< w_i + \hat{w}_i + c\ell_i T_\xi - 2\ell_i(f(T) - w_*) + \hat{F}_i , \hat{z} > = 0 .$$

where $< , >$ is the L_2-inner product. Since $cT_\xi - 2(f(T) - w_*) = 2T_{\xi\xi} - cT_\xi$ and $< 2T_{\xi\xi} - cT_\xi , \hat{z} > = 0$,

(3.16) $\quad < w_i , \hat{z} > + < \hat{w}_i , \hat{z} > + < \hat{F}_i , \hat{z} > = 0$.

(3. 8), (3.15) and (3.16) yield

(3.17) $\quad W_i^I(x_*)< 1-t , \hat{z} > + W_i^{II}(x_*)< t , \hat{z} > = \hat{\Delta}_i$,

where $\hat{\Delta}_i$ is a constant determined only by $\hat{u}_k$, $\hat{w}_k$, U_k^J , W_k^J and ℓ_k ($k \leq i - 1$, $J = I , II$). (3.14) and (3.17) determine $W_i^I(x_*)$ and $W_i^{II}(x_*)$. w_i and u_i are also determined by these $W_i^I(x_*)$ and $W_i^{II}(x_*)$ through (3. 8) and the last equaion of (3. 5). Since this w_i satisfies (3.16), we can obtain a unique solution $\hat{u}_i$ of the first equation of (3. 9; i) with $< u_i + \hat{u}_i , T_\xi > = 0$ if ℓ_i is given. Consequently, we can obtain $W_i^I(x_*)$, $W_i^{II}(x_*)$, and $\hat{w}_i$ if we know $\hat{u}_k$, $\hat{w}_k$, U_k^J , W_k^J and ℓ_k ($k \leq i - 1$, $J = I , II$). Moreover, if ℓ_i is also known, we can obtain $\hat{u}_i$.

Remark: In the above argument, we assumed the boundedness of

$\hat{g}_i$ and L_2-ness of the right-hand side of the first equation in (3.9; i). These can be shown inductively. Moreover, we can show that $\hat{u}_i$, $\hat{w}_i$ $\in \mathcal{S}$ (the class of the steepest decending functions) by noting exponential decays of $d^j t/d\xi^j$ (as $\xi \to -\infty$, $j = 0, 1, 2, \cdots$) and $d^j(1-t)/d\xi^j$ ($\xi \to +\infty$, $j = 0, 1, 2, \cdots$).

3-3. Inner expansions at $x \sim x^*$.

In a neighborhood of x^*, we introduce a shifted and stertched variable $\eta = \xi - a_0$, where a_0 is a constant determined later and $\xi = (x - x^*)/\varepsilon$. We assume that

$$(3.18)\quad \begin{cases} u \sim E^*u \equiv S(\eta) + \varepsilon(u^1(\eta) + \bar{u}_1(\eta)) + \varepsilon^2(u^2(\eta) + \bar{u}_2(\eta)) + \cdots, \\ w \sim E^*w \equiv w^* + \varepsilon(w^1(\eta) + \bar{w}_1(\eta)) + \varepsilon^2(w^2(\eta) + \bar{w}_2(\eta)) + \cdots, \end{cases}$$

and

$$u^i(\eta) = s(\eta)\,\Sigma_{k=0}^{i}\,(\eta + a_0)^k(d^kU^{II}_{i-k} / dx^k)(x^*) / k! + (1-s(\eta))\,\Sigma_{k=0}^{i}\,(\eta + a_0)^k(d^kU^{III}_{i-k} / dx^k)(x^*) / k!\,.$$

$$w^i(\eta) = s(\eta)\,\Sigma_{k=0}^{i}\,(\eta + a_0)^k(d^kW^{II}_{i-k} / dx^k)(x^*) / k! + (1-s(\eta))\,\Sigma_{k=0}^{i}\,(\eta + a_0)^k(d^kW^{III}_{i-k} / dx^k)(x^*) / k!$$

($i \geq 1$) where $s(\eta) = (S(\eta) - U_0^{III}(x^*))/(U_0^{II}(x^*) - U_0^{III}(x^*))$ and S is as in Section 2. Moreover, we assume that $\bar{u}_i$ has the form:

(3.19) $\quad \bar{u}_i(\eta) = \bar{\bar{u}}_i(\eta) + a_i S_\eta(\eta) \quad$ with $\langle \bar{\bar{u}}_i, S_\eta \rangle = 0 \quad (i \geq 1)$.

Hence, $\bar{w}_i$, $\bar{\bar{u}}_i$ and a_{i-1} ($i \geq 1$) are unknown to be determined here. Substituting (3.18) with (3.19) into (3. 1) and equating the terms of like powers of ε, we have

$$(3.20;\ 0)\quad \begin{cases} S_{\eta\eta} - cS_\eta + f(S) - w^* = 0, \\ \qquad\qquad\qquad\qquad\qquad\qquad -\infty < \eta < +\infty, \\ w^*_\eta = 0, \end{cases}$$

$$
(3.20;\ 1)\begin{cases} M\bar{\bar{u}}_1 \equiv \bar{\bar{u}}_{1\eta\eta} - c\bar{\bar{u}}_{1\eta} + f'(S)\bar{\bar{u}}_1 \\ \quad = -M u^1 + w^1 + \bar{w}_1 + c\ell_1 S_\eta - 2\ell_1 (f(S) - w^*), \\ \qquad\qquad\qquad -\infty < \eta < +\infty , \\ -c\bar{w}_{1\eta} = cw^1{}_\eta - (S - \gamma w^*) , \end{cases}
$$

$$
(3.20;\ i)\begin{cases} M\bar{\bar{u}}_i = -M u^i + w^i + \bar{w}_i + c\ell_i S_\eta - 2\ell_i (f(S) - w^*) \\ \qquad + a_{i-1}\{c\ell_1 S_{\eta\eta} - [2\ell_1 f'(S) + f''(S)(u^1 + \bar{u}_1)]S_\eta\} + \bar{F}_i , \\ \qquad\qquad\qquad -\infty < \eta < +\infty ,\ i \geq 2 , \\ -c\bar{w}_{i\eta} = cw^i{}_\eta - a_{i-1}S_\eta + \bar{G}_i , \end{cases}
$$

where $\bar{F}_i$ and $\bar{G}_i$ are functions determined only by $\bar{\bar{u}}_k$, $\bar{w}_k$, W_k^J , U_k^J , ℓ_k and a_{k-1} $(k \leq i-1 ,\ J = II ,\ III)$. By the definition of S , we see that (3.20; 0) holds. Impose the matching conditions on $\bar{\bar{u}}_i$ and $\bar{w}_i$ $(i \geq 1)$;

$$
(3.21) \qquad \bar{\bar{u}}_i(\eta) \to 0 ,\ \bar{w}_i(\eta) \to 0 , \quad \text{as } |\eta| \to +\infty .
$$

Solvability conditions of (3.20; i) with (3. 21) $(i \geq 1)$ can be obtained in the similar way as in Subsection 3-2:

$$
(3.22) \qquad W_i^{III}(x^*) - W_i^{II}(x^*) = c^{-1}a_{i-1}[U_0^{III}(x^*) - U_0^{II}(x^*)] = \bar{\Gamma}_i ,
$$

$$
(3.23) \qquad W_i^{II}(x^*)\langle s,\bar{z}\rangle + W_i^{III}(x^*)\langle 1-s,\bar{z}\rangle
$$

$$
- c^{-1}a_{i-1}\{[U_0^{II}(x^*) - U_0^{III}(x^*)]\langle s,\bar{z}\rangle + [U_0^{III}(x^*) - \gamma w^*]\langle 1,z\rangle\} = \bar{\Delta}_i
$$

$(i \geq 1)$, where $\bar{z} = S_\eta(\eta)e^{-c\eta}$, and $\bar{\Gamma}_i$, $\bar{\Delta}_i$ are constants determined only by $\bar{\bar{u}}_k$, $\bar{w}_k$, U_k^J , W_k^J , a_{k-1} and ℓ_k $(k \leq i-1 ,\ J = II,\ III)$. In the derivation of (3.22) and (3.23), we used

$$
\langle cS_\eta - (2f'(S) - w^*) ,\ \bar{z} \rangle = 0 ,
$$

$$
\langle (cf''(S) - 2\ell_1 f'(S))S_\eta - c\ell_1 S_{\eta\eta} ,\ \bar{z} \rangle
$$

$$
= \langle w^1{}_\eta + \bar{w}_\eta ,\ \bar{z} \rangle = c^{-1}\langle S - \gamma w^*, \bar{z}\rangle
$$

$$
= c^{-1}\{[U_0^{II}(x^*) - U_0^{III}(x^*)]\langle s,\bar{z}\rangle + [U_0^{III}(x^*) - \gamma w^*]\langle 1,z\rangle\} .
$$

Consequentry, if we know $\bar{\bar{u}}_k$, $\bar{w}_k$, U_k^J , W_k^J , a_{k-1} , ℓ_k $(k \leq i-1 ,\ J = II ,\ III)$ and $W_i^{II}(x^*)$, we can obtain $W_i^{III}(x^*)$ and a_{i-1}

from (3.22) and (3.23), and $\bar{w}_i$ from the second equation of (3.20; i) ($i \geq 1$). Moreover, if ℓ_i is also given, we can obtain $\bar{\bar{u}}_i$ from the first equation of (3.20, i) ($i \geq 1$).

3-4. Periodicity.

The series (3. 2), (3. 7) and (3.18) are asymptotic expansions of a priodic solution of (3. 1). Thus, coefficients of the series must be determined such that the series are also periodc, to say,

$$U_i^{III}(x^*) = U_i^I(0) \ , \quad (dU_i^{III}/dx)(x^*) = (dU_i^I/dx)(0) \ , \tag{3.24}$$

$$W_i^{III}(x^*) = W_i^I(0) \ . \tag{3.25}$$

In the case of $i = 0$, (3.24) and (3.25) are satisfied. From our construction of the series given in Subsections 3-1 ~ 3-3, we easily see that (3.25) implies (3.24) in the case of $i \geq 1$. Here, we show that (3.25) uniquely determines ℓ_i which was unknown in the previous subsections.

$W_i^I(x_*)$ and $W_i^{II}(x_*)$ ($= W_i^I(x_*) - \hat{\Gamma}_i$) are obtained from (3.14) and (3.17). Thus, by (3. 5), we have

$$W_i^I(0) = [A^I(x_*)]^{-1}\{W_i^I(x_*) - c\ell_i\int_0^{x_*} A^I(x_*-y)(U_0^I - \gamma W_0^I)(y)dy\} + C_i^I \ , \tag{3.26}$$

$$W_i^{II}(x^*) = A^{II}(x^*)W_i^I(x_*) + c\ell_i\int_{x_*}^{x^*} A^{II}(x_*-y)(U_0^{II} - \gamma W_0^{II})(y)dy + C_i^{II} , \tag{3.27}$$

where C_i^I and C_i^{II} are constants determined only by $\hat{u}_k$, $\hat{w}_k$, W_k^J , U_k^J and ℓ_k ($k \leq i-1$, $J = I$, II). On the other hand, (3.22) and (3.23) yield

$$W_i^{III}(x^*) = - K \ W_i^{II}(x^*) + D_i^{III} \ , \tag{3.28}$$

where $- K = (U_0^{III}(x^*) - \gamma w^*)/(U_0^{II}(x^*) - \gamma w^*)$ and D_i^{III} is a constant determined only by $\bar{\bar{u}}_k$, $\bar{w}_k$, W_k^J, U_k^J, ℓ_k and a_{k-1} ($k \leq i-1$, $J = II$, III). (3.27) and (3.28) yield

$$W_i^{III}(x^*) = -K A^{II}(x^*)W^I(x^*) - Kc^{-1}\ell_i\int_{x_*}^{x^*} A^{II}(x^*-y)(U_0^{II}-\gamma W_0^{II})(y)dy - K C_i^{II} + D_i^{III}. \tag{3.29}$$

By using (3.26) and (3.29), we can rewrite (3.25) into

$$c^{-1}B\ell_i = \{[A^I(x_*)]^{-1} + K A^{II}(x^*)\}W^{II}(x_*) + C_i^I + KC_i^{II} + D_i^{III}, \tag{3.30}$$

where $$B = \{[A^I(x_*)]^{-1}\int_0^{x_*} A^I(x_*-y)(U_0^I - \gamma W_0^I)(y)dy - K\int_{x_*}^{x^*} A^{II}(x^*-y)(U_0^{II}-\gamma W_0^{II})(y)dy\}.$$

Note that $A^I(x) > 0$ and $(U_0^I - \gamma W_0^I)(x) < 0$ for $x \in I$, $A^{II}(x) > 0$ and $(U_0^{II} - \gamma W_0^{II})(x) > 0$ for $x \in II$. Hence, $B < 0$ and there exists uniquely ℓ_i satisfying (3.30). (3.30) shows that ℓ_i is determined only by $\hat{u}_k$, $\hat{w}_k$, $\bar{\bar{u}}_k$, $\bar{w}_k$, a_{k-1}, W_k^J, U_k^J and ℓ_k ($k \leq i-1$, $J = I$, II, III). Moreover, (3.25) leads that $U_i^{III}(x) = U_i^I(x - x^*)$ and $W_i^{III}(x) = W_i^I(x - x^*)$ for $x \in III$.

From the argument in 3-1 ~ 3-4, we see that $\hat{u}_i$, $\hat{w}_i$, $\bar{\bar{u}}_i$, $\bar{w}_i$, a_{i-1}, W_i^J, U_i^J and ℓ_i ($J = I$, II, III) can be determined inductively, and that $U_i^{III}(x) = U_i^I(x - x^*)$ and $W_i^{III}(x) = W_i^I(x - x^*)$ for $x \in III$. The i-th step of the induction is as follows: 1) Determine $W_i^I(x_*)$ and $W_i^{II}(x_*)$ by solving (3.14) and (3.17), and ℓ_i by (3.30). 2) Obtain $W^{II}(x^*)$ by (3.27) and determin $W_i^{III}(x^*)$ and a_{i-1} by solving (3.22) and (3.23). 3) Set $W_i^I(0) = W_i^{III}(x^*)$ and obtain W_i^J, U_i^J ($J = I$, II, III) by

(3. 5). 4) Obtain $\hat{u}_i$ and $\hat{w}_i$ by solving (3. 9; i) with $\langle u_i + \hat{u}_i , T_\xi \rangle = 0$, $\hat{u}_i(\xi) \to 0$ and $\hat{w}_i(\xi) \to 0$ ($|\xi| \to +\infty$), and $\bar{\bar{u}}_i$ and $\bar{w}_i$ by (3.20; i) with $\langle \bar{\bar{u}}_i , S_\eta \rangle = 0$, $\bar{\bar{u}}_i(\eta) \to 0$ and $\bar{w}_i(\eta) \to 0$ ($|\eta| \to +\infty$).

4. Outline of the proof of Theorem 1.

Let d be a small positive number. Define Banach spaces X_ε and Y by the following way.

X_ε : The subspace in $C^2[d, x^* + d] \times C^1[d, x^* + d] \times \mathbb{R}$ whose elements (u, w, ℓ) satisfy

$$(d^j u/dx^j)(d) = (d^j u/dx^j)(x^* + d) \quad \text{for } j = 0, 1, 2,$$

$$(d^j w/dx^j)(d) = (d^j w/dx^j)(x^* + d) \quad \text{for } j = 0, 1.$$

The norm $\| \ \|_X^\varepsilon$ of X_ε is defined by

$$\|(u, w, \ell)\|_X^\varepsilon \equiv \Sigma_{j=0}^2 \varepsilon^j \|d^j u/dx^j\|_0 + \Sigma_{j=0}^1 \varepsilon^j \|d^j w/dx^j\|_0 + |\ell| ,$$

where $\|u\|_0 = \sup\{|u(x)| : d \le x \le x^* + d \}$.

Y : The subspace in $C[d, x^* + d] \times C[d, x^* + d] \times \mathbb{R}$ whose elemnts (h, g, r) satisfy

$$h(d) = h(x^* + d) , \quad g(d) = g(x^* + d).$$

The norm $\| \ \|_Y$ of Y is defined by

$$\|(h, g, r)\|_Y = \|h\|_0 + \|g\|_0 + |r| .$$

Define $P : X_\varepsilon \times \{ 0 < \varepsilon < 1 \} \to Y$ by

$$P(u, w, \ell; \varepsilon) = \Big(\varepsilon^2 u_{xx} - \varepsilon c \ell\, u_x + \ell^2 (f(u) - w) , \quad - c\, w_x + \ell (u - \gamma w) , \quad \int_{-d/\varepsilon}^{d/\varepsilon} (u(x_* + \varepsilon\xi) - T(\xi)) T_\xi(\xi) d\xi \Big) . \tag{4. 1}$$

Note that, if there exists a solution $(u^\varepsilon, w^\varepsilon, \ell^\varepsilon)$ of $P(u, w, \ell; \varepsilon) = 0$, ℓ^ε and the periodic extensions of u^ε and w^ε (with period x^*) satisfy (3. 1).

We denote the finite series of outer and inner expansions $H^J u$, $H^J w$ ($J = I, II, III$), $E_* u$, $E_* w$, $E^* u$ and $E^* w$ with terms of up to $O(\varepsilon^{m+2})$ of ε by $H^J_m u$, $H^J_m w$ ($J = I, II, III$), $E_{*m} u$, $E_{*m} w$, $E^*_m u$ and $E^*_m w$ respectively. Let τ be C^∞-function satisfying $0 \le \tau(x) \le 1$ for $x \in \mathbb{R}$, $\tau(x) \equiv 1$ for $|x| \le 1$ and $\tau(x) \equiv 0$ for $|x| \ge 2$, and set

$$\tau_1(x) = \tau((x - x_*)/\delta(\varepsilon)), \quad \tau_2(x) = \tau((x - x^*)/\delta(\varepsilon)),$$

$$\omega_J(x) = X_J(x)(1 - \tau_1(x) - \tau_2(x)) \quad (J = I, II, III),$$

where $\delta(\varepsilon) = -\varepsilon\log\varepsilon$ and X_J is the characteristic function of the interval $\bar{J}$ (the closure of J). Moreover, set

$$u^\varepsilon_m = \omega_I\, H^I_m u + \omega_{II}\, H^{II}_m u + \omega_{III}\, H^{III}_m u + \tau_1\, E_{*m} u + \tau_2\, E^*_m u,$$

$$w^\varepsilon_m = \omega_I\, H^I_m w + \omega_{II}\, H^{II}_m w + \omega_{III}\, H^{III}_m w + \tau_1\, E_{*m} w + \tau_2\, E^*_m w,$$

$$\ell^\varepsilon_m = 1 + \varepsilon\ell_1 + \varepsilon^2\ell_2 + \cdots + \varepsilon^{m+2}\ell_{m+2}.$$

We also denote the restriction of $(u^\varepsilon_m, w^\varepsilon_m)$ on $[d, x^* + d]$ by $(u^\varepsilon_m, w^\varepsilon_m)$. Then, we easily see that $(u^\varepsilon_m, w^\varepsilon_m, \ell^\varepsilon_m)$ belongs to X_ε and its norm is bounded uniformly in $0 < \varepsilon < 1$. Moreover, from the constructing method of the asymptotic expansions, we also see that

$$(4.\ 2) \qquad \| P(u^\varepsilon_m, w^\varepsilon_m, \ell^\varepsilon_m; \varepsilon) \|^\varepsilon_X = O(|\varepsilon\log\varepsilon|^{m+1}).$$

We show the existence of the solution $(u^\varepsilon, w^\varepsilon, \ell^\varepsilon)$ for $P(u, w, \ell; \varepsilon) = 0$ with $\|(u^\varepsilon - u^\varepsilon_m, w^\varepsilon - w^\varepsilon_m, \ell^\varepsilon - \ell^\varepsilon_m)\|^\varepsilon_X = O(\varepsilon^m|\log\varepsilon|^{m+1})$. This implies Theorm 1. We apply the implicit function theorem (Theorem 4. 2 in [5]) to show the existence of $(u^\varepsilon, w^\varepsilon, \ell^\varepsilon)$. We easily see that $P(u, w, \ell; \varepsilon)$ is twice Fréchet differentiable with respect to (u, w, ℓ) and its derivatives $DP(u_m^\varepsilon, w_m^\varepsilon, \ell_m^\varepsilon; \varepsilon) : X_\varepsilon \to Y$, and $D^2P(u_m^\varepsilon, w_m^\varepsilon, \ell_m^\varepsilon; \varepsilon) : X^\varepsilon \times X^\varepsilon \to Y$ are bounded uniformly in $0 < \varepsilon < 1$. Thus, for the proof of the existence of $(u^\varepsilon, w^\varepsilon, \ell^\varepsilon)$, it suffices to show the invertibility of $DP(u_m^\varepsilon, w_m^\varepsilon, \ell_m^\varepsilon; \varepsilon)$ and

$$(4.\ 3)\qquad \| [DP(u_m^\varepsilon, w_m^\varepsilon, \ell_m^\varepsilon; \varepsilon)]^{-1} \| \le O(\varepsilon^{-1}) \qquad (\varepsilon \to 0),$$

where $[DP(u_m^\varepsilon, w_m^\varepsilon, \ell_m^\varepsilon; \varepsilon)]^{-1}$ is the inverse operator of $DP(u_m^\varepsilon, w_m^\varepsilon, \ell_m^\varepsilon; \varepsilon)$ and $\| \ \|$ is the operator norm.

Proof of the invertivility and (4. 3). The invertivility of $DP(u_m^\varepsilon, w_m^\varepsilon, \ell_m^\varepsilon; \varepsilon)$ is equivalent to the solvability of

$$(4.\ 4)\quad \begin{cases} \varepsilon^2\varphi_{xx} - \varepsilon c\ell_m^\varepsilon \varphi_x + (\ell_m^\varepsilon)^2(f'(u_m^\varepsilon)\varphi - \psi) \\ \qquad - \nu[\varepsilon c u_{mx}^\varepsilon - 2\ell_m^\varepsilon(f(u_m^\varepsilon) - w_m^\varepsilon)] = h, \\ -c\,\psi_x + \ell_m^\varepsilon(\varphi - \gamma\psi) + \nu(u_m^\varepsilon - \gamma w_m^\varepsilon) = g, \\ \int_{-d/\varepsilon}^{d/\varepsilon} \varphi(x_* - \varepsilon\xi)\, T_\xi(\xi)d\xi = r, \end{cases}$$

for all $(h, g, r) \in Y$. To solve (4. 4), we first seek asymptotic expansions of (φ, ψ, ν) in the case where $h, g \in C^\infty$. Extend h, g periodically, and repesent them asymptotically, i.e.,

$$(4.\ 5)\quad \begin{cases} h \sim h(x), \quad g \sim g(x) & x \in J = I, II \text{ and } III, \\ h \sim \Sigma_{i=1}^\infty \varepsilon^i (d^i h/dx^i)(x_*)\xi^i/\, i! & x \sim x_*, \\ g \sim \Sigma_{i=1}^\infty \varepsilon^i (d^i g/dx^i)(x_*)\xi^i/\, i! & x \sim x_*, \\ h \sim \Sigma_{i=1}^\infty \varepsilon^i (d^i h/dx^i)(x^*)(\eta + a_0)^i/\, i! & x \sim x^*, \\ g \sim \Sigma_{i=1}^\infty \varepsilon^i (d^i g/dx^i)(x^*)(\eta + a_0)^i/\, i! & x \sim x^*. \end{cases}$$

Assume that φ, ψ and ν have the asymptotic expansions of the form:

$$\begin{cases} \nu \sim \nu_0 + \varepsilon\nu_1 + \varepsilon^2\nu_2 + \cdots, \end{cases}$$

$$
(4.6)\quad \begin{cases}
\varphi \sim H^J\varphi \equiv \Phi_0^J(x) + \varepsilon\Phi_1^J(x) + \varepsilon^2\Phi_2^J(x) + \cdots , & x \in J ,\\
\psi \sim H^J\psi \equiv \Psi_0^J(x) + \varepsilon\Psi_1^J(x) + \varepsilon^2\Psi_2^J(x) + \cdots , & x \in J ,\\
\varphi \sim E_*\varphi \equiv (1-t(\xi))H^I\varphi + t(\xi)H^{II}\varphi & \\
\qquad + \hat{\varphi}_0(\xi) + \varepsilon\hat{\varphi}_1(\xi) + \varepsilon^2\hat{\varphi}_2(\xi) + \cdots , & x \sim x_* ,\\
\psi \sim E_*\psi \equiv (1-t(\xi))H^I\psi + t(\xi)H^{II}\psi & \\
\qquad + \hat{\psi}_0(\xi) + \varepsilon\hat{\psi}_1(\xi) + \varepsilon^2\hat{\psi}_2(\xi) + \cdots , & x \sim x_* ,\\
\varphi \sim E^*\varphi \equiv s(\eta)H^{II}\varphi + (1-s(\eta))H^{III}\varphi & \\
\qquad + \varepsilon^{-1}\alpha_{-1}S_\eta(\eta) + [\alpha_0 S_\eta(\eta) + \bar{\bar{\varphi}}_0(\eta)] & \\
\qquad + \varepsilon[a_1 S_\eta(\eta) + \bar{\bar{\varphi}}_1(\eta)] + \cdots , & x \sim x^* ,\\
\psi \sim E^*\psi \equiv s(\eta)H^{II}\psi + (1-s(\eta))H^{III}\psi & \\
\qquad + \bar{\psi}_0(\eta) + \varepsilon\bar{\psi}_1(\xi) + \varepsilon^2\bar{\psi}_2(\eta) + \cdots , & x \sim x_* ,
\end{cases}
$$

with $\langle \bar{\bar{\varphi}}_i , S_\eta \rangle = 0$ $(i = 0, 1, \cdots)$. Substituting (4. 5) and (4. 6) as well as the asymptotic expansions of u_m^ε, w_m^ε , ℓ_m^ε into (4. 4), and equating terms of like powers of ε , we obtain

$$
(4.7)\quad \begin{cases}
f'(U_0^J)\Phi_i^J - \Psi_i^J = \mathcal{F}_i^J , & \\
 & x \in J ,\\
- c\Psi_{i\,x}^J + \Phi_i^J - \gamma\Psi_i^J + \nu_i(U_0^J - \gamma W_0^J) = \mathcal{G}_i^I , &
\end{cases}
$$

$$
(4.8)\quad \begin{cases}
L\hat{\varphi}_i = - L\varphi_i + \psi_i + \hat{\psi}_i + \nu_i(cT_\xi - 2(f(T)-w_*)) + \hat{\mathcal{F}}_i , & \\
- c\hat{\psi}_{i\xi} = c\psi_{i\xi} - \hat{\mathcal{G}}_i , & \xi \in \mathbb{R} ,\\
\langle \varphi_i + \hat{\varphi}_i , T_\xi \rangle = \delta_{0i} r , &
\end{cases}
$$

$$
(4.9)\quad \begin{cases}
M\bar{\bar{\varphi}}_i = - M\varphi^i + \psi^i + \bar{\psi}_i + \nu_i(cS_\eta - 2(f(S)-w^*)) & \\
\qquad + \alpha_{i-1}\{c\ell_1 S_{\eta\eta} - [2\ell_i f'(S)+f''(S)(u^1+\bar{u}_1)]S_\eta\} + \bar{\mathcal{F}}_i , & \\
- c\bar{\psi}_{i\eta} = c\psi^i{}_\eta - \alpha_{i-1}S_\eta + \bar{\mathcal{G}}_i , & \eta \in \mathbb{R} ,
\end{cases}
$$

where $\delta_{00} = 1$, $\delta_{0i} = 0$ $(i \geq 1)$, φ_i , ψ_i , φ^i and ψ^i are functions defined analogously as u_i , w_i , u^i and w^i respectively, and $\hat{\mathcal{F}}_i$, $\hat{\mathcal{G}}_i$, $\bar{\mathcal{F}}_i$, $\bar{\mathcal{G}}_i$, $\mathcal{F}_i^J$ and $\mathcal{G}_i^J$ (J = I, II, III) are functions determined only by $\hat{\varphi}_k$, $\hat{\psi}_k$, $\bar{\bar{\varphi}}_k$, $\bar{\psi}_k$, α_{k-1} , Φ_k^J ,

Ψ_k^J , ν_k ($k \le i-1$, J = I, II, III), h and g . Note that (4. 7), (4. 8), (4. 9) are of the same form as (3. 3;i), (3. 9; i) with $\langle u_i+\hat{u}_i , T_\xi\rangle = 0$ and (3.20; i) respectively. Hence, we can obtain $\hat{\varphi}_i$, $\hat{\phi}_i$, $\bar{\bar{\varphi}}_i$, $\bar{\psi}_i$, α_{i-1}, Φ_i^J , Ψ_i^J and ν_i in the same way as in $\hat{u}_{i+1}$, $\hat{w}_{i+1}$, $\bar{\bar{u}}_{i+1}$, $\bar{w}_{i+1}$, a_i , U_{i+1}^J, V_{i+1}^J and ℓ_{i+1} (J = I, II, III; i = 0, 1, 2, $\cdots$). Moreover, we can show that

$$\sup_x|\Phi_i^J(x)|,\ \sup_x|\Psi_i^J(x)| \quad (J = \mathrm{I, II, III}),\ |\alpha_{i-1}| ,$$
$$\sup_\xi|\hat{\varphi}_i(\xi)|,\ \sup_\xi|\hat{\phi}_i(\xi)|,\ \sup_\eta|\bar{\bar{\varphi}}_i(\eta)|,\ \sup_\eta|\bar{\psi}_i(\eta)|,\ |\nu_i|$$
$$\le \mathrm{const.}(\|h\|_i + \|g\|_i + |r|) ,$$

where $\|h\|_i = \Sigma_{k=0}^{i} \|d^kh/dx^k\|_0$. Let $n < m$, and put

$$B_n^\varepsilon(h, g, r) \tag{4. 10}$$
$$= (\omega_I H_n^I\varphi + \omega_{II}H_n^{II}\varphi + \omega_{III}H_n^{III}\varphi + \tau_1E_{*n}\varphi + \tau_2E_n^*\varphi ,$$
$$\omega_I H_n^I\psi + \omega_{II}H_n^{II}\psi + \omega_{III}H_n^{III}\psi + \tau_1E_{*n}\psi + \tau_2E_n^*\psi ,$$
$$\nu_0 + \varepsilon\nu_1 + \cdots + \varepsilon^{n+2}\nu_{\nu+2}) .$$

Then, we have

$$\|B_n^\varepsilon(h, g, r)\|_X^\varepsilon \le \varepsilon^{-1}\mathrm{const.}\ \Sigma_{i=0}^{n+3} \varepsilon^i(\|h\|_i+\|g\|_i+|r|). \tag{4. 11}$$

$$\|DP(u_m^\varepsilon, w_m^\varepsilon, \ell_m^\varepsilon)B_n(h, g, r) - (h, g, r)\|_Y \tag{4. 12}$$
$$\le \mathrm{const.}|\varepsilon\log\varepsilon|^{n+1}(\|h\|_{n+2} + \|g\|_{n+2} + |r|) .$$

Next we consider the case of $(h, g, r) \in Y$. Denote the periodic extentions of h and g also by h and g respectively. As is well known, there exists a family of smoothing operators S_t ($t > 1$): $C(\mathbb{R}) \to C^\infty(\mathbb{R})$ such that

$$\|S_th - h\|_0 \to 0 , \text{ as } t \to +\infty ,$$
$$\|S_th\|_i \le \mathrm{const.}\ t^i\|h\|_0 ,$$

for any $h \in C(\mathbb{R})$ (see for instance [17]). Define $\bar{B}_n^\varepsilon : Y \to X_\varepsilon$ by

$$\bar{B}_n^\varepsilon(h, g, r) = B_n^\varepsilon(S_{-\varepsilon\log\varepsilon}h , S_{-\varepsilon\log\varepsilon}g , r) .$$

Then, by (4.11) and (4.12), we have

$$(4.13)\quad \| \bar{B}_n^{\varepsilon}(h, g, r)\|_X^{\varepsilon} \le \varepsilon^{-1}\text{const.}\|(h, g, r)\|_Y ,$$

$$(4.14)\quad \| DP(u_m^{\varepsilon}, w_m^{\varepsilon}, \ell_m^{\varepsilon} ; \varepsilon)\bar{B}_n^{\varepsilon}(h, g, r) - (h, g, r)\|_Y = o(1)\|(h, g, r)\|_Y , \text{ as } \varepsilon \to 0 .$$

Thus, we see that $[DP(u_m^{\varepsilon}, w_m^{\varepsilon}, \ell_m^{\varepsilon} ; \varepsilon)]^{-1} \equiv [Id - (Id - DP(u_m^{\varepsilon}, w_m^{\varepsilon}, \ell_m^{\varepsilon} ; \varepsilon)\bar{B}_n^{\varepsilon})]^{-1} \bar{B}_n^{\varepsilon}$ exists for sufficiently small ε, is the inverse of $DP(u_m^{\varepsilon}, w_m^{\varepsilon}, \ell_m^{\varepsilon} ; \varepsilon)$, and satisfies (4. 3).

5. Outline of the proof of Theorem 2.

Let $(u^{\varepsilon}, w^{\varepsilon}, \ell^{\varepsilon})$ be the solution of $P(u, w, \ell ; \varepsilon) = 0$ obtained in the previous section. Denote the periodic extentions of u^{ε} and w^{ε} by the same notatins u^{ε} and w^{ε} respectively. The eigenvalue problem (2. 8) is written in the form,

$$(5.1)\quad \begin{cases} \varepsilon^2 p_{xx} - \varepsilon c \ell^{\varepsilon} p_x + (\ell^{\varepsilon})^2 (f'(u^{\varepsilon})p - q) = \varepsilon(\ell^{\varepsilon})^2 \lambda p , \\ \qquad\qquad\qquad\qquad\qquad\qquad\qquad\qquad x \in \mathbb{R} , \\ - c\, q_x + \ell^{\varepsilon}(p - \gamma q) = \ell^{\varepsilon} \lambda q , \end{cases}$$

because of the transformation $x \to \ell^{\varepsilon} x$.

Eigenvalues λ with eigenvector (p, q) can be also obtain through asymptotic expansions of the form:

$$(5.2)\quad \begin{cases} \lambda \sim \lambda_0 + \varepsilon\lambda_1 + \varepsilon^2\lambda_2 + \cdots, \\ p \sim H^J p \equiv P_0^J(x) + \varepsilon P_1^J(x) + \varepsilon^2 P_2^J(x) + \cdots , \quad x \in J , \\ q \sim H^J q \equiv Q_0^J(x) + \varepsilon Q_1^J(x) + \varepsilon^2 Q_2^J(x) + \cdots , \quad x \in J , \\ \qquad\qquad\qquad\qquad\qquad (J = I, II, III), \\ p \sim E_* p \equiv (1-t(\xi))H^I p + t(\xi)H^{II} p \\ \qquad + \varepsilon^{-1}\beta_{-1}T_{\xi}(\xi) + [\beta_0 T_{\xi}(\xi) + \check{p}_0(\xi)] \\ \qquad + \varepsilon[\beta_1 T_{\xi}(\xi) + \check{p}_1(\xi)] + \cdots , \quad x \sim x_* , \\ q \sim E_* q \equiv (1-t(\xi))H^I q + t(\xi)H^{II} q \end{cases}$$

$$
\left\{
\begin{array}{ll}
\quad + \hat{q}_0(\xi) + \varepsilon\hat{q}_1(\xi) + \varepsilon^2\hat{q}_2(\xi) + \cdots , & x \sim x_* , \\
p \sim E^*p \equiv s(\eta)H^{II}p + (1-s(\eta))H^{III}p & \\
\quad + \varepsilon^{-1}\delta_{-1}S_\eta(\eta) + [\delta_0 S_\eta(\eta) + \bar{\bar{p}}_0(\eta)] & \\
\quad + \varepsilon[\delta_1 S_\eta(\eta) + \bar{\bar{p}}_1(\eta)] + \cdots , & x \sim x^* , \\
q \sim E^*q \equiv s(\eta)H^{II}q + (1-s(\eta))H^{III}q & \\
\quad + \bar{q}_0(\eta) + \varepsilon\bar{q}_1(\eta) + \varepsilon^2\bar{q}_2(\eta) + \cdots , & x \sim x^* ,
\end{array}
\right.
$$

with $\langle \check{p}_i , T_\xi \rangle = \langle \bar{\bar{p}}_i , S_\eta \rangle = 0$ $(i = 0, 1, \cdots)$. Instead of the periodicity condition of the form of (3.25), we impose here the conditions;

(5. 2) $\quad |Q_i^{III}(x^*)| = |Q_i^I(0)|$, $i = 0, 1, 2, \cdots,$

which ensure the boundedness of the asymptotic expansions on $-\infty < x < +\infty$. Our main interest is the positivity (or the negativity) of Re λ which follows from the positivity (or the negativity) of Re λ_0 when ε is small enough. Thus, we give here only a part relating to the detemination of λ_0 .

Lemma 5. 1. Let λ_0 is a solution of

(5. 3) $\quad |\theta(\lambda)\exp(-\lambda x^*/c)A^I(x_*)A^{II}(x^*)| = 1$,

and $\lambda_0 \neq \Lambda_j$ (j=1, 2) . Then (5. 2) with i = 0 holds. Here,

$$\Lambda_1 = (U_0^I(x_*) - \gamma w_*)\langle 1, \hat{z}\rangle / c(U_0^{II}(x_*) - U_0^I(x_*))\langle t_\xi, \hat{z}\rangle ,$$
$$\Lambda_2 = (U_0^{II}(x^*) - \gamma w^*)\langle 1, \bar{z}\rangle / c(U_0^{II}(x^*) - U_0^{III}(x^*))\langle s_\eta, \bar{z}\rangle .$$

Proof. Substitute H^Jp , H^Jq , λ^ε as well as H^Ju , H^Jw , ℓ^ε into (5. 1), then we have the terms of $O(\varepsilon^0)$:

$$
\left\{
\begin{array}{ll}
f'(U_0^J(x))P_0^J - Q_0^J = 0 , & x \in J , \\
- c\, Q_{0\,x}^J + P_0^I - \gamma\, Q_0^J = \lambda_0\, Q_0^J , & x \in J .
\end{array}
\right.
$$

Thus,

$$(5.4)\quad \begin{cases} Q_0^{I}(x_*) = A^{I}(x_*)\exp(-\lambda_0 x_*/c)Q_0^{I}(0) \;, \\[2ex] Q_0^{II}(x^*) = A^{II}(x^*)\exp(-\lambda_0 (x^*-x_*)/c)Q_0^{II}(0) \;. \end{cases}$$

Solvability conditions of the equations governing $\check{p}_0$, $\hat{q}_0$ and $\bar{\bar{p}}_0$, $\bar{q}_0$ are of the similar type as (3.22) and (3.23), i. e.,

$$(5.5)\quad Q_0^{II}(x_*) - Q_0^{I}(x_*) = c^{-1}\beta_{-1}[U_0^{II}(x_*) - U_0^{I}(x_*)] \;,$$

$$(5.6)\quad Q_0^{I}(x_*)\langle 1-t, \hat{z}\rangle + Q_0^{II}(x_*)\langle t, \hat{z}\rangle + \beta_{-1}\{\lambda_0(U_0^{II} - U_0^{I})(x_*)\langle t_\xi, \hat{z}\rangle - c^{-1}[(U_0^{II} - U_0^{I})(x_*)\langle t, \hat{z}\rangle + (U_0^{I} - \gamma W_0^{I})(x_*)\langle 1, \hat{z}\rangle]\} = 0 \;,$$

$$(5.7)\quad Q_0^{III}(x^*) - Q_0^{II}(x^*) = c^{-1}\delta_{-1}[U_0^{III}(x^*) - U_0^{II}(x^*)] \;,$$

$$(5.8)\quad Q_0^{II}(x_*^*)\langle s, \bar{z}\rangle + Q_0^{III}(x_*^*)\langle 1-s, \bar{z}\rangle + \delta_{-1}\{\lambda_0(U_0^{II} - U_0^{III})(x^*)\langle s_\eta, \bar{z}\rangle - c^{-1}[(U_0^{II} - U_0^{III})(x^*)\langle s, \bar{z}\rangle + (U_0^{III} - \gamma W_0^{III})(x^*)\langle 1, \bar{z}\rangle]\} = 0 \;.$$

(5. 5) and (5. 6) yield

$$(5.9)\quad Q_0^{I}(x_*)\langle 1, \hat{z}\rangle = \beta_{-1}\{-\lambda_0(U_0^{II} - U_0^{I})(x_*)\langle t_\xi, \hat{z}\rangle + c^{-1}(U_0^{I} - \gamma W_0^{I})(x_*)\langle 1, \hat{z}\rangle\},$$

and

$$(5.10)\quad Q_0^{II}(x_*) = \left[1 - \frac{(U_0^{II} - U_0^{I})(x_*)\langle 1, \hat{z}\rangle}{c\lambda_0(U_0^{II} - U_0^{I})(x_*)\langle t_\xi, \hat{z}\rangle - (U_0^{I} - \gamma W_0^{I})(x_*)\langle 1, \hat{z}\rangle}\right]Q_0^{I}(x_*)$$

if $\lambda_0 \neq (U_0^{I} - \gamma W_0^{I})(x_*)\langle 1, \hat{z}\rangle / c(U_0^{II} - U_0^{I})(x_*)\langle t_\xi, \hat{z}\rangle \quad (< 0)$.

(5. 7) and (5. 8) yield

$$(5.11)\quad Q_0^{II}(x^*)\langle 1, \bar{z}\rangle = \delta_{-1}\{-\lambda_0(U_0^{II} - U_0^{III})(x^*)\langle s_\eta, \bar{z}\rangle + c^{-1}(U_0^{II} - \gamma W_0^{II})(x_*)\langle 1, \bar{z}\rangle\},$$

and

$$(5.12)\quad Q_0^{III}(x^*) = \left[1 - \frac{(U_0^{III} - U_0^{II})(x^*)\langle 1, \bar{z}\rangle}{c\lambda_0(U_0^{II} - U_0^{III})(x^*)\langle s_\eta, \bar{z}\rangle - (U_0^{II} - \gamma W_0^{II})(x^*)\langle 1, \bar{z}\rangle}\right]Q_0^{II}(x^*)$$

if $\lambda_0 \neq (U_0^{II} - \gamma W_0^{II})(x^*)\langle 1, \bar{z}\rangle / c(U_0^{II} - U_0^{III})(x^*)\langle s_\eta, \bar{z}\rangle \quad (<0)$.
(5. 4),(5.10) and (5.12) yield

$$Q_0^{III}(x^*) = \theta(\lambda_0)\exp(-\lambda_0 x^*/c)A^I(x_*)A^{II}(x^*)Q_0^I(x_*) \ .$$

The claim of the lemma follows from the above equation.

For λ_0 satisfying (5. 3) and not equal to Λ_j (j = i, 2), the asymptotic expansions (5. 2) can be obtained if $Q_0^I(0)$ is given. λ_i ($i \geq 1$) are determined to satisfy $Q_i^{III}(x^*) = Q_i^I(0) = 0$. Note that, for any eigenvector (p, q) of (5. 1) and any constant κ , $(\kappa p, \kappa q)$ is also an eigenvector of (5. 1) corresponding to the same eigenvalue. Thus, to determine (λ, p, q) uniquely , we impose a normalised conditon, namely, $q(d) = 1$ on (5. 1), which will detemines $Q_0^I(0)$ uniquely. The jastification of the asymptotic expansions obtained here can be done in the quite similar way as in the previous section. So we omit it.

Next, we note that (5. 1) has the eigenvalue $\lambda = 0$ with the eigenvector $(u^\varepsilon_x , w^\varepsilon_x)$ and that u^ε_x and w^ε_x are periodic functions with period x^* . Therefore,

$$\theta(0)\ A^I(x_*)A^{II}(x^*) = 1 \ .$$

This and (5. 3) yield (2. 9). This complete the proof of Theorm 2.

Proof of Corollary 3.

Noting that $0 < \alpha$, $0 < \beta$, $0 < A < 1$ and $0 < B < 1$, we have

$$\theta(0) = (1 - A^{-1})(1 - B^{-1}) > 0 \ ,$$

$$\theta'(0) = c\alpha A^{-2}(1 - B^{-1}) + c\beta B^{-2}(1 - A^{-1}) < 0 \ ,$$

and

$$\frac{d}{d\lambda}\ \theta(\lambda)\exp(-\lambda x^*/c)\Big|_{\lambda=0} = \theta'(0) - c^{-1}x^*\theta(0) < 0 \ .$$

Thus, it follows from the usual implicit function theorem that there exists solution $\lambda_0(\theta)$ of (2. 9) for small θ, and

$$\lambda_0(\theta) = i\,\sigma_1\theta + \sigma_2\theta^2 + O(\theta^3), \quad \text{as } \theta \to 0,$$

where

$$\sigma_1 = c\theta(0)/(c\theta'(0) - x^*\theta(0)) < 0,$$

$$\sigma_2 = 2^{-1}c^3\theta(0)[\theta''(0)\theta(0) - \theta'(0)^2][c\theta'(0) - x^*\theta(0)]^{-3} .$$

By the definition of θ, we have

$$\theta''(0)\theta(0) - \theta'(0)^2$$
$$= c^2\{\alpha^2A^{-3}(1 - B^{-1})^2(A^{-1} - 2) + \beta^2B^{-3}(1 - A^{-1})^2(B^{-1} - 2)\} .$$

By Lemma 2. 1, we easily see that, as $c \uparrow c_0$, A^{-1} grows infinitely while B^{-1} is bounded. Hence, for c closed to c_0,

$$\theta''(0)\theta(0) - \theta'(0)^2 \sim c_0^{\,2}\,\alpha^2A^{-3}(1 - B^{-1})^2 > 0$$

and $\sigma_2 < 0$. On the other hand, in the case of c closed to 0, we see that $A + B$ is closed to 1, $A < 1/2 < B$ and $\alpha = \beta$. Thus, in this case,

$$\theta''(0)\theta(0) - \theta'(0)^2 \sim \frac{c^2\alpha^2}{A(1 - A)}\left(\frac{1 - 2A}{A} - \frac{1 - 2A}{1 - A}\right) > 0$$

and $\sigma_2 < 0$. This completes the proof of Corollary 3.

References.

[1] G. A. Carpenter, A geometric approach to singular perturbation problems with application to nerve impulse equations, J. Differential Equations 23 (1977) 335-367.

[2] J. W. Evans, Nerve axon equations: II. Stability at rest, Indiana Univ. Math. J. 22 (1972), 75-90.

[3] J. W. Evans, Nerve axon equations: III. Stability of the nerve impulse, Indiana Univ. Math. J. 22 (1972) 577-593.

[4] J. W. Evans, Nerve axon equations: IV. The Stable and the unstable impulse, Indiana Univ. Math. J. 24 (1975) 1169-1190.

[5] P. C. Fife and W. M. Greenlee, Interior transition layers for elliptic boundary value problems with a small parameter, Russian Math. Surveys 29 (1974) 103-131.

[6] P. C. Fife and J. B. McLeod, The approach of nonlinear diffusion equations to travelling front solutions, Arch. Rat. Mech. Anal. 65 (1977) 335-361.

[7] A. van Harten and E. Vader-Burger, Approximate Green functions as a tool to prove correctness of a formal approximation in a model of competing and diffusing species, preprint No. 343 (1984) , Department of Mathematics, University of Utrecht.

[8] S. Hastings, The existence of periodic solutions to Naguno's equation, Quart. J. Math. Oxford 25 (1974) 369-378.

[9] S. Hastings, On the existence of homoclinic and periodic orbits for the FitzHugh-Nagumo equations, Quart. J. Math. Oxford 27 (1976) 123-134.

[9] H. Ikeda, M. Mimura and T. Tsujikawa, Slow traveling wave solutions to the Hodgkin-Huxley equations, preprint.

[10] H. Ikeda, M. Mimura and T. Tsujikawa, Pertubation analysis of the Hodgikin-Huxley equations, preprint.

[11] C. K. R. T. Jones, Stability of the travelling wave solution of the Fitzhugh-Nagumo system, Trans. Ame. Math. Soc. 286 (1984) 431-469.

[12] R. B. Langer, Existence and uniqueness of pulse solutions to the FitzHugh-Nagumo equations, Ph. D. Thesis, Northeastern Univ. (1980).

[13] K. Maginu, Existence and stability of periodic travelling wave solutions to Nagumo's Nerve Equation, J. Math. Biology 10 (1980) 133-153.

[14] R. N. Miller and J. Rinzel, The dependence of impulse propagation speed on firing frequency, dispersion, for the Hodgkin-Huxley model, Biophys. J. 34 (1981) 227-259.

[15] J. Rinzel and J. B. Keller, Traveling wave solutions of a nerve conduction equation, Biophys. J. 13 (1973) 1313-1337.

[16] E. Yanagida, Stability of fast travelling pulse solutions of the FitzHugh-Nagumo equations, J. Math. Biology 22 (1985) 81-104.

[17] E. Zehnder, Generalized implicit function theorems with applications to some small divisor problems, I, Comm. Pure Appl. Math. XXVIII (1975) 91-140.

Recent Topics in Nonlinear PDE III, Tokyo, 1986
Lecture Notes in Num. Appl. Anal., 9, 105–117 (1987)

Singular Perturbation of Domains and the Structure of the Solutions of Semilinear Elliptic Equation

Shuichi JIMBO

Department of Mathematics, Faculty of Science

University of Tokyo, Hongo, Tokyo, 113 Japan

§1. Introduction. We are concerned with the following semilinear elliptic boundary value problem :

$$(1.1)\quad \begin{cases} \Delta v + f(v) = 0 & \text{in } \Omega, \\ \dfrac{\partial v}{\partial \nu} = 0 & \text{on } \partial\Omega, \end{cases}$$

where Ω is a bounded domain in $\mathbb{R}^n$ with smooth boundary $\partial\Omega$, ν denotes the unit outer normal vector on $\partial\Omega$, $\Delta = \sum_{j=1}^{n} \frac{\partial^2}{\partial x_j^2}$ is the Laplace operator and f is a real valued smooth function on $\mathbb{R}$. It seems to be true that the solutions of (1.1) and their structure usually vary continuously under the smooth deformation of the domain Ω. On the other hand, not much is known as to what happens if Ω is perturbed singularly.

The purpose of this paper is to investigate the behavior of the solutions of (1.1) when the domain Ω is perturbed singularly in a certain sense. By doing so, we get some insight for a geometric factor which is important for understanding how the structure of the solution set varies. The domain $\Omega(\zeta)$ (parametrized by $\zeta > 0$) which we deal with is exhibited in Figure 1 and it is decomposed as follows:

$$\Omega(\zeta) = D_1 \cup D_2 \cup Q(\zeta),$$

where D_1 and D_2 are mutually disjoint bounded domains in $\mathbb{R}^n$, and $Q(\zeta)$ is changing its shape and approaches a segment as $\zeta \to 0$. We consider the behavior of the solutions of (1.1) and their structure for $\Omega = \Omega(\zeta)$ when ζ tends to 0 .

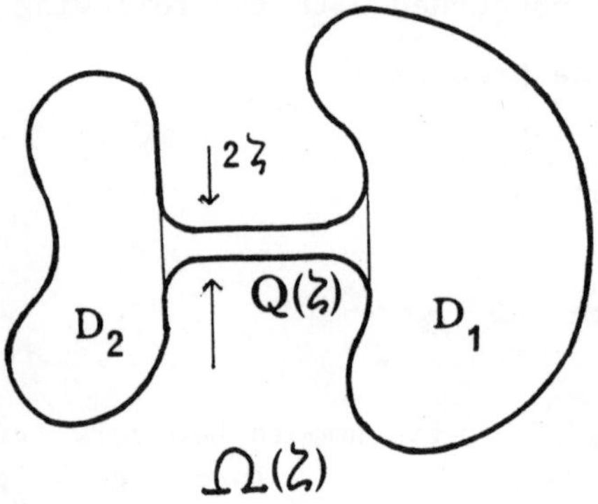

Figure 1

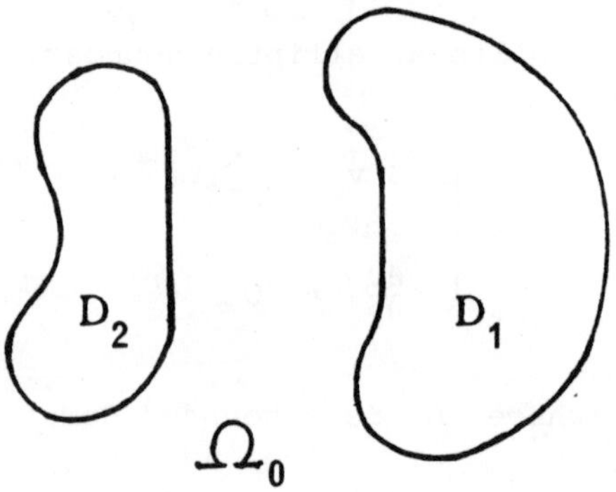

Figure 2

The volume of $Q(\zeta)$ tends to zero as $\zeta \to 0$ and $\Omega(\zeta)$ approaches the non-connected open set $\Omega_0 \equiv D_1 \cup D_2$ in some sense. Then, can we say that the influence of the varying portion $Q(\zeta)$ over the equation (1.1) vanishes as $\zeta \to 0$,i.e., that the structure of the solutions of (1.1) for $\Omega = \Omega(\zeta)$ (for small $\zeta > 0$) is equivalent to that of (1.1) for $\Omega = \Omega_0$ (Figure 2) ? Vegas [15], Hale and Vegas [6] have in fact considered (1.1) for the nonlinear term $f = f(\lambda,u) = \lambda u - u^p$

on the same domain as that in Figure 1 and have analyzed the bifurcation phenomenon for the bifurcation parameter ζ (when λ is a sufficiently small positive constant) . Their bifurcation diagram in the case when p is an odd natural number ($\geqq 3$) and the domain $\Omega(\zeta)$ is symmetric, is as in Figure 3 .

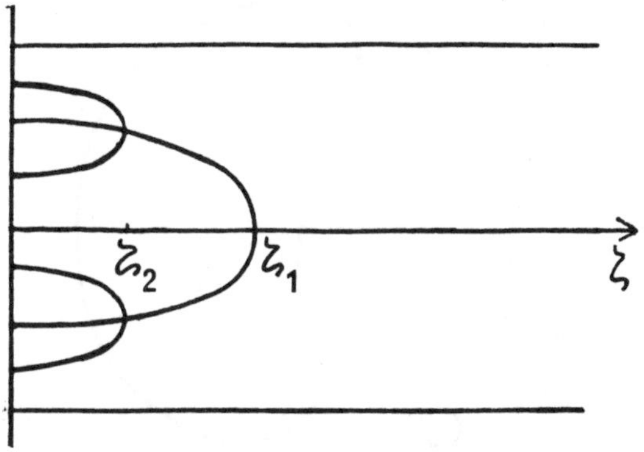

Figure 3: Bifurcation Diagram

In this situation when ζ is small ($0 < \zeta < \zeta_2$ in Figure 3), there are exactly nine solutions and each of them takes values near one of the values $\{ 0 , \lambda^{1/(p-1)}, -\lambda^{1/(p-1)} \}$ in D_i ($i = 1, 2$) ; its behavior on $Q(\zeta)$ being automatically determined by its behavior on D_1 and D_2 . Thus the structure of the solutions for $\Omega(\zeta)$ ($0 < \zeta < \zeta_2$) is equivalent to that for $\Omega = \Omega_0$. Notice that (1.1) for $\Omega = \Omega_0$ has nine solutions, each of which is equal to one of the values $\{ 0 , \lambda^{1/(p-1)}, -\lambda^{1/(p-1)} \}$ in D_i for each i (when $\lambda > 0$ is a small constant) . In this case $\Omega(\zeta)$ ($\zeta > 0$ small) can be regarded as a perturbation of Ω_0 not only from the point of view of geometric features but also from the point of view of the structure of the solution set. Nevertheless, in this paper, we assert that it is more natural and exact to regard $\Omega(\zeta)$ as a perturbation, rather from the set $\Omega_{*} = D_1 \cup D_2 \cup L$ (where $L \equiv \bigcap_{\zeta>0} Q(\zeta)$), rather than of the set $\Omega_0 = D_1 \cup D_2$ if we consider the perturbation of domain also with regard to the structure of the solution set. (See Figure 4.)

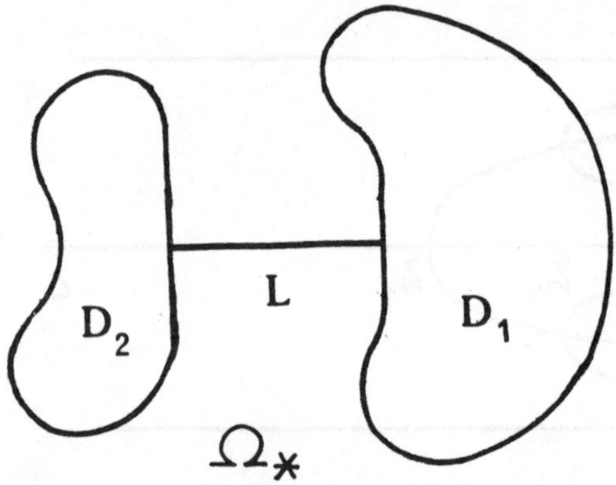

Figure 4

We remark that in the situation of Vegas [15], Hale and Vegas [6], $\frac{\partial f}{\partial u}$ is small around the solutions due to the smallness of $\lambda > 0$ and this may ensure the uniqueness of the behavior of the solution v on $Q(\zeta)$ if v is specified to take values near a_i in D_i $(i = 1, 2)$ with $f(a_i) = 0$ and $f'(a_i) < 0$.

We shall consider the behavior on $Q(\zeta)$ of certain solution of (1.1) (when $\zeta \to 0$) without any assumption on the bound of $\frac{\partial f}{\partial u}$ and we show that the behavior is described by the ordinary differential equation

$$(*) \quad \frac{d^2V}{dz^2} + f(V) = 0 \quad \text{along } L$$

with an appropriate boundary condition on $L \cap \partial D_1$ and $L \cap \partial D_2$ (Sec. 2).

Conversely we shall choose a nonlinear term f for which the ordinary differential equation (*) has three distinct solutions $V^{(0)} < V^{(1)} < V^{(2)}$, and we shall construct three solutions $v_\zeta^{(0)} < v_\zeta^{(1)} < v_\zeta^{(2)}$ of (1.1) for $\Omega = \Omega(\zeta)$ and the above f for small $\zeta > 0$ such that all $v_\zeta^{(i)}$ $(i = 0,1,2)$ take almost the same values in $D_1 \cup D_2$ and the behavior of $v_\zeta^{(i)}$ in $Q(\zeta)$ for small $\zeta > 0$ is approximated by that of $V^{(i)}$ on L for each i $(i = 0,1,2)$; $v_\zeta^{(0)}$, $v_\zeta^{(2)}$ are stable and $v_\zeta^{(1)}$ is unstable (Sec. 3). In this sense we can regard $\Omega(\zeta)$ as a perturbation from the set $\Omega_* = D_1 \cup D_2 \cup L$.

§2. Asymptotic Behavior on The Strip.

In this section we consider the behavior of certain solutions on the varying strip $Q(\zeta)$.

We define the domain $\Omega(\zeta)$ as follows :

$$\Omega(\zeta) = D_1 \cup D_2 \cup Q(\zeta)$$

where D_i $(i=1,2)$ and $Q(\zeta)$ are specified as follows in (A.1) and (A.2), where $x' = (x_2, x_3, \cdots, x_n) \in \mathbb{R}^{n-1}$.

(A.1) D_1 and D_2 are mutually disjoint bounded domains in $\mathbb{R}^n$ with smooth boundaries which satisfy the following conditions for some positive constant ζ_* :

$$\bar{D}_1 \cap \{ x = (x_1, x') \in \mathbb{R}^n \mid x_1 \leqq 1 , |x'| < 3\zeta_* \}$$
$$= \{ (1, x') \in \mathbb{R}^n \mid |x'| < 3\zeta_* \}$$

$$\bar{D}_2 \cap \{ x = (x_1,x') \in \mathbb{R}^n \mid x_1 \geqq -1 , |x'| < 3\zeta_* \}$$
$$= \{ (-1,x') \in \mathbb{R}^n \mid |x'| < 3\zeta_* \}$$

(A.2) $Q(\zeta) = R_1(\zeta) \cup R_2(\zeta) \cup \Gamma(\zeta)$

$$R_1(\zeta) = \{ (x_1,x') \in \mathbb{R}^n \mid 1 -2\zeta < x_1 \leqq 1, |x'| < \zeta\rho((x_1-1)/\zeta) \}$$

$$R_2(\zeta) = \{(x_1,x') \in \mathbb{R}^n \mid -1 \leqq x_1< -1+2\zeta, |x'| < \zeta\rho((-1-x_1)/\zeta) \}$$

$$\Gamma(\zeta) = \{ (x_1,x') \in \mathbb{R}^n \mid -1+2\zeta \leqq x_1 \leqq 1-2\zeta , |x'| < \zeta \},$$

where $\rho \in C^0((-2,0]) \cap C^\infty((-2,0))$ is a positive function with $\rho(0) = 2$, $\rho(s) = 1$ for $s \in (-2, -1)$ and $\frac{d\rho(s)}{ds} \geqq 0$ for $s \in (-2,0)$ and $\lim_{s\uparrow -0} \frac{d^k\rho}{ds^k}(s) = +\infty$ for any positive integer k .

(A.3) f is a real valued smooth function on $\mathbb{R}$ such that $\left\{ \xi \in \mathbb{R} \mid f(\xi) = 0 , f'(\xi) < 0 \right\} \neq \emptyset$ and $\overline{\lim_{\xi\to\infty}} f(\xi) < 0$, $\underline{\lim_{\xi\to-\infty}} f(\xi) > 0$ hold.

Remark. The domain $\Omega(\zeta)$ specified above has a smooth boundary $\partial\Omega(\zeta)$ for $\zeta \in (0,\zeta_*)$.

Under the conditions (A.1),(A.2) and (A.3), we analyze the asymptotic behavior on the strip $Q(\zeta)$ of certain solutions (which will be characterized by (A-4)) of the following semilinear elliptic boundary value problem (2.1):

$$(2.1) \quad \begin{cases} \Delta v + f(v) = 0 & \text{in } \Omega(\zeta) , \\ \dfrac{\partial v}{\partial \nu} = 0 & \text{on } \partial\Omega(\zeta) . \end{cases}$$

The condition (A.4) is as follows:

(A.4) v_ζ be is arbitrary solution of (2.1) indexed by ζ ($0 < \zeta < \zeta_*$) such that the family of functions $\{ v_\zeta \}_{0<\zeta<\zeta_*}$ satisfies:

$$\lim_{\zeta\to 0} \| v_\zeta - a_i \|_{L^2(D_i)} = 0 \qquad (i = 1 , 2)$$

where $f(a_i) = 0$ and $f'(a_i) < 0$ ($i = 1, 2$) (cf. (A.3)).

Definition 1. Let $\mu_1(\zeta)$ be the first eigenvalue of the following eigenvalue problem:

$$(2.2) \quad \begin{cases} \Delta \psi + f'(v_\zeta)\psi + \mu \psi = 0 & \text{in } \Omega(\zeta) , \\ \dfrac{\partial \psi}{\partial \nu} = 0 & \text{on } \partial\Omega(\zeta) . \end{cases}$$

Remark. The two values a_1 and a_2 are not necessarily distinct. In fact, we shall deal with the case $a_1 = a_2$ and construct some nontrivial solutions in Section 3.

We have the following theorems under (A.1) - (A.4).

Theorem 1. Assume $n \geqq 3$. Then we have, for each i

$$\lim_{\zeta\to 0} \sup_{x \in D_i \cup R_i(\zeta)} | v_\zeta(x) - a_i | = 0 \quad (i = 1, 2).$$

We construct the ordinary differential equation which describes the asymptotic behavior of v_ζ in $Q(\zeta)$ as $\zeta \downarrow 0$. First we let V denote the solution of

$$(2.3)\quad \begin{cases} \dfrac{d^2V}{dz^2} + f(V) = 0 & \text{in} \quad -1 < z < 1 , \\ V(1) = a_1 , \quad V(-1) = a_2 . \end{cases}$$

Definition 2. Let λ_V and Φ_V be the first eigenvalue and the first eigenfunction, respectively, of the following eigenvalue problem (2.4) for a solution V of (2.3):

$$(2.4)\quad \begin{cases} \dfrac{d^2\Phi}{dz^2} + f'(V(z))\,\Phi + \lambda\,\Phi = 0 & \text{in} \quad -1 < z < 1 \\ \Phi(1) = 0 , \quad \Phi(-1) = 0 . \end{cases}$$

Now we present one of the main results of this paper.

Theorem 2. Assume $n \geqq 3$. Then for any sequence of positive values $\{ \zeta_m \}_{m=1}^{\infty}$ such that $\lim_{m\to\infty} \zeta_m = 0$, there exist a subsequence $\{ \varkappa_m \}_{m=1}^{\infty} \subset \{ \zeta_m \}_{m=1}^{\infty}$ and a solution V of (2.3) with the following asymptotic property:

$$\lim_{m\to\infty} \sup_{x \in Q(\varkappa_m)} | v_{\varkappa_m}(x_1,x') - V(x_1) | = 0 .$$

Furthermore, if $\lambda_V > 0$ (resp. $\lambda_V < 0$), then $\underline{\lim}_{m\to\infty} \mu_1(\varkappa_m) > 0$ (resp. $\overline{\lim}_{m\to\infty} \mu_1(\varkappa_m) < 0$) holds.

§3. Construction of Stable and Unstable Solutions.

In this section, we shall consider the equation (2.1) in the domain $\Omega(\zeta)$ specified in Section 2. We shall construct an unstable solution $\{ v_\zeta^{(1)} \}_{\zeta>0}$ and stable solutions $\{ v_\zeta^{(0)} \}_{\zeta>0}$ and $\{ v_\zeta^{(2)} \}_{\zeta>0}$ in the case $a_1 = a_2$ in (A.4) for small $\zeta > 0$ by choosing an appropriate nonlinear term f .

The nonlinear term f is written in the following form.

$$f(\xi) = \vartheta\, g(\xi) \qquad (\vartheta > 0), \tag{3.1}$$

where $g \in C^\infty(\mathbb{R})$ satisfies the following conditions (A.5) and (A.6), and the parameter ϑ is to be chosen later.

(A.5) There exist three points $b_1 < b_2 < b_3$ such that

$$g(b_i) = 0 \ (1 \leqq i \leqq 3), \quad g'(b_1) < 0, \quad g'(b_3) < 0,$$
$$g(\xi) > 0 \quad \text{in} \quad (-\infty, b_1) \cup (b_2, b_3),$$
$$g(\xi) < 0 \quad \text{in} \quad (b_1, b_2) \cup (b_3, \infty).$$

(A.6) $\displaystyle\int_{b_1}^{b_3} g(\xi)\, d\xi > 0$

By (A.5)-(A.6), there exists a unique $d \in (b_2, b_3)$ such that $\displaystyle\int_{b_1}^{d} g(\xi)\, d\xi = 0$.

Under the conditions (A.5) and (A.6), we first construct the solutions of the following two point boundary value problem of the ordinary differential equation (3.2) (which is a special case of (2.3)), and determine their linearized stability.

$$\text{(3.2)} \quad \begin{cases} \dfrac{d^2V}{dz^2} + f(V) = 0 & \text{in } -1 < z < 1 \\ V(1) = b_1, \quad V(-1) = b_1. \end{cases}$$

Proposition. There exists a positive constant ϑ_0 such that for any $\vartheta \geqq \vartheta_0$, (3.2) has exactly three solutions

$V^{(0)}(z) \ (\equiv b_1) < V^{(1)}(z) < V^{(2)}(z) \quad (-1 < z < 1)$

with the following stability properties

$$\lambda_{V^{(0)}} > 0, \quad \lambda_{V^{(1)}} < 0, \quad \lambda_{V^{(2)}} > 0.$$

(See Definition 2 for $\lambda_{V^{(0)}}, \lambda_{V^{(1)}}, \lambda_{V^{(2)}}$.)

(Sketch of the proof of Proposition) To construct the nontrivial solution of (3.2) is almost equivalent to finding $\xi \in (d,b_3)$ for the following equation (3.3) or (3.3'):

$$(3.3) \qquad \int_{b_1}^{\xi} \left(2\int_{\sigma}^{\xi} f(\rho)\, d\rho \right)^{-1/2} d\sigma = 1 \qquad (d < \xi < b_3),$$

$$(3.3') \qquad \int_{b_1}^{\xi} \left(2\int_{\sigma}^{\xi} g(\rho)\, d\rho \right)^{-1/2} d\sigma = \vartheta^{1/2} \qquad (d < \xi < b_3)$$

If we denote the function on the left hand side of (3.3') by

$$s(\xi) \text{ i.e. } s(\xi) \equiv \int_{b_1}^{\xi} \left(2 \int_{\sigma}^{\xi} g(\rho)d\rho \right)^{-1/2} d\sigma \qquad (d < \xi < b_3),$$

then Proposition follows directly from the following Lemma and an argument in Maginu [11].

Lemma. $s(\xi)$ is a positive differentiable function on (d,b_3) with the following asymptotic conditions,

$$(4.3) \qquad \begin{cases} \lim\limits_{\xi \uparrow b_3} \dfrac{s(\xi)}{\left(-1/g'(b_3)\right)^{1/2} \log \dfrac{1}{b_3 - \xi}} = 1 \\[2ex] \lim\limits_{\xi \downarrow d} \dfrac{s(\xi)}{\left(-1/4g'(b_1)\right)^{1/2} \log \dfrac{1}{\xi - d}} = 1 \\[2ex] \lim\limits_{\xi \uparrow b_3} \dfrac{d}{d\xi} s(\xi) = +\infty , \quad \lim\limits_{\xi \downarrow d} \dfrac{d}{d\xi} s(\xi) = -\infty . \end{cases}$$

Now we state the main result.

Theorem 3. There exist two positive values $\zeta_0 > 0$ and $c > 0$ such that, for any $\zeta \in (0,\zeta_0)$, there are three solutions $v_\zeta^{(0)} \ (\equiv b_1) < v_\zeta^{(1)} < v_\zeta^{(2)}$ of (3.1) satisfying the following conditions:

$$\lim_{\zeta\to 0} \sup_{x \in D_1 \cup D_2} | v_\zeta^{(i)}(x) - b_1 | = 0 \quad (i = 0, 1, 2),$$

$$\lim_{\zeta\to 0} \sup_{x \in Q(\zeta)} | v_\zeta^{(i)}(x_1, x') - V^{(i)}(x_1) | = 0 \quad (i = 1, 2),$$

$$\mu_1(v_\zeta^{(0)}) \geqq c , \quad \mu_1(v_\zeta^{(1)}) \leqq - c , \quad \mu_1(v_\zeta^{(2)}) \geqq c \quad (0 < \zeta < \zeta_0).$$

Here $\mu_1(v_\zeta^{(i)})$ denotes the linearized first eigenvalue in Definition 1 , for the family $\{ v_\zeta^{(i)} \}_{0<\zeta<\zeta_0}$ for each i .

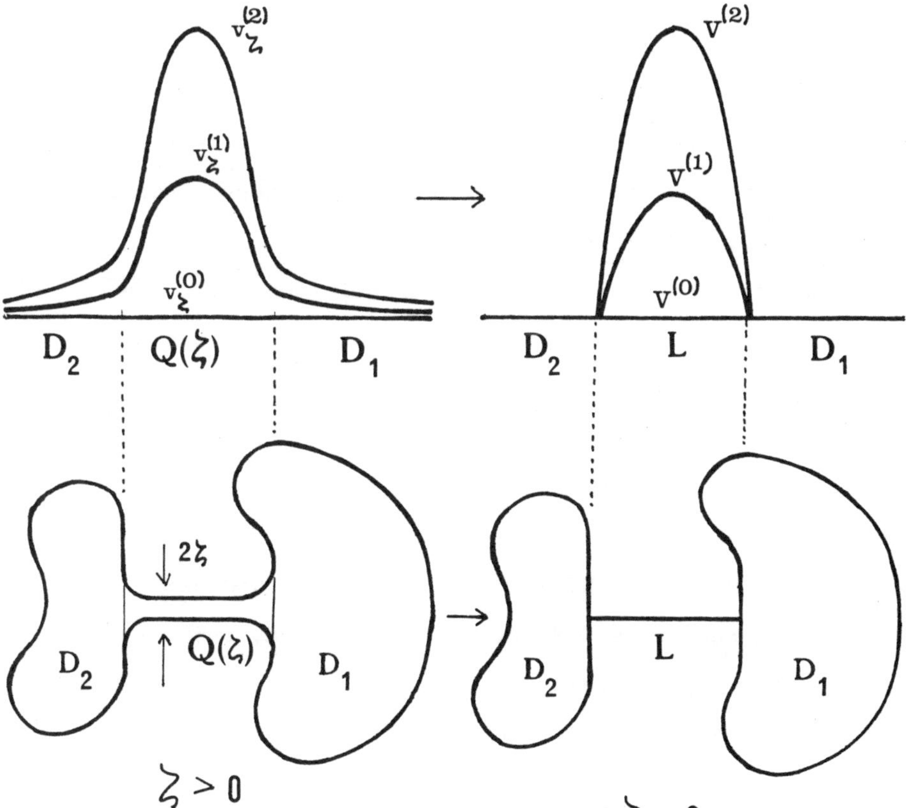

Figure 5

From the results in Theorem 3 (Figure 5), we see that the dependence of the equation (2.1) on the strip $Q(\zeta)$ does not vanish when $\zeta \to 0$. Moreover the behavior of the solution in $Q(\zeta)$ (which is described by the ordinary differential equation (3.2) for small $\zeta > 0$) plays an important role in determining the stability even if ζ is small. Thus it is natural to consider $\Omega(\zeta)$ as having the limit
$\Omega_* = D_1 \cup D_2 \cup L$, where $L = \bigcap_{\zeta>0} Q(\zeta)$.

We have not given the proofs of the main theorems. They will appear in [8].

References

[1] R.G.Casten and C.J.Holland, Instability results for reaction diffusion equation with Neumann boundary conditions, J.Diff.Eq. 27, (1978) 266-273 .

[2] N.Chafee, Asymptotic behavior for solutions of a one - dimensional parabolic equation with homogeneous Neumann boundary conditions. J.Diff.Eq. 18,((1975) 111-134.

[3] N.Chafee and E.F.Infante, A bifurcation problem for a nonlinear partial differential equation of parabolic type, Applicable Anal. 4 (1974), 17-37.

[4] E.A.Coddington and N.Levinson, "Theory of Ordinary Differential Equations," McGraw-Hill, New York, 1955.

[5] D.Gilbarg and N.Trudinger, Elliptic Partial Differential Equations of Second Order. Springer, New York, 1977.

[6] J.K.Hale and J.Vegas, A Nonlinear Parabolic Equation with Varying Domain. Arch.Rat.Mech.Anal.86,(1984),99-123.

[7] S.Jimbo, On a Semilinear Diffusion Equation on a Riemannian Manifold and its Stable Equilibrium Solutions. Proc.Japan Acad. Vol 60 (1984) 349-352.

[8] S.Jimbo, Singular Perturbation of Domains and Semilinear Elliptic Equation, in preparation.

[9] B.L.Keyfitz and H.J.Kuiper, Bifurcation resulting from changes in domain in a reaction-diffusion equation. J.Diif.Eq. 47,(1983) 378-405.

[10] K.Maginu, Stability of Stationary Solutions of a Semilinear Parabolic Partial Differential Equation. J.Math. Anal.Appl. 63, 224-243 (1978).

[11] H.Matano, Asymptotic behavior and stability of solutions of semilinear diffusion equations. Publ. RIMS, Kyoto Univ., 15, 401-454 (1979).

[12] H.Matano, Existence of nontrivial unstable sets for equilibriums of strongly order-preserving systems. J.Fac.Sci. Univ. Tokyo, 30,(1984), 645-673.

[13] H.Matano and M.Mimura, Pattern Formation in Competition-Diffusion Systems in Nonconvex Domains. Publ. RIMS,Kyoto Univ. 19 (1983), 1049-1079.

[14] Sattinger, Monotone Methods in Nonlinear Elliptic and Parabolic Boundary Value Problems. Indiana Univ.Math.J. Vol.21, (1972)979-1000.

[15] J.M.Vegas, Bifurcation Caused by Perturbing the Domain in an Elliptic Equation . J.Diff.Eq. 48,(1983)189-226.

Recent Topics in Nonlinear PDE III, Tokyo, 1986
Lecture Notes in Num. Appl. Anal., 9, 119–156 (1987)

Nonlinear Evolution Equations of Moser's Type

Hideo KAWARADA and Hideyuki KOSHIGOE

Institute of Applied Mathematics , Chiba University

Chiba 260, Japan

§ 1. Introduction

It is the purpose of this paper to prove the existence theorem for the nonlinear evolution equation;

(P) $\quad Px \equiv dx/dt + F(t,x) = 0 , \ 0 \leqq t \leqq T, \ x(0)=\phi$.

We keep in mind that F(t,x) in (P) is a nonlinear partial differential operator of order m .

In order to construct a relevant approximate solution, we shall deal with the following singularly perturbed equation (P_η) ($0 < \eta < 1$);

$$(P_\eta) \quad \begin{cases} P_\eta x \equiv dx/dt + \eta Hx + F(t,x) = 0 , \quad 0 \leqq t \leqq T , \\ x(0) = \phi \end{cases}$$

in place of (P) (J.L.Lions [8],J.Moser[10]) . In (P_η), H is a linear elliptic operator , the order of which is higher than m .

We try to construct the solution of (P) by a use of Newton method. Originally , this approach was studied by J. Moser [10] and recently was followed by M. Altman [1] . Let X and Z be Banach spaces .Then we define a mapping Φ ; for each $x \in X$,

$$(1.1) \quad \Phi \ : x \in X \rightarrow z \in Z$$

by using the solution z of the linearized equation for (P_η) ;

$$(1.2) \begin{cases} dz/dt + \eta Hz + F'(t,x)z + F(t,x) - F'(t,x)x = 0 , \quad 0 \leqq t \leqq T, \\ z(0) = \phi . \end{cases}$$

Here the linear operator $F'(t,x)$ is the Frechet derivative of $F(t,x)$ defined in the section 2 .

Then the sequence $\{x_n\}$ of approximate solutions by Newton method is constructed in the following:

$$(1.3) \quad \begin{cases} x_0 = \phi , \\ x_n = \Phi (x_{n-1}) \quad (n = 1,2,- - -) . \end{cases}$$

Generally, the mapping Φ induces the regularity loss i.e. $X \subset Z$. This fact makes it impossible to apply directly Newton method to the problem (P). So we construct new type of approximate solutions in the framework of m - normal Banach scale, which includes a parameter d(> 0).

In the case of d = 0, m - normal Banach scale becomes an inverted Banach scale, which M. Altman introduced in [1].

Generally, it is impossible to construct a bounded approximate solution of (1.2) in the framework of an inverted Banach scale. An existence of positive parameter d in normal Banach scale makes it possible to construct a bounded approximate solution, but induces some reduction of it.

In order to recover the regularity loss, we have to apply a smoothing operator with respect to the space variable to the singular perturbed solution of (1.2). And then we prove that our approximate solution converges to the solution of (P) in some topology.

Section 2 is devoted to the statement of assumptions with respect to the nonlinear term F(t,x) and our main Theorem . In section 3 , we construct an m-normal Banach scale for each m>0 and prepare the controll parameters and smoothing operators, which are needed to construct approximate solutions of degree μ of the linearized equation (1.2) . We choose a key parameter K_0 which depends upon the m-normal Banach scale , the initial value ϕ and the nonlinear term F(t,x). The choice of K_0 makes it possible to construst a set of the controll parameters . In section 4 , an approximate solution of degree μ of singularly perturbed equation of (1.2) are constructed in the framework of m-normal Banach scale . In section 5, we show that the approximate solution of degree μ of (1.2) becomes the approximate solution of degree λ of the nonlinear equation (P_η). There the controll parameters are used effectively . We prove our main Theorem in section 6. Finally in section 7, we apply our Theorem to the Navier- storkes equation in $[0,T]* R^n$.

§ 2 Assumptions and Main theorem

§ §2.1 Banach scale and fundamental set G(ϕ)

Following M.Altman , we shall use a scale of Banach spaces defined in the following way :

Definition 2.1 (Banach scale)

Let $X\equiv \{ X_0,X_{m_1},X_{m_2},X_s,X_p \}$ be a sequence of Banach spaces equipped with norms $|\cdot|_j$ ($0\leqq j\leqq p$) . If X satisfies

(2.1) $X_0 \supset X_{m_1} \supset X_{m_2} \supset X_s \supset X_p \quad (0 < m_1 < m_2 < s < p)$

and

(2.2) $|\cdot|_0 \leqq |\cdot|_{m_1} \leqq |\cdot|_{m_2} \leqq |\cdot|_s \leqq |\cdot|_p$,

then we call X a Banach scale .

Definition 2.2(Normal Banach scale) If a set of parameters $\{m_1, m_2, s, p\}$ of a Banach scale X and $\{\lambda, \mu\}$ satisfy

(2.3) $0 < m_1 < m_2 < s < p$,

(2.4) $0 < \lambda + 1 < (\mu + 1)/2$,

(2.5) $s/p < \lambda/(\lambda + 2)$

and

(2.6) $\mu = (m_1 + dm_2)/(p - m_2 - dm_2) > 0$ for $d > 0$,

we call X the normal Banach scale and denote it by $X = X(\lambda, \mu)$.

Remark 2.1 We call the conditions (2.3)-(2.6) Moser's condition .

Remark 2.2 The reason why we call $X(\lambda, \mu)$ a normal Banach scale is due to the following fact :

A Banach scale $Y \equiv \{X_0, X_{m_1}, X_s, X_{m_2}, X_p\}$ which M.Altman introduced in [1] satisfies Moser's condition in the case of d=0 only if $0<m_1<s<m_2<p$. For this reason , we called Y a inverted Banach scale in [5,6] , because of the inclution $X_s \supset X_{m_2}$.

Moreover because F(t,x) is a nonlinear partial differential operator of order m , we shall introduce the concept of the " m-normal Banach scale " .

Definition 2.3 (m-normal Banach scale) If a set of parameters $\{m_1, m_2, s, p\}$ of a normal Banach scale $X \equiv X(\lambda, \mu)$ satisfies the additional conditions ;

(2.7) $m \leqq m_1$, $m \leqq 2dm_2$,

(2.8) $m_1 + 3dm_2 \leqq m_2$,

and

(2.9) $m_2 + 2m \leqq s$,

then we call X an m-normal Banach scale and denote it by $X = X(\lambda, \mu; m)$.

Remark 2.3 When m is given , we are able to construct $X(\lambda, \mu; m)$ (see Proposition 3.2 in §§3.1) .

Denote by $C(0,T;X_j)$ the Banach space of all continuous functions $x = x(t)$ defined on the interval $[0,T]$ with values in X_j and set

$$\| x \|_{0(j)} = \sup \{ | x(t) |_j : 0 \leqq t \leqq T \} .$$

Denote by $C^1(0,T;X_j)$ the Banach space of all continuously differentiable functions $x = x(t)$ from $[0,T]$ into X_j and set

$$\| x \|_{1(j)} \equiv \| x \|_{0(j)} + \| dx/dt \|_{0(j)} .$$

Let $W_0 \subset X_s$ be an open ball with center $\phi \in X_p$ and radius $r > 0$. Put $V_0 = W_0 \cap X_p$ i.e. $V_0 = \{ x \in X_p ; | x-\phi |_s < r \}$.

Now we shall introduce the fundamental set $G(\phi)$.

Definition 2.4 (Fundamental set $G(\phi)$)

If $G(\phi)$ is a set of functions

$$x \in C^1(0,T; X_p) , x(t) \in V_0 \text{ for } 0 \leqq t \leqq T \text{ and } x(0) = \phi ,$$

then we call $G(\phi)$ a fundamental set .

§§2.2 Assumptions

Now we shall state some assumptions in the framework of $X(\lambda, \mu; m)$;

(A_1) F is a nonlinear mapping from $[0,T]*X_j$ to X_{j-m} $(j>m)$,

(2.10) F is continuous in the following sense :

$x_n \in G(\phi)$ and $\| x_n - x \|_{0(s)} \to 0$ implies

$$\| F(t,x_n)-F(t,x) \|_{0(0)} \to 0 \quad \text{as } n \to \infty ,$$

(2.11) For each $x \in V_0$, there exists the Frechet derivative $F'(t,x)$ of $F(t,x)$;

$$F'(t,x) \in L(X_{j+m},X_j) \ (0 \leq j \leq m_2 + m) \quad \text{for any } t \in [0,T]$$

and $F'(t,x(t))$ is continuous from $[0,T]$ into $L(X_{j+m},X_j)$ for each $x(t) \in G(\phi)$ and each j $(0 \leq j \leq m_2 + m)$.

And also

(2.12) $F'(\cdot,x)$ satisfies the following relation :

there exists positive constants M and β such that

$$\| F(\cdot,x+h) - F(\cdot,x) - F'(\cdot,x)h \|_{0(0)} \leq M \|h\|_{0(0)}^{2-\beta} \|h\|_{0(p)}^{\beta}$$

for $x \in G(\phi)$ and $h \in C(0,T;X_p) \cap C^1(0,T;X_0)$ where M and β are independent of x and h . And β satisfies

(2.13) $0 < \beta < \{\lambda\mu / (\lambda+1)(\mu+1)\}\{1-2(\lambda+1) / (\mu+1)\}$.

(A_2) There exists a constant L_1 such that

(2.14) $\| F'(t,x)h \|_0 \leq L_1 \| h \|_m$

for all $(t,x) \in [0,T]*V_0$ and $h \in X_m$

and

(2.15) $\| F'(t,x)h \|_{m_1+dm_2} \leq L_1 \| h \|_{m_2}$

for all $(t,x) \in [0,T]*V_0$ and $h \in X_{m_2}$.

(2.16) Also there exists a constant D_1 such that

$$\| F(t,x) - F'(t,x)(x-\phi) \|_{0(m_2)} \leq D_1 \quad \text{for all } x \in G(\phi) .$$

(A_3) We shall introduce a linear elliptic operator H with constant coefficients ;

(2.17) $\quad | Hx |_j \leq L_2 \; | x |_{j+2dm_2} \quad$ for $x \in X_{j+2dm_2}$.

Then we shall assume that for $x \in G(\phi)$ and $\eta \in (0,1)$, the equation

$$\begin{cases} dz_\eta/dt + \eta H z_\eta + F'(t,x)z_\eta + F(t,x) - F'(t,x)(x-\phi) + \eta H\phi = 0 , \\ z_\eta(0) = 0 \quad , \quad 0 \leq t \leq T \; . \end{cases}$$

has a solution $z_\eta \in C^1(0,T;\, X_{m_2}) \cap C(0,T;\, X_{m_2+2dm_2})$ satisfying the following estimates;

(2.18) $\quad \| z_\eta \|_{0(m_2)} \leq D_2 \quad$ and

(2.19) $\quad \| z_\eta \|_{0(m_2+dm_2)} \leq D_2 \eta^{-k} \qquad (0 < k < 1)$

where the positive constant D_2 is independent of x and η .

(A_4) For $x \in G(\phi)$ and $g \in C(0,T;X_0)$, the linear equation

$$\begin{cases} dh/dt + \eta Hh + F'(t,x)h + g = 0 \; , \; 0 \leq t \leq b \; (0 < b \leq T) \\ h(0)=0 \end{cases}$$

has a solution $h \in C^1(0,b;X_0)$ which is estimated in the following way;

(2.20) $\quad \| h \|_{0(0)} \leq bD_3 \| g \|_{0(0)}$

where the constant D_3 is independent of b , x and η .

(A_5) For any initial data $\phi \in X_{m_2+m+2dm_2}$, we choose b which satisfies

(2.21) $\quad (bD_3)^{1/2} [\| F(t,\phi) \|_{0(0)} + | H\phi |_0] \leq K_0^{-\lambda}$

and

$$(2.22) \quad \begin{cases} bD_3 \leq 1 \; , \\ 4M(bD_3)^{1-\beta/2} \leq 1 \; , \\ 2^{1-2s/p} C(bD_3)^{1/2-s/2p} \sum_{n=0}^{\infty} K_n^{-\alpha} < r \qquad (\alpha = \lambda(1-s/p) - \tau s/p \;) \end{cases}$$

where K_0 is a key parameter satisfying the condition (k_0) defined in the section 5 , and K_n ($= K_{n-1}^{\tau} > 1$) . τ and C will be defined in the section 3 .

Remark 2.4 Note that α in (2.22) is positive because of (2.5) and

(3.28) stated later in section 3 .

§§2.3 Main Theorem

Finally we shall state our main theorem:

THEOREM Take an m-normal Banach scale $X = X(\lambda, \mu; m)$ and suppose that the assumptions (A_1) - (A_5) are satisfied . Then the nonlinear evolution equation (P) has a solution $x \in \dot{C}^1(0,b;X_0)$ for each $\phi \in X_{m_2+m+2dm_2}$.

§ 3 m-Normal Banach scale , controll parameters and smoothing operator

§ § 3.1 m-Normal Banach scale

In this subsection , we shall construct the m-normal Banach scale $X(\lambda, \mu; m)$ defined in §§2.1 .

Lemma 3.1 For each $d>0$, there exists a couple of $\{ m_1, m_2, s, p \}$ and $\{ \lambda, \mu \}$ which satisfies the following conditions ;

(3.1) $0 < m_1 < m_2 < s < p$,

(3.2) $0 < \lambda + 1 < (\mu + 1)/2$,

(3.3) $s/p < \lambda/(\lambda + 2)$

and

(3.4) $\mu = (m_1 + dm_2)/(p - m_2 - dm_2) > 0$

Proof. (1st step) Set

(3.5) $s/p = a, \ m_2/s = \omega, \ m_1/m_2 = \varepsilon$.

Then the statement of this Lemma is equivalent to the following fact(A);

There exists a , ω and ε ($0 < a, \omega, \varepsilon < 1$) satisfying

(3.6) $1 - (1 + d)a\omega > 0$

and

(3.7) $(3a + 1)/(1 - a) < (\varepsilon + d)a\omega / \{1 - (1 + d)a\omega\}$.

Indeed, from the conditions (3.1)-(3.5), one can easily derive the conditions (3.6) and (3.7). Conversely we assume that the fact (A) holds.

Fix some $m_1 > 0$. Then we can represent m_2, s and p in the following way: $m_2 = (1/\varepsilon)m_1$, $s = (1/\omega\varepsilon)m_1$ and $p = (1/a\omega\varepsilon)m_1$ by using (3.5). Then we easily see $0 < m_1 < m_2 < s < p$. This means (3.1).

Also we shall set μ by

(3.8) $\qquad \mu = (\varepsilon + d)a\omega / \{1-(1+d)a\omega\} > 0 \qquad$ from (3.7).

By (3.5), we get $\mu = (m_1 + dm_2) / (p - m_2 - dm_2)$.

This means (3.4).

By using (3,7), we have $(1+3a)/(1-a) < \mu$, from which follows $(\mu-1)/2 > 2a/(1-a)$. Hence we can take λ which satisfies

(3.9) $\qquad (\mu-1)/2 > \lambda > 2a/(1-a)$.

Then the first inequality of (3.9) means (3.2) and also the second inequality of (3.9) implies that (3.3) holds. Here we should note that the conditions (3.6) and (3.7) do not depend on m_1.

(2nd step) The fact (A) is also equivalent to the following fact (B);

There exists a set of parameters $\{a, \omega, \varepsilon\}$ $(0 < a, \omega, \varepsilon < 1)$ satisfying (3.6) and

(3.10) $$f(a) \equiv \{3(1+d)\omega - (\varepsilon+d)\omega\}a^2 + \{(\varepsilon + d)\omega + (1+d)\omega - 3\}a - 1 > 0.$$

We can easily check that the fact (B) is equivalent to the fact (A).

(3rd step) We shall prove the fact (B). Now we shall take any ε $(0 < \varepsilon < 1)$ and any δ $(0 < \delta < d)$ and put

(3.11) $\qquad \omega = (1 + \delta)/(1 + d) \quad (0 < \delta < d)$.

Then we get $0 < \varepsilon, \omega < 1$, $f(0) = -1 < 0$ and $f(1) = 4\delta > 0$.
Moreover the coefficient of a^2 in f(a) is positive for $0 < \varepsilon < 1$.
Hence there exists a_0 $(0 < a_0 < 1)$ satisfying

(3.12) $f(a_0) = 0$ and $f(a) > 0$ $(a_0 < a < 1)$.

On the other hand , we get

$$f(1/(1+\delta)) = (\varepsilon + d)\delta / (1+d)(1+\delta) > 0 .$$

This implies that the following inequality

(3.13) $a_0 < 1/(1+\delta) = 1/(1+d)\omega$

holds by (3.12) . Therefore taking a constant a satisfying

$$a_0 < a < 1/(1+\delta) ,$$

we get (3.6) and (3.10). ■

Proposition 3.1 For each d>0 and each $m_1 > 0$, there exists a normal Banach scale $X(\lambda, \mu)$.

Example 3.1 $\{m_1, m_2, s, p\} = \{2, 4, 8, 40/3\}$ and $\{\lambda, \mu\} = \{3.2, 7.5\}$ satisfy Moser's condition .

Lemma 3.2 For each d (0<d<1/3)and each m , there exists a couple of $\{m_1, m_2, s, p\}$ and $\{\lambda, \mu\}$ of a normal Banach scale $X = X(\lambda, \mu)$ which satisfies the additional conditions ;

(3.14) $m \leqq m_1$, $m \leqq 2dm_2$,

(3.15) $m_1 + 3dm_2 \leqq m_2$,

(3.16) $m_2 + 2m \leqq s$

and

(3.17) $s < m_2 + dm_2 < p$.

Proof. For each d(0<d<1/3), we shall choose the positive numbers δ and ε used in the proof of Lemma 3.1 such that

(3.18) $0 < \varepsilon < 1 - 3d$

and

(3.19) $0 < \delta < d$.

Also we take a positive number α which satisfies

(3.20) $\alpha = \min [(d-\delta)/\{2\varepsilon(1+\delta)\} , 1]$

Then for m, we can choose a positive integer m_1 such that

(3.21) $m \leqq \alpha m_1$.

Then from Lemma3.1 , we can determine the numbers m_2 , s and p according to this m_1 and we know that (3.1)-(3.4) hold . Moreover from (3.20) and (3.21),we get (3.14) .

Using the relation

(3.22) $m_1/m_2 = \varepsilon$, $m_2/s = \omega = (1+\delta)/(1+d)$, $s/p=a$ and $a < 1/(1+\delta)$

in the proof of Lemma 3.1, we have

$$(1/m_2)(m_1 + 3dm_2) = \varepsilon + 3d \leqq 1 \quad \text{by (3.18)}$$

Hence we get $m_1 + 3dm_2 \leqq m_2$.

Similarly,we get

$$(1/s)(m_2 + 2\alpha m_1) = (1 + 2\alpha\varepsilon)\omega$$

$$\leqq \{1 + (d - \delta) / (1 + \delta)\}(1+\delta)/(1+d) \quad \text{by (3.20) and (3.22)}$$

$$= 1$$

Therefore it follows from (3.21) that

$$m_2 + 2m \leqq m_2 + 2\alpha m_1 \leqq s .$$

From (3.22) , we get

$$(1/s)(m_2 + dm_2) = (1+d)\omega = (1+d)\cdot(1+\delta)/(1+d) = 1+\delta > 1 .$$

Hence we have

$$m_2 + dm_2 > s .$$

Similarly by (3.22) , we get

$$(1/p)(m_2 + dm_2) = (1+d)m_2/p = (1+d)a\omega < 1 ,$$

which implies

$$m_2 + dm_2 < p . \quad \blacksquare$$

Proposition 3.2 For each d ($0<d<1/3$) and each $m > 0$, there exists an m-normal Banach scale $X(\lambda, \mu; m)$.

Example 3.2 $\{ m, m_1, m_2, s, p \} = \{ 2, 5, 20, 24.75, 25 \}$ and $\{ \lambda , \mu \} = \{ 200, 1999.3 \}$.

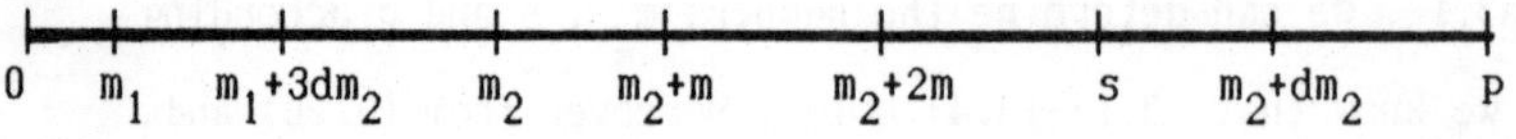

§ § 3.2 Controll parameters.

Here we shall define a set of controll parameters and discuss their properties , which will be used effectively in the section 4 and 5 .

Lemma 3.3. From the inequalities (2.4) and (2.13) , we have

$$(3.23)\quad 1 < \{ 1 - (\lambda+1)/(\mu+1)\}^{-1} < 2\{ 1 + (\lambda+1)(\mu+1)\beta/\lambda\mu \}^{-1} < 2$$

Proof. From (2,4), we get

$$(3.24)\quad 1 > 1 - (\lambda+1)/(\mu+1) > 1/2 ,$$

which implies

$$(3.25)\quad 1 < \{ 1 - (\lambda+1)/(\mu+1)\}^{-1} < 2 .$$

Similary from (2.13), we get

$$(3.26)\quad 2\{ 1 - (\lambda+1)/(\mu+1)\} > 1 + (\lambda+1)(\mu+1)\beta/\lambda\mu ,$$

from which follows

$$(3.27)\quad \{ 1 - (\lambda+1)/(\mu+1)\}^{-1} < 2\{ 1 + (\lambda+1)(\mu+1)\beta/\lambda\mu\}^{-1} .$$

Therefore (3.25) and (3.27) lead to (3.23) . ■

Then we can fix some τ ($1 < \tau < 2$) such that

$$(3.28)\quad \{ 1 - (\lambda+1)/(\mu+1)\}^{-1} < \tau < 2\{ 1 + (\lambda+1)(\mu+1)\beta/\lambda\mu \}^{-1} .$$

Lemma 3.4. From the inequality (3.28), we have

(3.29) $\tau\lambda + 1 < \mu(\tau - 1)$,

(3.30) $\tau\lambda + 1 < \mu\{ -1 + \lambda(2-\beta)/\beta - \tau\lambda/\beta \}$.

Proof. From the first inequality of (3.28), we get

(3.31) $(\lambda+1)/(\mu+1) < 1 - 1/\tau = (\tau-1)/\tau$.

which implies (3.29).

Similary from the second inequality of (3.28), we get

(3.32) $(2-\tau)/\tau = 2/\tau - 1 > (\lambda+1)(\mu+1)\beta/\lambda\mu$.

From (3.32) and $1 < \tau < 2$, we get

$$\begin{aligned}\tau\lambda+1 < \tau(\lambda+1) &< \mu\{-\tau(\lambda+1) + (2-\tau)\lambda/\beta\} \\ &< \mu\{-(\lambda+1) + (2-\tau)\lambda/\beta\} \\ &= \mu\{-1+\lambda(2-\beta)/\beta-\tau\lambda/\beta\} ,\end{aligned}$$

which implies (3.30) . ■

Set

(3.33) $e = \min\{ \tau-1, -1+\lambda(2-\beta)/\beta - \tau\lambda/\beta \}$.

Let K_0 be positive and large enough . Then we shall define a set of the controll parameters $\{ K_n, Q_n, \theta_n, \eta_n \}$ as follows (n = 0,1,2,- -) :

(3.34) $K_{n+1} = K_n^{\tau}$,

(3.35) $Q_n = K_n^{\{(\tau\lambda+1)/\mu+e\}/2}$,

(3.36) $\theta_n = Q_n^{1/(p-m_2-dm_2)}$ and

(3.37) $\eta_n^k = 2D/K_n$ for n = 0,1,2,3,-,-,-,- .

where D in (3.37) is defined in (4.16) .

Note that the above controll parameters $\{ K_n, Q_n, \theta_n, \eta_n \}$ are determined by a choice of a key parameter K_0 and that $e>0$ and $e-(\tau\lambda+1)/\mu > 0$ by Lemma 3.4 . Then we get

Proposition 3.3 Let K_0 satisfy

$$K_0^{\{e-(\tau\lambda+1)/\mu\}/2} > \max.\{4, 2^{1/\beta}, 2^{1/\mu}\} \tag{3.38}$$

$$K_0 > 2^{1/(\tau-1)}, \tag{3.39}$$

Then $\{K_n, Q_n\}$ satisfies the following inequalities ;

$$4K_nQ_n < K_{n+1} \tag{3.40}$$

$$2(K_nQ_n)^{\beta} K_n^{-\lambda(2-\beta)} \leqq K_{n+1}^{-\lambda} \tag{3.41}$$

$$2K_nQ_n^{-\mu} \leqq K_{n+1}^{-\lambda} \tag{3.42}$$

$$K_0 + (1/2)\sum_{j=1}^{n} K_i < K_n \tag{3.43}$$

Proof. From (3.38) and (3.34), we have

$$K_n^{\{e-(\tau\lambda+1)/\mu\}/2} > K_0^{\{e-(\tau\lambda+1)/\mu\}/2} > \max.\{4, 2^{1/\beta}, 2^{1/\mu}\}. \tag{3.44}$$

From (3.44), we get

$$2^{1/\mu} < K_n^{\{e-(\tau\lambda+1)/\mu\}/2} \quad \text{and} \tag{3.45}$$

$$K_n^{\{(\tau\lambda+1)/\mu-e\}/2} < \min\{1/4, (1/2)^{1/\beta}\}. \tag{3.46}$$

Hence (3.45) and (3.46) lead to

$$2^{1/\mu} K_n^{(1+\tau\lambda)/\mu} < K_n^{\{(\tau\lambda+1)/\mu+e\}/2} < \min\{1/4, (1/2)^{1/\beta}\}K_n^{e}. \tag{3.47}$$

Thus (3.47) and (3.35) imply

$$2^{1/\mu} K_n^{(1+\tau\lambda)/\mu} < Q_n < \min\{1/4, (1/2)^{1/\beta}\}K_n^{e}. \tag{3.48}$$

Therefore the first inequality of (3.48) leads to (3.42) . Also from the sefond inequality of (3.48) , we get (3.40) and (3.41) .

Finally we shall prove (3.43) by use of the induction . From (3.39), we get $K_0 < (1/2)K_0^{\tau}$. Hence it follows that

$$K_0 + (1/2)K_1 = K_0 + (1/2)K_0^{\tau} < (1/2)K_0^{\tau} + (1/2)K_0^{\tau} = K_0^{\tau}$$
$$= K_1$$

Therefore (3.43) holds for n=1. Now we assume that (3.43) holds for $1 \leqq n \leqq k$. Using $K_n = K_{n-1}^{\tau}$ and (3.39) , we have

$$K_n > K_0 > 2^{1/(\tau-1)} \qquad (n=1,2,\dots,k)$$

from which, we get

$$K_n < (1/2)K_n^{\tau} \qquad (n=1,2,\dots,k).$$

Therefore using the assumption of the induction, we get

$$K_0 + (1/2)\sum_{j=1}^{k+1} K_j = [\, K_0 + (1/2)\sum_{j=1}^{k} K_j \,] + (1/2)K_{k+1}$$
$$< K_k + (1/2)K_{k+1} < (1/2)K_k^{\tau} + (1/2)K_k^{\tau} = K_k^{\tau}$$
$$= K_{k+1} \quad .$$

Hence (3.43) holds for all n . This completes the proof . ■

§ 3.3. Smoothing operator

In this subsection , we let the symbol i and j represent { $0, m_1, m_2$, s,p } respectively .

Definition 3.4 (Tame Banach scale)

If a Banach scale X= { X_j } admits smoothing oparators S_θ ($\theta \geqq 1$) such that , for $0 \leqq i \leqq j \leqq p$,

(3.49) $\quad | S_\theta u |_j \leqq M_{i,j}\, \theta^{j-i} | u |_i \quad$ for $u \in X_i$

(3.50) $\quad | (I - S_\theta)u |_i \leqq M_{i,j}\, \theta^{-(j-i)} | u |_j \quad$ for $u \in X_j$

where $M_{i,j}$ are nonnegative constants independent of u and θ , then we shall call X a tame Banach scale .

Remark 3.1 When X is a tame Banach scale , it is well known that the following inequality

$$(3.51) \qquad |x|_s \leqq M_{0,s,p} |x|_0^{1-s/p} |x|_p^{s/p} \quad \text{for } x \in X_p$$

holds for some constant $M_{0,s,p}$.

Hereafter we set $C = \max \{ M_{0,s,p} , M_{i,j} ; 0 \leqq i \leqq j \leqq p \}$.

Lemma 3.5 Let $X=\{X_j\}$ be a tame Banach scale.Then we have

$$(3.52) \quad \| S_\theta x \|_{0(j)} \leqq C \theta^{j-i} \|x\|_{0(i)}$$

$$\text{for} \quad 0 \leqq i \leqq j , x \in C(0,T; X_i)$$

$$(3.53) \quad \| (I - S_\theta) x \|_{0(i)} \leqq C \theta^{-(j-i)} \| x \|_{0(j)}$$

$$\text{for } 0 \leqq i \leqq j \leqq p , \quad x \in C(0,T;X_j)$$

Proof. We can easily prove this Lemma from the definition 3.1 . ■

§ 4 Construction of an approximate solution of degree μ of the linearized equation (1.2)

In this section ,we shall construct an approximate solution of degree μ for the linearized equation (1.2) .

From the assumption (A_3) , the linearized equation

$$(4.1) \begin{cases} dz_\eta/dt + \eta H z_\eta + F'(t,x)z_\eta + F(t,x)-F'(t,x)(x-\phi) + \eta H\phi = 0, \\ z_\eta(0)=0 \quad , \quad 0 \leqq t \leqq T , \end{cases}$$

has a solution $z_\eta \in C^1(0,T;X_{m_2}) \cap C(0,T;X_{m_2+2dm_2})$ for $x=x_n \in G(\phi)$ and $\eta = \eta_n$. Hence we define x_{n+1} by

$$(4.2) \qquad x_{n+1} = S_{\theta_n} z_{\eta_n} + \phi \quad (n = 0,1,2,-,-),$$

and in this way get a sequence $\{ x_n \}$ with $x_0 = \phi$.

Here we used smoothing operators and controll parameters defined in § 3 .

Remark 4.1 Let us note that $x_{n+1} \in C^1(0,T;X_p)$.

Also define z_n and y_n by

(4.3) $$z_n = S_\theta z_\eta + \phi$$

and

(4.4) $$-y_n = dz_n/dt + \eta Hz_n + F'(t,x)z_n + F(t,x) - F'(t,x)x$$

where $\theta = \theta_n$, $x = x_n$ and $\eta = \eta_n$.

Then we shall note that $z_n = x_{n+1}$ by (4.2) .

Now we fix a large number K_0 satisfying (3.38), (3.39) and (4.16), (4.17) defined later.

Proposition 4.1 Suppose (A_2) and (A_3) . Let $x_n \in G(\phi)$.
Then z_n and y_n defined by (4.3) and (4.4) have the following properties in the framework of m-normal Banach scale $X = X(\lambda, \mu; m)$ and the controll parameters $\{K_n, Q_n\}$ for each $m>0$:

(4.5) $$z_n \in C^1(0,T;X_p), \quad y_n \in C(0,T;X_0) \quad \text{with}$$
$$\| y_n \|_{0(0)} < K_n Q_n^{-\mu} \quad \text{and} \quad \| z_n \|_{0(p)} < K_n Q_n$$

and

(4.6) z_n is a solution of the following linear equation with residual function y_n ;

$$\begin{cases} dz_n/dt + \eta Hz_n + F'(t,x_n)z_n + F(t,x_n) - F'(t,x_n)x_n + y_n = 0 , \\ z_n(0) = \phi , \quad 0 \leqq t \leqq T, \end{cases}$$

where $\eta = \eta_n$.

Definition 4.1. When z_n satisfies the above properties(4.5)and (4.6), we call z_n an approximate solution of degree μ of the linearized equation (1.2) .

Lemma 4.1 For a solution z_η of (4.1), put

$$z = S_\theta z_\eta + \phi \quad .$$

Then z is the solution of the following linear equation :

$$dz/dt + \eta Hz + F'(t,x)z + [S_\theta , \eta H + F'(t,x)]z_\eta$$

(4.7) $$+ (S_\theta - I)[F'(t,x)\phi + \eta H\phi] + S_\theta [F(t,x) - F'(t,x)x] = 0 ,$$

$$z(0) = \phi \quad , \quad 0 \leqq t \leqq T .$$

where [A,B]=AB-BA .

Proof. Operating S_θ on the both sides of (4.1) , using the linearity of S_θ and $z = S_\theta z_\eta + \phi$, we get

$$0 = dz/dt + \eta S_\theta Hz_\eta + S_\theta F'(t,x)z_\eta$$
$$+ S_\theta [F(t,x) - F'(t,x)(x-\phi)+\eta H\phi]$$
$$= dz/dt + \eta Hz + F'(t,x)z + S_\theta (\eta H + F'(t,x))z_\eta$$
$$- (\eta H + F'(t,x))S_\theta z_\eta - \eta H\phi - F'(t,x)\phi$$
$$+ S_\theta [F(t,x) - F'(t,x)(x-\phi) + \eta H\phi]$$
$$= dz/dt + \eta Hz + F'(t,x)z + [S_\theta , \eta H + F'(t,x)]z_\eta$$
$$+ (S_\theta - I)(F'(t,x)\phi + \eta H\phi) + S_\theta [F(t,x) - F'(t,x)x] .$$

Also we get $z(0)= S_\theta z_\eta(0)+ \phi = \phi$ by (4.1) . ■

Hereafter we set

(4.8) $$f \equiv [S_\theta , \eta H + F'(t,x)]z_\eta + (S_\theta - I)(F'(t,x)\phi + \eta H\phi] + S_\theta [F(t,x) - F'(t,x)x] .$$

(Proof of proposition 4.1)

By Lemma 4.1 and (4.4) ,we get for $y=y_n$, $z=z_n$, $x=x_n$ and $\eta = \eta_n$,

(4.9) $$\|y\|_{0(0)}$$
$$= \|dz/dt + \eta Hz + F'(t,x)z + F(t,x) - F'(t,x)x \|_{0(0)}$$
$$\leqq \|dz/dt + \eta Hz + F'(t,x)z + f\|_{0(0)}$$
$$+ \|f - (F(t,x) - F'(t,x)x)\|_{0(0)}$$
$$= \|f - (F(t,x) - F'(t,x)x)\|_{0(0)} \quad .$$

It follows from (4.8) that

(4.10) $$f - (F(t,x) - F'(t,x)x) = \eta [S_\theta ,H]z_\eta + [S_\theta , F'(t,x)]z_\eta + (S_\theta - I) [F(t,x) - F'(t,x)(x - \phi) + \eta H\phi] .$$

We estimate the first term on the right hand side of (4.10) .

(4.11) $$\| \eta [S_\theta , H]z_\eta \|_{0(0)}$$

$$\leq \| (S_\theta - I)Hz_\eta + H (I - S_\theta)z_\eta \|_{0(0)} \qquad (0 < \eta < 1)$$

$$\leq C\theta^{-(m_1+dm_2)} \| Hz_\eta \|_{0(m_1 + dm_2)}$$

$$+ L_2 \| (I - S_\theta)z_\eta \|_{0(2dm_2)} \qquad \text{by (3.53) and (2.17)}$$

$$\leq 2CL_2 \theta^{-(m_1+dm_2)} \| z_\eta \|_{0(m_1+ 3dm_2)} \qquad \text{by (2.17) and (3.53)}$$

$$\leq 2CL_2 \theta^{-(m_1+dm_2)} \| z_\eta \|_{0(m_2)} \qquad \text{by (3.15)}$$

$$\leq 2CL_2D_2 \theta^{-(m_1+dm_2)} \qquad \text{by (2.18) .}$$

As for the second term , we have

(4.12) $$\| [S_\theta , F'(t,x)]z_\eta \|_{0(0)}$$

$$\leq \| (S_\theta - I) F'(t,x)z_\eta \|_{0(0)} + \| F'(t,x)(I - S_\theta)z_\eta \|_{0(0)}$$

$$\leq C\theta^{-(m_1+dm_2)} \| F'(t,x)z_\eta \|_{0(m_1+dm_2)}$$

$$+ L_1 \| (I - S_\theta)z_\eta \|_{0(m)} \qquad \text{by (3.53) and (2.14)}$$

$$\leq CL_1 \theta^{-(m_1+dm_2)} \| z_\eta \|_{0(m_2)}$$

$$+ L_1 C\theta^{-(m_1+dm_2)} \| z_\eta \|_{0(m_1+dm_2+m)} \qquad \text{by (2.15) and (3.53)}$$

$$\leqq 2L_1 C\theta^{-(m_1+dm_2)} \| z_\eta \|_{0(m_2)} \qquad \text{by (3.14) and (3.15)}$$

$$\leqq 2L_1 CD_2 \theta^{-(m_1+dm_2)} \qquad \text{by (2.18)} .$$

As for the third term , we have

$$\text{(4.13)} \qquad \| (I - S_\theta)[F(t,x) - F'(t,x)(x-\phi) + \eta H\phi] \|_{0(0)}$$

$$\leqq C\theta^{-(m_1+dm_2)} \{ \| F(t,x) - F'(t,x)(x-\phi) \|_{0(m_1+dm_2)} + \eta \, | H\phi |_{(m_1+dm_2)} \} \qquad \text{by (3.53)}$$

$$\leqq C\theta^{-(m_1+dm_2)} \{ \| F(t,x) - F'(t,x)(x-\phi) \|_{0(m_2)} + \eta L_2 | \phi |_{m_1+3dm_2} \} \qquad \text{by (3.15) and (2.17)}$$

$$\leqq C\theta^{-(m_1+dm_2)} \{ D_1 + \eta L_2 | \phi |_{m_2} \} \qquad \text{by (2.16) and (3.15)} .$$

$$\leqq C\theta^{-(m_1+dm_2)} \{ D_1 + L_2 | \phi |_{m_2} \} \qquad (0 < \eta < 1) .$$

Hence from (4.9)-(4.13) , we get

$$\text{(4.14)} \qquad \| y \|_{0(0)} \leqq D_4 \theta^{-(m_1+dm_2)}$$

where $D_4 = \max\{ C(D_1 + L_2 | \phi |_{m_2}), 2CL_1D_2, 2CL_2D_2 \}$.

Similarly , we get

$$\text{(4.15)} \qquad \| z \|_{0(p)} \leqq \| S_\theta z_\eta \|_{0(p)} + | \phi |_p$$

$$\leqq C\theta^{p-m_2-dm_2} \| z_\eta \|_{0(m_2+dm_2)} + | \phi |_p \qquad \text{by(3.52)}$$

$$\leqq CD_2 \theta^{p-m_2-dm_2} \eta^{-k} + | \phi |_p \qquad \text{by (2.19)}$$

$$= D_5 \theta^{p-m_2-dm_2} \eta^{-k} + | \phi |_p \quad .$$

where $D_5 = CD_2$.

Now let

$$\text{(4.16)} \qquad K_0 > D = \max \{ D_4, D_5 \} .$$

Then we get from (4.14)-(4.16),(3.4),(3.36),(3.37) and (4.4) ,

$y_n \in C(0,T;X_0)$, $z_n \in C^1(0,T;X_p)$ with

$$\| y_n \|_{0(0)} \leqq K_n Q_n^{-\mu} \quad ,$$

$$\| z_n \|_{0(p)} \leqq (1/2) K_n Q_n + | \phi |_p$$

and

$$\begin{cases} dz_n/dt + \eta H_\eta z_n + F'(t,x_n) z_n + F(t,x_n) - F'(t,x_n) x_n + y_n = 0 \\ z_n(0) = \phi , \quad 0 \leqq t \leqq T . \end{cases}$$

where $\eta = \eta_n$.

Finally we choose K_0 such that K_0 satisfies (3.38),(3.39),(4.16) and further

(4.17) $$| \phi |_p < K_0 \quad .$$

Then from (3.39) , we get

(4.18) $$K_0 < (1/2) K_0^{\tau} = (1/2) K_1 < (1/2) K_n .$$

Therefore it follows from (4.18) that

$$\| z_n \|_{0(p)} \leqq (1/2) k_n Q_n + | \phi |_p \leqq (1/2) K_n Q_n + K_0$$

$$< K_n Q_n \quad .$$

This completes the proof of the proposition 4.1 . ■

Remark 4.1 Note that the condition (4.17) can be relaxed .

§ 5 An approximate solution of degree λ of (P_η)

In this section ,we shall prove the existence of an approximate solution of degree λ of the nonlinear evolution equation (P_η) .

Here we shall prove that the sequence { x_n } constructed in § 4 has the following properties ;

(5.1) $$\begin{cases} x_n \in G(\phi) \quad (n=0,1,2,3,- - - -) , \\ (bD_2)^{1/2} \| P_\eta x_n \|_{0(0)} \leqq K_n^{-\lambda} \quad (n=0,1,2,- -) . \end{cases}$$

Definition 5.1 If the sequence $\{ x_n \}$ satisfies (5.1), we shall call $\{ x_n \}$ an approximate solution of degree λ of the nonlinear evolution evolution (P_η).

Recall that for $x_n \in G(\phi)$, z_n and y_n defined by (4.2), (4.4) satisfy the equation

$$\begin{cases} dz_n / dt + \eta H_\eta z_n + F'(t,x_n)z_n + F(t,x_n) - F'(t,x_n)x_n + y_n = 0, \\ z_n(0) = \phi, \quad 0 \leqq t \leqq T. \end{cases}$$

by Theorem 4.1.

Now we define h_n by

$$z_n \equiv x_{n+1} = x_n + h_n .$$

Then one can easily see that h_n is a solution of the following equation;

$$(5.2)\begin{cases} dh_n/dt + \eta Hh_n + F'(t,x_n)h_n + P_\eta x_n + y_n = 0, 0 \leqq t \leqq T, \\ h_n(0) = 0 . \end{cases}$$

Similarly, we see that x_{n+1} satisfies the following relation ;

$$(5.3) \quad P_\eta x_{n+1} = P_\eta (x_n + h_n) = [F(t,x_n + h_n) - F(t,x_n) - F'(t,x_n)h_n]$$
$$+ [dh_n/dt + \eta Hh_n + F'(t,x_n)h_n + P_\eta x_n + y_n] - y_n$$
$$= [F(t,x_n + h_n) - F(t,x_n) - F'(t,x_n)h_n] - y_n \quad \text{by (5.2)} .$$

Definition 5.2 When K_0 meets (3.38),(3.39),(4.16) and (4.17), we say that K_0 satisfies the condition (K_0).

Proposition 5.1 Assume that (A_1) - (A_5) and choose K_0 satisfying the condition(K_0). Then for $\{ x_n \}$, it holds that

$$(5.4) \qquad x_n \in G(\phi) \qquad (n = 0,1,2,3,\cdots)$$

$$(5.5) \qquad (bD_3)^{1/2} \| P_\eta x_n \|_{0(0)} \leqq K_n^{-\lambda} \qquad (n = 0,1,2,3,\cdots)$$

(5.6) $\| h_{n-1} \|_{0(0)} \leqq 2(bD_3)^{1/2} K_{n-1}^{-\lambda}$ $(n = 1,2,3,\cdots)$

and

(5.7) $\| h_{n-1} \|_{0(p)} \leqq (1/2)K_n$ $(n = 1,2,3,\cdots)$

where K_n was defined in the subsection 3.2.

proof. We shall prove the proposition 5.1 by the induction .

For $n = 0$, it is clear that (5.4) - (5.5) hold by (2.21) .

Now we assume that Proposition 5.1 holds for $i = 0,1,\ldots,n$.

Then $x_i \in G(\phi)$ $(i = 1,\ldots,n)$ where $x_i = S_\theta z_\eta + \phi$ $(\theta = \theta_{i-1}, \eta = \eta_{i-1})$.

Hence from Theorem 4.1 ,we know that there exist y_i and z_i $(i = 0,\ldots,n)$ satisfying

(5.8) $$\begin{cases} \| y_i \|_{0(0)} < K_i Q_i^{-\mu} , \\ \| z_i \|_{0(p)} < K_i Q_i \end{cases}$$

and

(5.9) $$\begin{cases} dz_i/dt + \eta H z_i + F'(t,x_i)z_i + F(t,x_i) - F'(t,x_i)x_i + y_i = 0 \\ 0 \leqq t \leqq T , \ z_i(0) = \phi . \end{cases}$$

From $x_{n+1} = z_n = x_n + h_n$, we get

(5.10) $$\| x_n \|_{0(p)} \leqq \| \phi \|_p + \sum_{i=0}^{n-1} \| h_i \|_{0(p)}$$

$$\leqq K_0 + (1/2) \sum_{i=1}^{n} K_i < K_n \quad \text{by (3.43)} .$$

We shall prove (5.7). From (5.8) and (5.10), we get

(5.11) $$\| h_n \|_{0(p)} \leqq \| z_n \|_{0(p)} + \| x_n \|_{0(p)} < K_n Q_n + K_n$$

$$< 2K_n Q_n < (1/2)K_{n+1} \quad \text{by (3.40)} .$$

We shall prove (5.6). From (5.2),(2.20) and the assumption of the induction ,we also get

$$(5.12)\qquad \| h_n \|_{0(0)} \leqq bD_3\{ \|P_\eta x_n\|_{0(0)} + \|y_n\|_{0(0)}\}$$

$$\leqq (bD_3)^{1/2}\{(bD_3)^{1/2}\|P_\eta x_n\|_{0(0)} + \|y_n\|_{0(0)}\} \qquad \text{by } (2.22)$$

$$\leqq (bD_3)^{1/2}(K_n^{-\lambda} + K_nQ_n^{-\mu})$$

$$< (bD_3)^{1/2}\{K_n^{-\lambda} + (1/2)K_{n+1}^{-\lambda}\} \qquad \text{by } (3.42)$$

$$< 2(bD_3)^{1/2}K_n^{-\lambda} \qquad \text{by } (3.34)\ .$$

Next we shall prove (5.4) (i.e. $x_{n+1} \in G(\phi)$) .

From (3.51),(5.11) and (5.12),it follows that

$$(5.13)\qquad \|h_n\|_{0(s)} \leqq C\ \|h_n\|_{0(0)}^{1-s/p}\|h_n\|_{0(p)}^{s/p}$$

$$\leqq C\{ 2(bD_3)^{1/2}K_n^{-\lambda}\}^{1-s/p}\{ (1/2)K_{n+1}\}^{s/p}$$

$$= 2^{1-2s/p}C(bD_3)^{(1/2)(1-s/p)}\ K_n^{-\lambda(1-s/p)+\tau(s/p)} \qquad \text{by } (3.34)$$

$$= 2^{1-2s/p}C(bD_3)^{(1/2)(1-s/p)}\ K_n^{-\alpha} \qquad \text{by } (2.22).$$

Hence we get

$$\| x_{n+1} - \phi \|_{0(s)} \leqq \sum_{i=0}^{n} \| h_i \|_{0(s)}$$

$$< \sum_{i=0}^{n} 2^{1-2s/p}C(bD_3)^{(1/2)(1-s/p)}\ K_i^{-\alpha} < r \quad \text{by } (2.22)\ .$$

This implies (5.4) .

Finally we shall prove (5.5).

Using (5.3),(2.12),(5.11),(5.12) and (5.8),we get

$$\| P_\eta x_{n+1} \|_{0(0)}$$

$$\leqq M\| h_n \|_{0(0)}^{2-\beta}\| h_n \|_{0(p)}^{\beta} + \| y_n \|_{0(0)}$$

$$\leqq M\{2(bD_3)^{1/2}K_n^{-\lambda}\}^{2-\beta}(2K_nQ_n)^{\beta} + K_nQ_n^{-\mu}$$

$$= 4M(bD_3)^{1-\beta/2}\ K_n^{-\lambda(2-\beta)}\ (K_nQ_n)^{\beta} + K_nQ_n^{-\mu}$$

$$< K_n^{-\lambda(2-\beta)}(K_nQ_n)^{\beta} + K_nQ_n^{-\mu} \qquad \text{by (2.22)}$$

$$< K_{n+1}^{-\lambda} \qquad \text{by (3.41) and (3.42)}.$$

Hence it follows that

$$(bD_3)^{1/2}\| P_\eta x_{n+1}\|_{0(0)} < K_{n+1}^{-\lambda} \quad . \quad ■$$

§ 6 The proof of Main Theorem

First we show that there exists a limit function $x \in C(0,b;X_s)$ such that

(6.1) $\qquad x_n \to x \quad \text{in } C(0,b;X_s)$

where $\{ x_n \}$ is the approximating sequence constructed in § 4 .

In fact , it holds that for $n > m$,

$$\| x_n - x_m \|_{0(s)} \leq \sum_{j=m}^{n-1} \| h_j \|_{0(s)}$$

$$\leq \sum_{j=m}^{n-1} 2^{1-2s/p}C(bD_3)^{(1/2)(1-s/p)} K_j^{-\alpha}$$

$$\to 0 \quad \text{as } n , m \to \infty \quad .$$

by virtue of (5.13) and (2.22) .

Using the relation $dx_n/dt = P_\eta x_n - F(t,x_n) - \eta Hx_n$, (2.10) and (6.1) , we have

(6.2) $$\| dx_n/dt - dx_m/dt \|_{0(0)} \leq \| P_\eta x_n - P_\eta x_m \|_{0(0)}$$

$$+ \| F(t,x_n) - F(t,x_m) \|_{0(0)} + \eta_n \| Hx_n \|_{0(0)}$$

$$+ \eta_m \| Hx_m \|_{0(0)}$$

$$\leq (bD_3)^{-1/2}(K_n^{-\lambda} + K_m^{-\lambda}) + \| F(t,x_n) - F(t,x_m) \|_{0(0)}$$

$+ D_6(\eta_n + \eta_m)$

$\to 0$ as $n, m \to \infty$.

Here we used the inequality

(6.3) $\eta_n \| Hx_n \|_{0(0)} \leqq D_6 \eta_n$

where $D_6 = L_2(r + | \phi |_s)$.

The inequality (6.3) is showed in the following way ;

$$\| \eta_n Hx_n \|_{0(0)} \leqq \eta_n L_2 \| x_n \|_{0(2dm_2)} \quad \text{by (2.17)}$$

$$\leqq \eta_n L_2 \| x_n \|_{0(m_2)} \quad \text{by (3.15)}$$

$$\leqq \eta_n L_2 \{ r + | \phi |_s \} \quad \text{by (5.4)}$$

$$= D_6 \eta_n \quad .$$

Hence from (6.1) and (6.2) , we get

(6.4) $x \in C^1(0,b;X_0)$ and $x_n \to x$ in $C^1(0,b;X_0)$.

Therefore

$$P_\eta x_n = dx_n/dt + \eta Hx_n + F(t,x_n) \quad (0 \leqq t \leqq b) , \ u_n(0)=\phi$$

converges

(6.5) $0 = dx/dt + F(t,x) \quad (0 \leqq t \leqq b) , \ x(0)=\phi$

as $n \to \infty$ by (5.5),(6.3),(6.4),(6.1) and (2.10) .

This means that x is a local solution (in time) of the nonlinear evolution equation (P) .

§7 An application of Main Theorem to the Navier-Stokes equation

By using our main theorem, we try to seek a vector function $u=(u_1, u_2, - - -, u_n)$ representing the velocity of the field, and a scalar function p representing the pressure, which are defined in $[0,T]*R^n$ and satisfy the initial value problem of the nonstationary Navier-Stokes equation ([2],[3],[7],[9],[11],[13]) ;

$$(7.1)\quad \begin{cases} du/dt = \Delta u - (u\cdot\nabla)u - \nabla p\ ,\ (t,x)\in [0,T]*R^n, \\ \nabla\cdot u = 0\ ,\quad (t,x)\in [0,T]*R^n\ , \\ u(0,x) = u_0(x)\ ,\quad x\in R^n\ , \end{cases}$$

where $\nabla\cdot u_0 = 0$.

§§ 7.1 Modification of the problem by Fourier transform

By eliminating the pressure function p , we get the nonlinear evolution equation including only the velocity field u as an unknown function ;

$$(7.2)\quad \begin{cases} du/dt + F(u) = 0\ ,\ 0 \leqq t \leqq T\ , \\ u(0) = u_0\ . \end{cases}$$

Where

$$(7.3)\qquad F(u) = -\Delta u + (u\cdot\nabla)u + \nabla p\ .$$

p in (7.3)is determined by u as the solution of the following poisson equation for any $t \in [\,0,T\,]$;

$$(7.4)\qquad -\Delta p = \nabla\cdot\{(u\cdot\nabla)u\}\ .$$

Denote by $\hat{u}$ the Fourier transform of u . Then we can rewrite (7.3) in the following way ;

$$(7.5)\qquad F(u) = -\Delta u + Nu\ ,$$

where

$$(7.6)\qquad N u = -\sum_{j=1}^{n} (d/dx_j)(N^{(j)}u)\ .$$

Here the k-th component of $N^{(j)}u$ is defined by

$$(7.7)\qquad \widehat{(N^{(j)}u)}_k(\xi) = (\xi_k/|\xi|^2)\ \xi\cdot\widehat{(u_j u)}(\xi) - \widehat{(u_j u_k)}(\xi)$$
$$(k = 1,2, ---, n)\ .$$

Now we shall try to apply main Thorem to the transformd problem (7.2) and (7.5)-(7.7) .

§§ 7.2 Choice of 2 - normal Banach scale $X(\lambda, \mu : 2)$

As a Banach scale $\{X_j\}$, we adopt the Sobolev space

$$X_j = [H^{[n/2]+j+1}(R^n)]^n$$

and denote its norm by $|\cdot|_j$ for $j \geq 0$.

Now assume $u_0 \in X_p$ and set

(7.8) $V_0 = \{u \in X_p \ ; \ |u - u_0|_s < r\}$

for a fixed positive number r .

Then we define the fundamental set $G(u_0)$:

(7.9) $G(u_0)$

$$= \{ u \in C^1(0,T;X_p),\ u(t) \in V_0 \text{ for } 0 \leq t \leq T \text{ and } u(0) = u_0 \} .$$

In the case of the Navier - Stokes equation (7.2), F(u) is a nonlinear partial differential operator of order 2 .

Hence using Lemma 3.2 , we construct 2-normal Banach scale $\{X_0, X_{m_1}, X_{m_2}, X_s, X_p\}$, one of which is

(7.10) $\begin{cases} \{ m, m_1, m_2, s, p \} = \{ 2, 5, 20, 24.75, 25 \} \text{ and} \\ \{\lambda, \mu\} = \{ 200, 1999.3 \} . \end{cases}$

§§ 7.3 Differentiability of F(u)

In this subsection , we define Fréchet derivative of F(u) and describe its properties in detail .

Lemma 7.1 For each i (i = 1,2,-,-,-,n) , the nonlinear mapping

$$N^{(i)} : X_j \rightarrow X_j$$

is continuous for each $j \geq 0$ and

(7.11) $|N^{(i)}u|_j \leq C(n)\, |u|_j^2$

holds for $u \in X_j$ ($j \geqq 0$) .

Proof. If we use the definition (7.7) of $N^{(j)}u$ and the estimate of functional product , by which the elements of the Sobolev space X_j form algebra , we have (7.11) . ■

Lemma 7.2 (Fréchet derivative of F(u)) For $u \in V_0$, Fréchet derivative $F'(u)$ of $F(u)$; $X_{i+2} \to X_i$ is defined by

$$(7.12) \qquad F'(u)v = -\Delta v - \sum_{j=1}^{n}(d/dx_j)(N_j(u)v)$$

for $v \in X_{i+2}$ $(0 \leqq i \leqq m_2+2)$ where the k-th component of $N_j(u)v$ is

$$(7.13) \qquad \widehat{(N_j(u)v)_k}(\xi) = (\xi_k/|\xi|^2)\,\xi\cdot[\widehat{(u_jv)}(\xi) + \widehat{(v_ju)}(\xi)] - [\widehat{(u_jv_k)}(\xi) + \widehat{(v_ju_k)}(\xi)].$$

Proof. From the definition (7.5)-(7.7) of F(u) , we have only to show

$$(7.14) \qquad \| (d/dx_j)[N^{(j)}(u+v) - N^{(j)}(u) - N_j(u)v \|_i \leqq C(n)\|v\|_{i+1}^2 \quad \text{for } 0 \leqq i \leqq m_2+2 \text{ and } 1 \leqq j \leqq n .$$

Let us calculate

$$\widehat{(N^{(j)}(u+v))_k}(\xi) - \widehat{(N^{(j)}(u))_k}(\xi)$$
$$= (\xi_k/|\xi|^2)\,\xi\cdot[\widehat{((u_j+v_j)(u+v))}(\xi) - \widehat{(u_ju)}(\xi)]$$
$$- [\widehat{((u_j+v_j)(u_k+v_k))}(\xi) - \widehat{(u_ju_k)}(\xi)]$$
$$= (\xi_k/|\xi|^2)\,\xi\cdot[\widehat{(u_jv+v_ju)}(\xi) + \widehat{(v_jv)}(\xi)]$$
$$- [\widehat{(u_jv_k+v_ju_k)}(\xi) + \widehat{(v_jv_k)}(\xi)] .$$

Hence we get

$$[\,(N^{(j)}(u+v))^{\wedge}_k(\xi) - (N^{(j)}(u))^{\wedge}_k(\xi)\,] - (N_j(u)v)^{\wedge}_k(\xi)$$

$$= [\,(\xi_k/|\xi|^2)\xi \cdot (v_j v)^{\wedge}(\xi) - (v_j v_k)^{\wedge}(\xi)\,] ,$$

from which

$$|\,[\,N^{(j)}(u+v) - N^{(j)}u\,] - N_j(u)v\,|_i$$

$$\leq \sum_{k=1}^{n} \|\,(1+|\xi|^2)^{i/2}[\,(N^{(j)}(u+v))^{\wedge}_k(\xi) - (N^{(j)}u)^{\wedge}_k(\xi)$$

$$- (N_j(u)v)^{\wedge}_k(\xi)\,]\,\|_{L^2}$$

$$\leq 2\sum_{k=1}^{n} \|(1+|\xi|^2)^{i/2}(v_j v_k)^{\wedge}(\xi)\|_{L^2}$$

$$\leq 2\sum_{k=1}^{n} \|v_j\|_i \|v_k\|_i \leq 2n\|v\|_i^2$$

$$\leq C(n)\|\,v\,\|_i^2$$

Therefore we have (7.14) . ■

Lemma 7.3 For each i (i = 1, 2, - -, n) , the linear mapping $N_i(u)$

$$N_i(u) : X_j \rightarrow X_j$$

is continuous for each $j \geq 0$ and

(7.15) $\quad |\,N_i(u)v\,|_j \leq C(n)\,|u|_j\,|v|_j$

holds for $u \in v_0$ and $v \in X_j$ $\quad (0 \leq j \leq m_2+2)$.

Proof. Using the definition (7.13) of $N_i(u)$ and the estimate of functional product in the same way as in lemma 7.1 , we have (7.15) . ■

Lemma 7.4 For $u \in G(u_0)$, $F'(u(t))v$ is continuously differentiable from [0,T] into X_i for each $v \in X_{i+2}$, $0 \leq i \leq m_2+2$.

Proof. By use of the definition (7.12) of $F'(u)v$, we have

(7.16) $$(d/dt)F'(u)v = -\sum_{j=1}^{n}(d/dx_j)N_j(du/dt)v \in C(0,T;X_i)\ ,$$

which implies this lemma . ■

Lemma 7.5 For $u \in G(u_0)$, $F(u) - F'(u)(u - u_0)$ is continuously differentiable from $[0,T]$ into X_i for $0 \leqq i \leqq m_2+2$.

Proof . By using (7.5) and (7.12) , we have

(7.17) $$(d/dt)[\ F(u) - F'(u)u\ ] = \sum_{j=1}^{n}(d/dx_j)N_j(du/dt)u \in C(0,T;X_i)\ .$$

Combining (7.17) with (7.16) , we can prove this lemma . ■

Lemma 7.6 There exists a constant D_6 such that

(7.18) $$|F'(u)v|_j \leqq D_6\ |V|_{j+2} \text{ for } u \in V_0\ ,\ v \in X_{j+2} \text{ and } 0 \leqq j \leqq m_2+2$$

and

(7.19) $$\|F(u+v) - F(u) - F'(u)v\|_{0(0)} \leqq D_6 \|v\|_{0(0)}^{2(1-1/p)} \|v\|_{0(p)}^{2/p}$$

for $u \in G(u_0)$ and $v \in C(0,T;X_p)$ and $\beta = 2/p$.

Where D_6 is independent of u and v .

Proof . By (7.12) and (7.15) , we have

$$|\ F'(u)v\ |_j \leqq |\ v\ |_{j+2} + C(n)\,|u|_{j+1}\,|v|_{j+1}$$

$$\leqq (\ 1 + C(n)\,|u|_{j+1}\ )\,|v|_{j+2} \leqq D_6\ |v|_{j+2}$$

by $u \in v_0$ $(0 \leqq j \leqq m_2+2)$.

Also using the equality

(7.20) $$F(\ u + v\ ) - F(u) - F'(u)v$$

$$= -\sum_{j=1}^{n}(d/dx_j)[\ N^{(j)}(u+v) - N^{(j)}u - N_j(u)v\ ]$$

and (7.14) , we have

$$| F(u+v) - F(u) - F'(u)v |_0 \leqq C(n) \; | v |_1^2$$

$$\leqq D_6 \; | v |_0^{2-\beta} | v |_p^{\beta} \quad \text{where } \beta = 2/p$$

by (3.51) , from which we get (7.19) . ■

Remark 7.1 We easily check that $\beta = 2/p$ satisfies (2.13) under our choice of 2-normal Banach scale .

Lemma 7.7 There exists constant D_7 such that

(7.21) $\| F(u) - F'(u)(u - u_0) \|_{0(j)} \leqq D_7$

for $u \in G(u_0)$ and $0 \leqq j \leqq m_2+2$.

Proof. Using the equality

(7.22) $$F(u) - F'(u)u = - \sum_{j=1}^{n} (d/dx_j)[N^{(j)}u - N_j(u)u]$$
$$= \sum_{j=1}^{n} (d/dx_j)N^{(j)}u \quad ,$$

and (7.11) , we get

$$|F(u) - F'(u)(u-u_0)|_i \leqq C(n)|u|_{i+1}^2 + |F'(u)u_0|_i$$
$$\leqq C(n)|u|_{i+1}^2 + D_6 \; |u_0|_{i+2} \quad \text{by (7.18)}$$
$$\leqq D_7 \quad \text{for } 0 \leqq i \leqq m_2+2 \quad \text{by } u(t) \in V_0 \; (0 \leqq t \leqq T) . \quad ■$$

Remark 7.2 Lemmas 7.6 - 7.7 and Remark 7.1 ensure the assumptions (A_1) and (A_2) in §§2.2 .

§§7.4 Controll parameters,smoothing operator and singular perturbation

The smoothing operater which we shall use here is defined as follows; Let $\rho \in C^{\infty}(R^n)$ satisfy

(7.23) $$\begin{cases} |\rho(\xi)| \leqq 1 \quad (\xi \in R^n) \text{ and} \\ \rho(\xi) = 1 \quad \text{for} \quad |\xi| \leqq 1 \; . \end{cases}$$

Moreover put

(7.24) $\zeta(x) = (1/2\pi)^n \int_{R^n} e^{ix\cdot\xi} \rho(\xi)d\xi$

and define the smoothing operator S_θ by

(7.25) $(S_\theta f)(x) = (\zeta_\theta * f)(x)$ for $f \in X_j$

where $\zeta_\theta(x) = \theta^n \zeta(\theta x)$ $(\theta \geqq 1)$.

Then we easily check that S_θ satisfies (3.49) and (3.50) in Definition3.1 .

Next we introduce the singular perturbation ηH ($0 < \eta < 1$);

(7.26) $\eta Hu = \eta[(-\Delta+1)^{dm_2}]u$.

Lemma 7.8 For each $u \in X_j$, we have

(7.27) $|Hu|_j \leqq D_8 |u|_{j-2dm_2}$ for $u \in X_j$ $(j>2dm_2)$ and some $D_8 > 0$,

(7.28) $(Hu,u)_j = |u|^2_{j+dm_2}$

Proof. From the definition of ηH , (7.27) is obvious .
Using the fact $((-\Delta+I)u,u)_j = (\nabla u,\nabla u)_j + (u,u)_j$ $= |u|^2_{j+1}$, we can prove (7.28) by induction . ■

Finally if we consider the facts stated above , then we are able to choose the key parameter K_0 , which makes it possible to construct the controll parameters for this case .

§§ 7.5 The existence and the estimate of the solution of the singularly perturbed linear equation

By use of (7.12) and (7.22), we obtain the linearized equation for (7.2) ;

$$(7.29)\quad \begin{cases} dv/dt + \eta Hv - \Delta v - \sum_{j=1}^{n} (d/dx_j)N_j(u(t))v \\ \qquad\qquad + \sum_{j=1}^{n} (d/dx_j)N^{(j)}u(t) = 0 , \quad 0 \leqq t \leqq T , \\ v(0) = u_0 . \end{cases}$$

For $u \in G(u_0)$, we define the linear operator $A_\eta(t)$ ($0 \leqq t \leqq T$) ;

$$(7.30)\quad \begin{cases} D(A_\eta(t)) = X_{i+2dm_2} \qquad (0 \leqq i \leqq m_2+2) \\ A_\eta(t)v = \eta Hv - \Delta v - \sum_{j=1}^{n} (d/dx_j)N_j(u(t))v \quad \text{for } v \in X_{i+2dm_2} . \end{cases}$$

Lemma 7.9 The linear operator $-A_\eta(t)$ generates the uniformly bounded evolution operator $U_\eta(t,s)$ ($0 \leqq s \leqq t \leqq T$) in X_i ($0 \leqq i \leqq m_2+2$) for $\eta \in (0,1)$.

Proof. By using (7.15) in Lemma 7.3, we have for $u \in G(u_0)$,

$$(7.31)\quad (A_\eta(t)v,v)_i = (\eta Hv - \Delta v - \sum_{j=1}^{n} (d/dx_j)N_j(u(t))v , v)_i$$

$$= \eta |v|_{i+dm_2}^2 + | \nabla v |_i^2 - \sum_{j=1}^{n} (N_j(u(t))v , (d/dx_j)v)_i$$

$$\geqq \eta |v|_{i+dm_2}^2 + |v|_{i+1}^2 - (1+C(n)) |v|_i |v|_{i+1}$$

$$\geqq \eta |v|_{i+dm_2}^2 + (1/2) |v|_{i+1}^2 - (1/2)(1+C(n))^2 |v|_i^2 \qquad (0 \leqq t \leqq T)$$

which implies that

$$(7.32)\qquad -A_\eta(t) \in G(X_i,1,\beta) \quad (0 \leqq t \leqq T) \text{ where } \beta = (1+C(n))^2/2 .$$

Therefore using Kato's Theorem on the construction of the fundamental solutions of hyperbolic type ([4],[12]) . we can construct the evolution opetator $U_\eta(t,s)$ satisfying

$$(7.33)\qquad | U_\eta(t,s)g |_i \leqq \exp(\beta(t-s)) |g|_i$$

for $\eta \in (0,1)$ and $g \in X_i$ ($0 \leqq i \leqq m_2+2$) .

Here we used (7.31) and lemma 7.4 . ■

Now put

$$(7.34)\qquad f(t) \equiv -\{ F(u(t)) - F'(u(t))(u(t)-u_0) - \eta Hu_0 \}$$
$$= -\sum_{j=1}^{n} (d/dx_j)N^{(j)}u(t) - F'(u(t))u_0 - \eta Hu_0 .$$

Lemma 7.10 For $u \in G(u_0)$, the singularly perturbed linear equation (7.29) of (7.2);

$$(7.35)\quad \begin{cases} dv/dt + A_\eta(t)v = f(t) & (0 \leqq t \leqq T) \\ v(0) = 0 \end{cases}$$

has a unique solution $v = v_\eta(t) \in C(0,T;X_{i+2dm_2}) \cap C^1(0,T;X_i)$ $(0 \leqq i \leqq m_2+2)$. And v_η is estimated by

$$(7.36)\qquad \|v_\eta\|_{0(0)} \leqq bD_9 \|f\|_{0(0)} \qquad (0 < b \leqq T),$$

$$(7.37)\qquad \|v_\eta\|_{0(m_2+2)} \leqq D_9$$

where the constant D_9 is independent of $\eta \in (0,1)$.

Proof. From Lemma 7.9 and Lemma 7.5, we know that the linear equation (7.35) has a unique solution $v_\eta \in C(0,T;X_{i+2dm_2}) \cap C^1(0,T;X_i)$, which is represented by

$$(7.38)\qquad v_\eta(t) = \int_0^t U_\eta(t,s)f(s)ds \qquad (0 < t \leqq b \leqq T).$$

(See H.Tanabe [12]). From (7.33), (7.21) and (7.27), we have (7.36). Similarly for $i = m_2 + 2$, (7.35) has a unique solution $v_\eta \in C^1(0,T;X_{m_2+2})$. By using (7.33),(7.21),(7.27) and (7.38), we get (7.37). ■

Lemma 7.11 For $u \in G(u_0)$, the solution v_η of (7.35) has the estimate ;

$$(7.39)\qquad \|v_\eta\|_{0(m_2+dm_2)} \leqq D_{10}\eta^{-1/2} .$$

Proof. By (7.31), $-\eta H$ generates a holomorphic semigroup $T_\eta(t)$ such that

(7.40) $$|T_\eta(t)f|_X \leqq |f|_X$$

and

(7.41) $$|T_\eta(t)f|_V \leqq \eta^{-1/2}t^{-1/2}|f|_X \quad \text{for } f \in X$$

where $X=X_{m_2}$ and $V=X_{m_2+dm_2}$.

Hence the solution of (7.35)in X_{m_2+2} satisfies the following integral equation in X_{m_2};

(7.42) $$v_\eta(t) = -\int_0^t T_\eta(t-s)[\,F'(u)v_\eta + F(u) - F'(u)(u-u_0) + \eta Hu_0]ds\,.$$

Therefore using (7.42), (7.41), (7.21) and (7.37), we get .

$$|v_\eta(t)|_{m_2+dm_2}$$

$$\leqq \int_0^t \eta^{-1/2}(t-s)^{-1/2}|F'(u)v_\eta + F(u) - F'(u)(u-u_0) + \eta Hu_0|_{m_2}ds$$

$$\leqq \eta^{-1/2}\sqrt{t}\,(\,D_6\|v_\eta\|_{0(m_2+2)} + D_7 + D_8|u_0|_{m_2+2dm_2})$$

$$\leqq \eta^{-1/2}\sqrt{T}\,(\,D_6D_9 + D_7 + D_8|u_0|_{m_2+2dm_2}\,)$$

$$\equiv D_{10}\eta^{-1/2} \qquad \blacksquare$$

Remark 7.3 Lemma 7.8 , 7.10 and 7.11 ensure the assumptions (A_3) and (A_4) in §§2.2 .

§§7.6 Existence Theorem

In the above subsections, we showed that the assumptions (A_1) - (A_4) are satisfied for the nonlinear evolution equation (7.2). Therefore using main theorem , we get

Theorem 7.1 The initial value problem of the transformed equation (7.2) has a local solution (in time) for any $u_0 \in X_{32}$.

Moreover we easily check that the solution of (7.2) satisfies

$$d(\nabla\cdot u)/dt = \Delta(\nabla\cdot u) \quad , \quad (t,x) \in [0,T]\ R^n ,$$

$$(\nabla\cdot u)(0,x) = \nabla\cdot u_0 = 0 \quad , x \in R^n \quad .$$

Hence we have

$$(\nabla\cdot u)(t,x) = 0 \qquad \text{for } t \in [0,T] \quad .$$

Thus we get

Theorem 7.2 There exists a local solution { u , p } for the Navier-Stokes equation (7.1) .

References

[1] M.Altman, Nonlinear equations of evolution in Banach spaces, Nonlinear Analysis 8, 491-499 (1984) .

[2] H.Fujita and T.Kato,On the Navier-Stokes initial value problem I , Arch.Rational Mech.Anal.,16,269-315 (1964)

[3] Y.Giga and T.Miyakawa,Solutions in L_r of the Navier-Stokes initial value problem , Arch. Rational Mech.Anal., 267-281 (1985)

[4] T.Kato, Linear evolution equation of "hyperbolic" type, J. Fac. Sci. Univ. Tokyo, Sec. I. 17, 241-258 (1970) .

[5] H.Kawarada and H.Koshigoe, On a comstruction of an approximate solution of the linearized equation of Moser's type, Tech. Rep. Math. Sci. Chiba Univ. No.5 (1985) .

[6] H.Kawarada and H.Koshigoe,Nonlinear evolution equation of Moser's type, Surikaisekiken kokyuroku(Kyoto Univ.)579,30-40(1985)(in Japanese).

[7] O.A.Ladyzenhenskaya,The mathematical theory of viscous incompressible flow , New York : Gordon and Breach (1969)

[8] J.L.Lions, Perturbations singulieres dans les problems aux limites et en controle optimal, Springer-Verlag, 1973 .

[9] K.Masuda, Weak solutions of Navier-Stokes Equations , Tohoku Math.J.36,623-646 (1984)

[10] J.Moser, A rapidly convergent iteration method and nonlinear partial differential equations I, Annali Scu. norm. sup. Pisa 20, 265-315 (1966) .

[11] S.Ukai, On the exterior problem to a linearized Boltzmann equation with the reverse reflection boundary condition , Lecture Notes in Numerical and Applied Analysis,No.2,39-57 (1980) Kinokuniya,Tokyo .

[12] H.Tanabe, Equations of Evolution, Pitman, (1979) .

[13] R.Temam, Navier-Stokes equations, Amsterdam-New York-Oxford : North Holland (1984)

Recent Topics in Nonlinear PDE III, Tokyo, 1986
Lecture Notes in Num. Appl. Anal., 9, 157–172 (1985)

The Boltzmann Equation and Thirteen Moments

Shuichi KAWASHIMA

Department of Mathematics
Nara Women's University
Nara 630, Japan

1. Introduction

This is a summary of the author's recent paper [5].

We consider the initial value problem for the Boltzmann equation:

$$F_t + v\cdot\nabla_x F = Q(F,F)\ , \tag{1.1}$$

$$F(0,x,v) = F_0(x,v)\ . \tag{1.2}$$

Here $F = F(t,x,v)$ denotes the mass density of gas molecules with velocity $v = (v_1,v_2,v_3) \in \mathbb{R}^3$ at time $t \geq 0$ and position $x = (x_1,x_2,x_3) \in \mathbb{R}^3$, ∇_x is the gradient with respect to x and $Q(F,F)$ is the term related to the binary collisions of molecules, which is given explicitly as follows:

$$Q(F,G)(v) = \frac{1}{2}\iint_{S^2\times\mathbb{R}^3} q(\theta,|v_*-v|)\{F(v')G(v_*') + F(v_*')G(v') - F(v)G(v_*) - F(v_*)G(v)\}d\omega dv_*\ . \tag{1.3}$$

In (1.3) we use abbreviations such as $F(v) = F(t,x,v)$; v' and v_*' are molecular velocites which produce v and v_* after a collision, namely, $v' = v + ((v_*-v)\cdot\omega)\omega$, $v_*' = v_* - ((v_*-v)\cdot\omega)\omega$ for $\omega \in S^2$; $q(\theta,|v_*-v|)$ (where θ is defined by $(v_*-v)\cdot\omega = |v_*-v|\cos\theta$) is a function determined by the intermolecular potentials and is assumed to be of the cutoff hard type of Grad [2].

We study the problem concerning the existence of global solutions of (1.1),(1.2) in a neighborhood of a Maxwellian. The key of the problem is to get a suitable decay estimate for the linearized Boltzmann equation around the Maxwellian (see [6],[7]). In the previous works [6],[7], such a decay estimate was obtained by a method based on the spectral theory for the linearized Boltzmann operator investigated in [1]. Our aim is to show the same decay estimate by quite a different method. Our method is the so-called energy method and makes use of the matrix represetation of $v\cdot\xi$, the symbol of the streaming operator $v\cdot\nabla_x$, which maps the null space of the linearized collision operator into the subspace associated with the thirteen moments.

2. Preliminaries

We consider the problem (1.1),(1.2) in a neighborhood of the normalized Maxwellian $M = M(v)$:

$$(2.1)\qquad M(v) = (2\pi)^{-3/2}\exp(-|v|^2/2) .$$

M is an equilibrium of (1.1) since $Q(M,M) = 0$. Following Grad [2],[3], we introduce the new unknown function $f = f(t,x,v)$ by

$$(2.2)\qquad F = M + M^{1/2}f .$$

The problem (1.1),(1.2) is then transformed into

$$(2.3)\qquad f_t + v\cdot\nabla_x f + Lf = \Gamma(f,f) ,$$

$$(2.4)\qquad f(0,x,v) = f_0(x,v) .$$

Here $f_0(x,v) = M(v)^{-1/2}(F_0(x,v) - M(v))$ and

(2.5)
$$Lf = -2M^{-1/2}Q(M,M^{1/2}f) ,$$
$$\Gamma(f,g) = M^{-1/2}Q(M^{1/2}f,M^{1/2}g) .$$

First we summarize some known properties of the linearized collision operator L. (For the details, see [2].) L is decomposed in the form

$$Lf = \nu f - Kf , \tag{2.6}$$

where $\nu = \nu(v)$ is the function satisfying $\nu_1 \le \nu(v) \le \nu_2(1+|v|)$ for positive constants ν_1, ν_2, and K is a compact selfadjoint operator on $L^2(v)$. Therefore L is a (unbounded) symmetric operator on $L^2(v)$. Also, L is nonnegative, namely, $(Lf,f) \ge 0$ for $f \in L^2(v)$ with $Lf \in L^2(v)$, where $(\, , \,)$ is the standard inner product of $L^2(v)$. We denote the null space of L by $N(L)$. It is known that

$$N(L) = \text{linear span of } \{\psi_1 M^{1/2},\cdots,\psi_5 M^{1/2}\} , \tag{2.7}$$

where

$$\psi_1 = 1 , \quad \psi_{j+1} = v_j , \quad j=1,2,3, \quad \psi_5 = |v|^2 . \tag{2.8}$$

(Recall that v_j is the j-th component of v.) Each ψ_k is called a summational invariant. The following five functions form an orthonormal basis of $N(L)$.

$$e_1 = M^{1/2} , \quad e_{j+1} = v_j M^{1/2} , \quad j=1,2,3, \quad e_5 = \frac{1}{\sqrt{6}}(|v|^2 - 3)M^{1/2} . \tag{2.9}$$

From the properties of L stated above we deduce that for $f \in L^2(v)$ with $Lf \in L^2(v)$,

$$(Lf,f) \ge \delta_1 |(I - P_0)f|_2^2 , \tag{2.10}$$

where δ_1 is a positive constant, $|\cdot|_2$ denotes the norm of $L^2(v)$, and P_0 is the orthogonal projection from $L^2(v)$ onto $N(L)$:

$$P_0 f = \sum_{k=1}^{5} (f,e_k)e_k \ .$$

We remark that (2.10) holds true also for $f \in L_1^2(v)$, where $L_1^2(v)$ is the space of functions $f \in L^2(v)$ such that $(1+|v|)f \in L^2(v)$.

Next we introduce the following thirteen functions.

$$\phi_1 = 1\ , \quad \phi_{j+1} = v_j\ , \quad j=1,2,3, \quad \phi_{j+4} = v_j^2\ , \quad j=1,2,3,$$

$$\text{(2.11)} \qquad \phi_8 = v_1v_2\ , \quad \phi_9 = v_2v_3\ , \quad \phi_{10} = v_3v_1\ ,$$

$$\phi_{j+10} = |v|^2 v_j\ , \quad j=1,2,3.$$

Notice that each summational invariant in (2.8) is a linear combination of the above functions: $\psi_k = \phi_k$, $k=1,\cdots,4$, and $\psi_5 = \phi_5+\phi_6+\phi_7$. We denote by W the subspace of $L^2(v)$ spanned by the thirteen functions $\phi_k M^{1/2}$, $k=1,\cdots,13$, namely,

$$\text{(2.12)} \qquad W = \text{linear span of } \{\phi_1 M^{1/2},\cdots,\phi_{13}M^{1/2}\}\ .$$

W is the subspace associated with the thirteen moments, since the quantities $\int \phi_k F\,dv = (M^{1/2}+f, \phi_k M^{1/2})$ are called moments of the distribution function F. We shall introduce an orthonormal basis of W. Since $N(L) \subset W$ and the five functions $e_1,\cdots,e_5$ given by (2.9) form an orthonormal basis of $N(L)$, we choose additional eight functions $e_6,\cdots,e_{13}$ such that $\{e_1,\cdots,e_{13}\}$ becomes an orthonormal basis of W. They are given as follows:

$$e_{k+4} = \sum_{j=1}^{3} c_{kj}\tilde{e}_{j+4}\ , \quad k=2,3,$$

$$\text{(2.13)} \qquad e_8 = v_1v_2M^{1/2}\ , \quad e_9 = v_2v_3M^{1/2}\ , \quad e_{10} = v_3v_1M^{1/2}\ ,$$

$$e_{j+10} = \frac{1}{\sqrt{10}} (|v|^2 - 5) v_j M^{1/2}, \quad j = 1,2,3.$$

Here

(2.14) $$\tilde{e}_{j+4} = \frac{1}{\sqrt{2}} (v_j^2 - 1) M^{1/2}, \quad j = 1,2,3,$$

and the coefficients c_{kj} are chosen such that the three vectors $c_1 = (1/\sqrt{3}, 1/\sqrt{3}, 1/\sqrt{3})$, $c_2 = (c_{21}, c_{22}, c_{23})$ and $c_3 = (c_{31}, c_{32}, c_{33})$ form an orthonormal basis of $\mathbb{R}^3$. This choice of c_{kj} is based on the following observation: The three functions in (2.14) form an orthonormal system of $L^2(v)$ and $e_5 = (\tilde{e}_5 + \tilde{e}_6 + \tilde{e}_7)/\sqrt{3}$.

Now we consider $v \cdot \xi$ ($\xi \in \mathbb{R}^3$), the symbol of the streaming operator $v \cdot \nabla_x$, on the null space $N(L)$. For each $\xi \in \mathbb{R}^3$, $v \cdot \xi$ is regarded as a linear operator from $N(L)$ into W, and therefore can be represented by the 13×5 matrix with the entries $((v \cdot \xi) e_k, e_\ell)$, $1 \le k \le 13$, $1 \le \ell \le 5$. Hence we introduce for $\xi \in \mathbb{R}^3$,

(2.15) $$V(\xi) = (((v \cdot \xi) e_k, e_\ell))_{1 \le k, \ell \le 13},$$

which is a real symmetric matrix. Consider the decomposition

(2.16) $$V(\xi) = \begin{pmatrix} V_{11}(\xi) & V_{12}(\xi) \\ V_{21}(\xi) & V_{22}(\xi) \end{pmatrix},$$

where $V_{11}(\xi)$, $V_{12}(\xi)$, $V_{21}(\xi)$ and $V_{22}(\xi)$ are 5×5, 5×8, 8×5 and 8×8 matrices, respectively. We have $V_{11}(\xi)^T = V_{11}(\xi)$, $V_{12}(\xi)^T = V_{21}(\xi)$ and $V_{22}(\xi)^T = V_{22}(\xi)$, where the superscript T denotes transpose. By straightfoward calculation, using (2.9) and (2.13), we have the following expressions:

$$(2.17)\qquad V_{11}(\xi) = \left(\begin{array}{c|ccc|c} 0 & \xi_1 & \xi_2 & \xi_3 & 0 \\ \hline \xi_1 & & & & a_1\xi_1 \\ \xi_2 & & 0 & & a_1\xi_2 \\ \xi_3 & & & & a_1\xi_3 \\ \hline 0 & a_1\xi_1 & a_1\xi_2 & a_1\xi_3 & 0 \end{array}\right)$$

$$(2.18)\qquad V_{12}(\xi) = \left(\begin{array}{c|ccc|c} 0 & a_{21}\xi_1 & a_{22}\xi_2 & a_{23}\xi_3 & 0 \\ 0 & a_{31}\xi_1 & a_{32}\xi_2 & a_{33}\xi_3 & 0 \\ \hline 0 & \xi_2 & \xi_1 & 0 & 0 \\ 0 & 0 & \xi_3 & \xi_2 & 0 \\ 0 & \xi_3 & 0 & \xi_1 & 0 \\ \hline 0 & & & & a_4\xi_1 \\ 0 & & 0 & & a_4\xi_2 \\ 0 & & & & a_4\xi_3 \end{array}\right)$$

where $\xi = (\xi_1,\xi_2,\xi_3)$, $a_1 = \sqrt{2/3}$, $a_{kj} = \sqrt{2}c_{kj}$, $k = 2,3$, $j = 1,2,3$, and $a_4 = \sqrt{3/5}$.

3. Construction of a compensating function

We introduce the notion of a compensating function for the Boltzmann equation (2.3). Let $\mathbb{B}(L^2(v))$ be the Banach space of bounded linear operators on $L^2(v)$, with the operator norm.

Definition 3.1. Let $S(\omega)$ be a bounded linear operator on $L^2(v)$ with a parameter $\omega \in S^2$, i.e., $S(\omega) \in \mathbb{B}(L^2(v))$ for each $\omega \in S^2$. $S(\omega)$ is called a compensating function for the Boltzmann equation (2.3), if the following conditions are satisfied:

(i) $S(\cdot) \in C^{\infty}(S^2; \mathbf{B}(L^2(v)))$ and $S(-\omega) = -S(\omega)$ for each $\omega \in S^2$.

(ii) $iS(\omega)$ is a selfadjoint operator on $L^2(v)$ for each $\omega \in S^2$.

(iii) There exists a positive constant δ such that for any $\omega \in S^2$ and $f \in L_1^2(v)$, the following inequality holds.

$$\mathrm{Re}\,(S(\omega)(v\cdot\omega)f,f) + (Lf,f) \geq \delta|f|_2^2 .$$

In order to show the existence of a compensating function for the Boltzmann equation, we prepare the following

Lemma 3.1. *There exist matrices* R^j, $j = 1,2,3$, *which satisfy the following properties: Each* R^j *is a* 13×13 *real skew-symmetric matrix with constant entries. Moreover, there exist positive constants* c_1 *and* C_1 *such that for any* $\omega \in S^2$ *and* $w = (w_1,\cdots,w_{13})^T \in \mathbf{C}^{13}$,

$$\text{(3.1)} \qquad \mathrm{Re} < R(\omega)V(\omega)w,w > \ \geq c_1|w_{I}|^2 - C_1|w_{II}|^2 ,$$

where $R(\omega) = \sum R^j\omega_j$ *for* $\omega = (\omega_1,\omega_2,\omega_3)$, $V(\omega)$ *is the matrix defined by* (2.15) *with* ξ *replaced by* ω, $w_I = (w_1,\cdots,w_5)^T$ $w_{II} = (w_6,\cdots,w_{13})^T$, *and* $<\ ,\ >$ *denotes the standard inner product of* $\mathbf{C}^{13}$.

Proof. We define R^j, $j = 1,2,3$, by

$$\text{(3.2)} \qquad \sum_{j=1}^{3} R^j\xi_j = R(\xi) = \begin{pmatrix} \alpha\tilde{R}_{11}(\xi) & V_{12}(\xi) \\ -V_{21}(\xi) & 0 \end{pmatrix} ,$$

where α is a positive constant which will be determined later, $V_{12}(\xi)$ and $V_{21}(\xi)$ are the matrices in (2.16), and

$$(3.3)\qquad \tilde{R}_{11}(\xi) = \left(\begin{array}{c|ccc|c} 0 & \xi_1 & \xi_2 & \xi_3 & 0 \\ \hline -\xi_1 & & & & 0 \\ -\xi_2 & & 0 & & 0 \\ -\xi_3 & & & & 0 \\ \hline 0 & 0 & 0 & 0 & 0 \end{array}\right).$$

By the definition, each R^j is a 13×13 real skew-symmetric matrix with constant entries. We shall show (3.1). Put $U(\xi) = R(\xi)V(\xi)$ and let $U(\xi) = (U_{pq}(\xi))_{1\le p,q\le 2}$ be the decomposition of the same type as in (2.16). From (2.16) and (3.2) we have

$$U_{11}(\xi) = \alpha\tilde{R}_{11}(\xi)V_{11}(\xi) + V_{12}(\xi)V_{21}(\xi).$$

By a simple calculation, using (2.7) and (3.3), we know that for $\omega \in S^2$ and $w_I = (w_1,\cdots,w_5)^T \in \mathbf{C}^5$,

$$(3.4)\qquad \mathrm{Re} < \tilde{R}_{11}(\omega)V_{11}(\omega)w_I, w_I > \ \ge\ c_2|w_1|^2 - C_2\sum_{k=2}^{5}|w_k|^2 ,$$

where c_2 and C_2 are positive constants. On the other hand, it follows from (2.18) that $\mathrm{rank}\, V_{21}(\omega) = 4$ for any $\omega \in S^2$ and hence

$$(3.5)\qquad < V_{12}(\omega)V_{21}(\omega)w_I, w_I > \ = |V_{21}(\omega)w_I|^2 \ge c_3\sum_{k=2}^{5}|w_k|^2 ,$$

where c_3 is a positive constant. We multiply (3.4) by $\alpha > 0$ and then add the resulting inequality to (3.5). Choosing α such that $\alpha C_2 = c_3/2$, we obtain

$$(3.6)\qquad \mathrm{Re} < U_{11}(\omega)w_I, w_I > \ \ge\ c|w_I|^2$$

with $c = \min\{\alpha c_2, c_3/2\}$. The desired estimate (3.1) is an easy consequence of (3.6). Therefore the proof of Lemma 3.1 is complete.

We denote the components of the matrix $R(\omega)$ in Lemma 3.1 by $r_{k\ell}(\omega)$, $k,\ell = 1,\cdots,13$, and define the operator $S(\omega)$ with a parameter $\omega \in S^2$ by

(3.7) $$S(\omega)f = \sum_{k,\ell=1}^{13} \beta r_{k\ell}(\omega)(f,e_\ell)e_k , \qquad f \in L^2(v) ,$$

where β is a positive constant. We shall show that the above $S(\omega)$ is a compensating function for the Boltzmann equation.

Proposition 3.2. *The operator* $S(\omega)$ *defined by* (3.7) *is a compensating function for the Boltzmann equation, provided that* $\beta > 0$ *is sufficiently small. Moreover, for each* $\omega \in S^2$, $S(\omega)$ *maps* $L^2(v)$ *into the subspace* W *defined by* (2.12).

Proof. Since $\{e_1,\cdots,e_{13}\}$ is an orthonormal basis of W, the last statement of the proposition is obvious from the definition (3.7). We shall check conditions (i), (ii) and (iii) of Definition 3.1. Condition (i) is an easy consequence of $R(\omega) = \sum R^j\omega_j$. Let $f, g \in L^2(v)$. We have from (3.7),

(3.8) $$(S(\omega)f,g) = \sum_{k,\ell=1}^{13} \beta r_{k\ell}(\omega)(f,e_\ell)\overline{(g,e_k)} .$$

Let w and u be the vectors in $\mathbb{C}^{13}$ whose k-th components are (f,e_k) and (g,e_k), respectively. The equality (3.8) then gives $(S(\omega)f,g) = \beta < R(\omega)w,u >$, where $< , >$ is the standard inner product of $\mathbb{C}^{13}$. This relation shows that $iS(\omega)$ is a selfadjoint operator on $L^2(v)$, since $R(\omega)$ is real skew-symmetric. Thus condition (ii) is verified. Finally, we check condition (iii). Let $f \in L^2_1(v)$. From (3.8) we have

(3.9) $$(S(\omega)(v\cdot\omega)f,f) = \sum_{k,\ell=1}^{13} \beta r_{k\ell}(\omega)((v\cdot\omega)f,e_\ell)\overline{(f,e_k)} .$$

We denote the orthogonal projection from $L^2(v)$ onto W by P, namely,

$$Pf = \sum_{k=1}^{13} (f,e_k)e_k .$$

We substitute the decomposition $f = Pf + (I-P)f$ into the right hand side of (3.9) to obtain

$$(3.10) \qquad (S(\omega)(v\cdot\omega)f,f) = \beta < R(\omega)V(\omega)w,w > + \sum_{k,\ell=1}^{13} \beta r_{k\ell}(\omega)((I-P)f,(v\cdot\omega)e_\ell)\overline{(f,e_k)} ,$$

where $V(\omega)$ is the matrix defined by (2.15), and w is the vector in $\mathbb{C}^{13}$ whose k-th component is (f,e_k). The second term on the right hand side of (3.10) is bounded by $\beta C|(I-P_0)f|_2|f|_2$, where C is a constant independent of β and P_0 is the orthogonal projection from $L^2(v)$ onto $N(L)$. On the other hand, by virtue of Lemma 3.1, the real part of the first term on the right side of (3.10) is bounded from below by $\beta c_1|P_0f|_2^2 - \beta C_1|(I-P_0)f|_2^2$, where c_1 and C_1 are the positive constants in (3.1) and hence do not depend on β. Therefore we obtain

$$(3.11) \qquad \mathrm{Re}\,(S(\omega)(v\cdot\omega)f,f) \geq \beta(c_1-\varepsilon)|P_0f|_2^2 - \beta C_\varepsilon|(I-P_0)f|_2^2$$

for any $\varepsilon > 0$, where C_ε is a constant depending on ε but not on β. We add (2.10) to (3.11) and choose ε and β such that $\varepsilon = c_1/2$ and $\beta C_\varepsilon = \delta_1/2$. Then we get the inequality

$$(3.12) \qquad \mathrm{Re}\,(S(\omega)(v\cdot\omega)f,f) + (Lf,f) \geq \delta_2|f|_2^2$$

with $\delta_2 = \min\{\beta c_1/2, \delta_1/2\}$. Thus condition (iii) has been checked. This completes the proof of Proposition 3.2.

4. Decay estimate for the linearized equation

We consider the initial value problem for the linearized Boltzmann equation:

(4.1) $f_t + v\cdot\nabla_x f + Lf = g$,

(4.2) $f(0,x,v) = f_0(x,v)$,

where g is a given function of $(t,x,v) \in [0,\infty) \times \mathbb{R}^3 \times \mathbb{R}^3$. Our aim is to show a decay estimate of solutions of (4.1),(4.2) by an energy method similar to the one employed in [4] (see also [8]) for the discrete Boltzmann equation. Our method is based on the existence of a compensating function for the Boltzmann equation.

Let us introduce function spaces. $H^\ell(x)$ denotes the usual Sobolev space on $\mathbb{R}^3_x$ of order ℓ. We denote by $\mathbb{H}^\ell$ the space of $L^2(v)$-functions with values in $H^\ell(x)$, with the norm $\|\cdot\|_\ell$. $\mathbb{H}^\ell_1$ is the space of $L^2_1(v)$-functions with values in $H^\ell(x)$. $L^{p,2}$ denotes the space of $L^2(v)$-functions with values in $L^p(x)$. The norm of $L^{p,2}$ is denoted by $[\![\cdot]\!]_{p,2}$.

Our result is then stated as follows.

Theorem 4.1. *Let* $\ell \geq 0$ *and* $p, q \in [1,2]$. *Suppose that* $f_0 \in \mathbb{H}^\ell \cap L^{p,2}$. *Moreover we assume that* $g \in L^\infty([0,\infty);\mathbb{H}^\ell \cap L^{q,2})$ *and* $(P_0 g)(t,x,v) = 0$ *for* $(t,x,v) \in [0,\infty) \times \mathbb{R}^3 \times \mathbb{R}^3$, *where* P_0 *is the orthogonal projection from* $L^2(v)$ *onto* $N(L)$. *Let* f *be a solution of the problem* (4.1),(4.2) *satisfying* $f \in L^\infty([0,\infty);\mathbb{H}^\ell_1)$ *and* $f_t \in L^\infty([0,\infty);\mathbb{H}^{\ell-1})$. *Then we have*

$$\|f(t)\|_\ell^2 \leq C(1+t)^{-2\gamma}(\|f_0\|_\ell + [\![f_0]\!]_{p,2})^2 + C\int_0^t (1+t-\tau)^{-2\gamma'}(\|g(\tau)\|_\ell + [\![g(\tau)]\!]_{q,2})^2 d\tau \tag{4.3}$$

for $t \in [0,\infty)$, *where* $\gamma = (3/2)(1/p - 1/2)$, $\gamma' = (3/2)(1/q - 1/2)$ *and* C *is a constant.*

The decay estimate (4.3) with $g = 0$ has been obtained in [6],[7] by a method based on the spectral theory for the linearized Boltzmann operator.

In order to prove Theorem 4.1, we consider (4.1),(4.2) in the Fourier transform:

$$(4.4)\qquad \hat{f}_t + i|\xi|(v\cdot\omega)\hat{f} + L\hat{f} = \hat{g}, \qquad \omega = \xi/|\xi| \in S^2,$$

$$(4.5)\qquad \hat{f}(0,\xi,v) = \hat{f}_0(\xi,v),$$

where $\hat{f} = \hat{f}(t,\xi,v)$ denotes the Fourier transform of $f = f(t,x,v)$. Let $S(\omega)$ be the compensating function for the Boltzmann equation constructed in Proposition 3.2 and let μ be a positive constant. Put

$$(4.6)\qquad E[\hat{f}](t,\xi) = |\hat{f}(t,\xi)|_2^2 - \frac{\mu|\xi|}{1+|\xi|^2}(iS(\omega)\hat{f}(t,\xi),\hat{f}(t,\xi)), \quad \omega = \xi/|\xi|.$$

We shall show that for a suitably chosen $\mu > 0$, $E[\hat{f}]$ is a Ljapunov function of (4.4), which is regarded as an ordinary differential equation in $L^2(v)$ with a parameter $\xi \in \mathbb{R}^3$. More precisely we have

<u>Lemma 4.2</u>. *For a suitably chosen* $\mu > 0$, *the function* $E[\hat{f}]$ *defined by* (4.6) *satisfies the following inequalities.*

$$(4.7)\qquad \frac{1}{2}|\hat{f}|_2^2 \le E[\hat{f}] \le 2|\hat{f}|_2^2,$$

$$(4.8)\qquad \frac{\partial}{\partial t}E[\hat{f}] + \delta\rho(\xi)E[\hat{f}] \le C|\hat{g}|_2^2,$$

where δ *and* C *are positive constants, and* $\rho(\xi) = |\xi|^2/(1+|\xi|^2)$.

Theorem 4.1 can be proved by using Lemma 4.2. In fact, applying Gronwall's inequality to (4.8) and using (4.7), we obtain for $(t,\xi) \in [0,\infty)\times\mathbb{R}^3$,

$$(4.9)\qquad |\hat{f}(t,\xi)|_2^2 \le Ce^{-\delta\rho(\xi)t}|\hat{f}_0(\xi)|_2^2 + C\int_0^t e^{-\delta\rho(\xi)(t-\tau)}|\hat{g}(\tau,\xi)|_2^2\,d\tau,$$

where δ is the constant in (4.8) and C is some constant. The desired estimate (4.3) is then obtained from (4.9) by the standard technique and so we omit the arguments. See, for example, [6] or [8].

Proof of Lemma 4.2. We first note that (4.7) holds true for sufficiently small $\mu > 0$, say, $\mu \in (0,\mu_1]$. To show (4.8), we use the argument analogous to that employed in [4],[8]. We take the inner product (of $L^2(v)$) of (4.4) and $\hat{f}$. Its real part is

$$(4.10) \qquad (\tfrac{1}{2}|\hat{f}|_2^2)_t + (L\hat{f},\hat{f}) = \mathrm{Re}\,(\hat{g},\hat{f}) \ .$$

We apply $-i|\xi|S(\omega)$, $\omega = \xi/|\xi|$, to (4.4) and then take the inner product with $\hat{f}$. Since $iS(\omega)$ is a selfadjoint operator, the real part of the resulting equality is

$$(4.11) \qquad \{-\tfrac{1}{2}|\xi|(iS(\omega)\hat{f},\hat{f})\}_t + |\xi|^2\mathrm{Re}\,(S(\omega)(v\cdot\omega)\hat{f},\hat{f})$$
$$= |\xi|\,\mathrm{Re}\,\{(iS(\omega)L\hat{f},\hat{f}) - (iS(\omega)\hat{g},\hat{f})\} \ .$$

We calculate $(4.10)\times(1+|\xi|^2)+(4.11)\times\mu$ with a positive constant μ to obtain

$$(4.12) \qquad \{\tfrac{1}{2}(1+|\xi|^2)E[\hat{f}]\}_t + \{1+(1-\mu)|\xi|^2\}(L\hat{f},\hat{f}) +$$
$$+ \mu|\xi|^2\{\mathrm{Re}\,(S(\omega)(v\cdot\omega)\hat{f},\hat{f}) + (L\hat{f},\hat{f})\}$$
$$= (1+|\xi|^2)\,\mathrm{Re}\,(\hat{g},\hat{f}) + \mu|\xi|\,\mathrm{Re}\,\{(iS(\omega)L\hat{f},\hat{f}) - (iS(\omega)\hat{g},\hat{f})\} \ ,$$

where $E[\hat{f}]$ is the function defined by (4.6). We assume that $\mu \in (0,1]$. Then the second term on the left hand side of (4.12) is bounded from below by $(1-\mu)(1+|\xi|^2)(L\hat{f},\hat{f}) \geq (1-\mu)\delta_1(1+|\xi|^2)|(I-P_0)\hat{f}|_2^2$, where we used (2.10). On the other hand, by virtue of (3.12), the third term on the left side is bounded from below by $\mu\delta_2|\xi|^2|\hat{f}|_2^2$. Therefore we have the following lower bound for the left side of (4.12).

(4.13) $\{\frac{1}{2}(1+|\xi|^2)E[\hat{f}]\}_t + (1-\mu)\delta_1(1+|\xi|^2)|(I-P_0)\hat{f}|_2^2 + \mu\delta_2|\xi|^2|\hat{f}|_2^2$.

Next we estimate the right side of (4.12). Since $P_0\hat{g} = 0$ by the assumption, the first term on the right side of (4.12) is majorized by $(1+|\xi|^2)|(I-P_0)\hat{f}|_2|\hat{g}|_2$. Also, from (3.8), we see that the second term on the right side is estimated by $\mu C|\xi||\hat{f}|_2(|(I-P_0)\hat{f}|_2 + |\hat{g}|_2)$, where C is a constant independent of μ. Therefore, the right side of (4.12) is bounded by

$$(4.14)\qquad (\varepsilon+\mu C_\varepsilon)(1+|\xi|^2)|(I-P_0)\hat{f}|_2^2 + \mu\varepsilon|\xi|^2|\hat{f}|_2^2 + C_\varepsilon(1+|\xi|^2)|\hat{g}|_2^2$$

for any $\varepsilon > 0$, where C_ε is a constant depending on ε but not on $\mu \in (0,1]$. We choose ε and μ_2 such that $\varepsilon = \min\{\delta_1/6, \delta_2/2\}$ and $\mu_2 = \min\{1/6, \delta_1/6C_\varepsilon\}$. Then we have for $\mu \in (0,\mu_2]$,

$$(4.15)\qquad \frac{\partial}{\partial t}E[\hat{f}] + \delta_1|(I-P_0)\hat{f}|_2^2 + \mu\delta_2\rho(\xi)|\hat{f}|_2^2 \le C|\hat{g}|_2^2 ,$$

where C is a constant. Now we put $\mu = \min\{\mu_1, \mu_2\}$. For this choice of μ, the inequality (4.15) combined with (4.7) gives (4.8) with $\delta = \mu\delta_2/2$. This completes the proof of Lemma 4.2.

5. Global solutions of the nonlinear equation

With the aid of the decay estimate (4.3) we can show the existence of global solutions to the problem (2.3),(2.4) in the same way as in [6],[7]. Of course the result obtained is the same as that in [6],[7].

<u>Theorem 5.1</u>. *Let* $\ell > 3/2$, $\beta > 5/2$ *and* $p \in [1,2]$. *We assume that* $f_0 \in \dot{\mathbb{B}}_\beta^\ell \cap L^{p,2}$. *If* $\|f_0\|_{\ell,\beta} + [\![f_0]\!]_{p,2}$ *is suitably small, then the problem* (2.3),(2.4) *has a unique global solution* f *in* $C^0([0,\infty);\dot{\mathbb{B}}_\beta^\ell) \cap C^1([0,\infty);\dot{\mathbb{B}}_{\beta-1}^{\ell-1})$. *Moreover, the solution satisfies*

(5.1) $\|f(t)\|_{\ell,\beta} \leq C(1+t)^{-\gamma}(\|f_0\|_{\ell,\beta} + [\![f_0]\!]_{p,2})$

for $t \in [0,\infty)$, *where* $\gamma = (3/2)(1/p - 1/2)$ *and* C *is a constant.*

Here we have employed the following notations: $\dot{\mathbb{B}}^{\ell}_{\beta}$ is the space of $\dot{L}^{\infty}_{\beta}(v)$-functions with values in $H^{\ell}(x)$, where $\dot{L}^{\infty}_{\beta}(v)$ denotes the space of functions $f = f(v)$ such that $(1+|v|)^{\beta}f \in L^{\infty}(v)$ and $(1+|v|)^{\beta}f(v) \to 0$ uniformly as $|v| \to \infty$. The norm of $\dot{\mathbb{B}}^{\ell}_{\beta}$ is denoted by $\|\cdot\|_{\ell,\beta}$.

References

[1] R.S. Ellis and M.A. Pinsky, The first and second fluid approximations to the linearized Boltzmann equation, J. Math. pures et appl., 54 (1975), 125-156.

[2] H. Grad, Asymptotic theory of the Boltzmann equation, II, Rarefied Gas Dynamics, 1 (J.A. Laurmann, ed.), 26-59, Academic Press, New York, 1963.

[3] H. Grad, Asymptotic equivalence of the Navier-Stokes and nonlinear Boltzmann equations, Proc. Symp. Appl. Math., 17 (R. Finn, ed.), 154-183, Amer. Math. Soc., Providence, 1965.

[4] S. Kawashima, Global existence and stability of solutions for discrete velocity models of the Boltzmann equation, Lecture Notes in Numerical and Applied Analysis, 6, 59-85, Kinokuniya, 1983.

[5] S. Kawashima, The Boltzmann equation and 13 moments, to appear in Japan J. Appl. Math.

[6] T. Nishida and K. Imai, Global solutions to the initial value problem for the nonlinear Boltzmann equation, Publ. RIMS, Kyoto Univ., 12 (1976), 229-239.

[7] S. Ukai, Les solutions globales de l'équation de Boltzmann dans l'espace tout entier et dans le demi-espace, C.R. Acad. Sci., Paris, 282 A (1976), 317-320.

[8] T. Umeda, S. Kawashima and Y. Shizuta, On the decay of solutions to

the linearized equations of electro-magneto-fluid dynamics, Japan J. Appl. Math., 1 (1984), 435-457.

Recent Topics in Nonlinear PDE III, Tokyo, 1986
Lecture Notes in Num. Appl. Anal., 9, 173–183 (1987)

On Compactly Supported Solutions of the Compressible Euler Equation

Tetu MAKINO*, Seiji UKAI** and Shuichi KAWASHIMA***
Department of Liberal Arts, Osaka Industrial University
Osaka 574, Japan
**Department of Applied Physics, Osaka City University
Osaka 558, Japan
***Department of Mathematics, Nara Women's University
Nara 630, Japan

§0. Introduction

This is a brief representation of our recent work [6] on the classical solutions of the compressible Euler equation:

$$(1\text{-}0)\qquad \frac{\partial\rho}{\partial t} + \sum_{j=1}^{3} v_j\frac{\partial\rho}{\partial x_j} + \rho\sum_{j=1}^{3}\frac{\partial v_j}{\partial x_j} = 0,$$

$$(1\text{-}i)\qquad \rho\Big(\frac{\partial v_i}{\partial t} + \sum_{j=1}^{3} v_j\frac{\partial v_i}{\partial x_j}\Big) + \frac{\partial p}{\partial x_i} = 0 \quad (i=1,2,3),$$

$$(1\text{-}4)\qquad \frac{\partial s}{\partial t} + \sum_{j=1}^{3} v_j\frac{\partial s}{\partial x_j} = 0,$$

$$(2)\qquad p = \rho^{\gamma} e^{s},$$

$$(3)\qquad \rho|_{t=0} = \rho^0(x) \geqq 0,\quad v_i|_{t=0} = v_i^{\,0}(x)\quad (i=1,2,3),\quad s|_{t=0} = s^0(x),$$

where γ is a positive constant such that $\gamma > 1$. The unknowns are $\rho = \rho(t, x)$, $v = {}^t(v_1, v_2, v_3) = v(t, x)$ and $s = s(t, x)$ of $t \geqq 0$

and $x \varepsilon R^3$.

First we will establish the existence of a local solution of (1)(2)(3) for the case where $\inf \rho^0 = 0$. For the case $\inf \rho^0 > 0$ the existence has been well established by Lax [3], Kato [1], Majda [4] and Klainerman and Majda [2] by applying the theory of quasi-linear symmetric hyperbolic systems. However their symmetrization does not work if $\inf \rho^0 = 0$. In §1 we shall propose another symmetrization which works well for solutions with compact support and for those vanishing at infinity.

Secondly we will discuss the existence of global classical solutions. Recently Sideris [8] gave a sufficient condition on the initial data for the non-existence of global C^1-solution for the case $\inf \rho^0 > 0$. We will find a similar condition for compactly supported ρ^0. This study, as in [7], requires the estimate of the evolution of the support. In our case the support of (ρ, v) of the solution does not change as long as the solution is regular. The proof will be given in §2.

Using this we shall give in §3 a verification of a conjecture of T. Nishida: Any nontrivial compactly supported C^1-soluiton cannot be global!

§1 Existence of classical solutions

We will show that even if $\inf \rho^0 = 0$, the Cauchy problem (1)(2)(3) has a local classical solution. To do this we wish to apply Theorem II of [1] to an associated evolution equation, just as was done in [4] for the case $\inf \rho^0 > 0$. Then we have to transform the equation (1)(2) to a symmetric hyperbolic system.

The symmetrization employed in [4] is

(4) $$B_0(V)\frac{\partial V}{\partial t} + \sum B_j(V)\frac{\partial V}{\partial x_j} = 0,$$

where $V = {}^t(p, v_1, v_2, v_3, s)$,

$$B_0 = \begin{pmatrix} \frac{1}{\gamma p} & 0 & 0 \\ 0 & \rho I & 0 \\ 0 & 0 & 1 \end{pmatrix}, \quad B_j = \begin{pmatrix} \frac{1}{\gamma p} v_j & {}^t e_j & 0 \\ e_j & \rho v_j I & 0 \\ 0 & 0 & v_j \end{pmatrix},$$

I being the unit matrix, e_j the unit vector. However the coefficients become singular if p or ρ vanishes. To avoid this difficulty we must find another symmetrization.

Here we introduce, as in [5], the new variable

(5) $$w = p^{\frac{\gamma-1}{2\gamma}} = \rho^{\frac{\gamma-1}{2}} e^{\frac{\gamma-1}{2\gamma}s}.$$

Then the problem (1)(2)(3) is reduced to the problem

(6) $$A_0(U)\frac{\partial U}{\partial t} + \sum A_j(U)\frac{\partial U}{\partial x_j} = 0,$$

(7) $$U\big|_{t=0} = U^0,$$

where $U = {}^t(w, v_1, v_2, v_3, s)$,

$$A_0 = \begin{pmatrix} 1 & 0 & 0 \\ 0 & \frac{(\gamma-1)^2}{4\gamma} e^{-s/\gamma} I & 0 \\ 0 & 0 & 1 \end{pmatrix}, \quad A_j = \begin{pmatrix} v_j & \frac{\gamma-1}{2} w\, {}^t e_j & 0 \\ \frac{\gamma-1}{2} w e_j & \frac{(\gamma-1)^2}{4\gamma} e^{-s/\gamma} v_j I & 0 \\ 0 & 0 & v_j \end{pmatrix}$$

(j=1,2,3). We see that the matrices $A_j(U)$, j=0,1,2,3, are all symmetric and of C^∞ in U and that $A_0(U)$ is positive definite uniformly whenever s is bounded from below. Therefore we can apply Theorem II of [1] to the problem (6)(7) without restriction on inf w^0. Thus we have the following

Lemma 1. *Given* $U^0 = (w^0, v^0, s^0) \in H^3$, *there exist a positive number* T *and a unique solution of the problem (6)(7) such that*

$$U \in C([0, T]; H^3) \cap C^1([0, T]; H^2).$$

MOreover, if $w^0(x) \geqq 0$ *everywhere, then* $w(t, x) \geqq 0$ *for all* t *and* x.

Here $H^\ell = H^\ell(R^3)$, ℓ=2,3, denotes the usual Sobolev space.

Proof of Lemma 1. The existence and the uniqueness of the solution are an immediate consequence of Theorem II of [1]. We are going to show that $w \geqq 0$ under the hypothesis that $w^0 \geqq 0$.

Let (τ, ξ) be an arbitrary point in $[0, T] \times R^3$. Consider the problem

$$\frac{dx}{dt} = v(t, x), \quad x\Big|_{t=\tau} = \xi.$$

Since $v \in C([0, T]; H^3)$ is bouded and continuously differentiable in x, we have a unique solution $x = \psi(t) \in C^1([0, T]; R^3)$ by the Cauchy-Lipschitz theorem of the theory of ordinary differential equations. From the equation (6) it follows that

$$\frac{d}{dt}w(t, \psi(t)) = -\frac{\gamma-1}{2}\left(\sum\frac{\partial v_j}{\partial x_j}\right)w.$$

Integrating this from $t=0$ to $t=\tau$ yields

$$w(\tau, \xi) = w^0(\psi(0))\exp\left[-\frac{\gamma-1}{2}\int_0^\tau \left(\sum \frac{\partial v_j}{\partial x_j}\right)(t,\psi(t))dt\right]$$

from which $w(\tau, \xi) \geqq 0$ if $w^0 \geqq 0$. This completes the proof of Lemma 1.

Let us return to the problem (1)(2)(3).

Theorem 1. *Suppose that* $1 < \gamma \leqq 3$, $\rho^0 \in C^1(R^3)$, $\rho^0 \geqq 0$ *and*

$$U^0 = ((\rho^0)^{\frac{\gamma-1}{2}} e^{\frac{\gamma-1}{2\gamma}s^0}, \; v^0, \; s^0) \in H^3.$$

Then there exist a positive number T *and a unique solution* (ρ, v, s) $C^1([0, T] \times R^3)$ *such that the function*

$$U = (\rho^{\frac{\gamma-1}{2}} e^{\frac{\gamma-1}{2\gamma}s}, \; v, \; s)$$

belongs to $C([0,T]; H^3) \cap C^1([0,T]; H^2)$ *and satisfies* (6).

Proof. Applying Lemma 1, we have a unique solution $U = (w, v, s)$ of (6)(7) such that $U \in C([0,T]; H^3) \cap C^1([0,T]; H^2)$ and $w \geqq 0$. Put

$$\rho(t, x) = w(t, x)^{\frac{2}{\gamma-1}} e^{-\frac{1}{\gamma}s(t, x)}.$$

Note that, since $2/(\gamma-1) \geqq 1$ for $1 < \gamma \leqq 3$, the function $w \to (\operatorname{sign} w)|w|^{2/(\gamma-1)}$ is continuously differentiable. Since $w, s \in C([0,T]; H^3) \cap C^1([0,T]; H^2) \subset C^1([0,T] \times R^3)$ by the Sobolev imbedding theorem, we see that $\rho(t, x) \in C^1([0,T] \times R^3)$ as the composed function. It is easy to verify that the function (ρ, v, s) solves the problem (1)(2)(3). This completes the proof of Theorem 1.

§2. Support of regular solutions

In this section we shall prove that the support of a regular solution does not change.

First we define the regular solution.

Definition. *A function* (ρ, v, s) *is called regular solution of* (1)(2) *if the following conditions are satisfied:*

i) $(\rho, v, s) \in C^1([0,T) \times R^3)$, $\rho \geq 0$ *and* (ρ, v, s) *satisfies* (1)(2) *on* $0 \leq t < T$ *and* $x \in R^3$*;*

ii) $\rho^{(\gamma-1)/2} \in C^1([0,T) \times R^3)$ *and the equations*

$$\frac{\partial v_i}{\partial t} + \sum v_j \frac{\partial v_i}{\partial x_j} = 0 \qquad (i=1,2,3)$$

are satisfied on the exterior of the support of ρ*. A regular solution is said to be global if* $T = +\infty$.

It is clear that if (ρ, v, s) is a regular solution,

$$U = (\rho(t, x)^{\frac{\gamma-1}{2}} e^{\frac{\gamma-1}{2\gamma}s(t, x)}, v(t, x), s(t, x))$$

is of class $C^1([0,T) \times R^3)$ and satisfies (6). The solution whose existence was established in Theorem 1 is a regular solution.

Theorem 2. *If* $(\rho(t), v(t), s(t))$ *is a regular solution on* $[0, T)$*, then*

$$supp\ (\rho(t), v(t)) = supp\ (\rho(0), v(0))$$

for all $t < T$.

Proof. We noted that $U(t) = (w(t), v(t), s(t))$ is a C^1-solution of the system (6). This implies

$$\frac{\partial u}{\partial t} + \sum a_j(u, s)\frac{\partial u}{\partial x_j} = 0 ,$$

where $u = {}^t(w, v_1, v_2, v_3)$ and

$$a_j(u, s) = \begin{pmatrix} v_j & \frac{\gamma-1}{2} w\,{}^te_j \\ \frac{2}{\gamma-1}e^{s/\gamma}we_j & v_jI \end{pmatrix} .$$

Let (τ, ξ) be an arbitrary point on $[0, T) \times R^3$. We see that there exists a constant C such that

$$|a_j(u, s(t, x))| \leqq C|u|$$

along the segment L: $0 \leqq t \leqq T$, $x = \xi$. For $s(t, x)$ is bounded on L. On the other hand

$$C' = \sup_{(t,x)\in L, j=1,2,3} \left|\frac{\partial u}{\partial x_j}(t, x)\right|$$

is clearly finite. Then we have

$$\left|\frac{\partial u}{\partial t}\right| \leq 3CC' |u|$$

along L. Therefore $u(\tau, \xi) = 0$ if and only if $u(0, \xi) = 0$. This completes the proof of Theorem 2.

§3. Non-existence of global solutions

First we rewrite the equations (1-0),-1),-2),-3) in the form of conservation laws:

$$(1\text{-}0)' \qquad \frac{\partial \rho}{\partial t} + \sum_j \frac{\partial}{\partial x_j}(\rho v_j) = 0,$$

$$(1\text{-}i)' \qquad \frac{\partial}{\partial t}(\rho v_i) + \sum_j \frac{\partial}{\partial x_j}(\rho v_i v_j) + \frac{\partial p}{\partial x_i} = 0 \quad (i=1,2,3).$$

Moreover it follows from (1) with (2) that

$$(1\text{-}4)' \qquad \frac{\partial}{\partial t}\left(\frac{1}{2}\rho|v|^2 + \frac{1}{\gamma-1}p\right) + \sum_j \frac{\partial}{\partial x_j}\left(\frac{1}{2}\rho|v|^2 + \frac{\gamma}{\gamma-1}p\right)v_j = 0.$$

Using these equations, we shall prove the following

Theorem 3. *If $(\rho(t), v(t), s(t))$ is a regular solution on $[0, T)$ such that $(\rho(0), v(0))$ is compactly supported and if $\rho(0)$ is not identically zero, then the solution cannot be global, that is $T < +\infty$.*

Proof. Put

$$H(t) = \frac{1}{2} \int \rho(t, x) |x|^2 dx.$$

Using (1-0)' and integrating by parts, we have

$$H'(t) = \frac{1}{2} \int \frac{\partial \rho}{\partial t} |x|^2 dx = -\frac{1}{2} \int \sum_j \frac{\partial}{\partial x_j}(\rho v_j) |x|^2 dx$$

$$= \int \sum \rho v_j x_j dx.$$

Moreover, using (1-1)',-2)',-3)', we have

$$H''(t) = \int \sum \frac{\partial}{\partial t}(\rho v_j) x_j dx = - \int \sum (\sum_k \frac{\partial}{\partial x_k}(\rho v_j v_k) + \frac{\partial p}{\partial x_j}) x_j dx$$

$$= \int (\rho |v|^2 + 3p) dx.$$

But it follows from (1-4)' that the quantity

$$E = \int (\frac{1}{2} \rho |v|^2 + \frac{1}{\gamma - 1} p) dx$$

is independent of t. It is a positive constant since $\rho(0) \not\equiv 0$. Therefore

$$H''(t) \geqq \alpha E,$$

where $\alpha = \min(2, 3/(\gamma-1)) > 0$, from which

$$H(t) \geqq H(0) + H'(0)t + \frac{\alpha E}{2} t^2.$$

On the other hand it follows from (1-0)' that

$$M = \int\rho(t, x)dx$$

is a constant. Thanks to Theorem 2, there is a finite number R such that the support of $\rho(t)$ is contained in the ball $\{ x \mid |x| \leq R \}$. Then

$$H(t) = \frac{1}{2}\int \rho|x|^2dx \leq \frac{1}{2} R^2M.$$

Consequently we have the estimate

$$t \leq -\frac{H'(0)}{\alpha E} + \sqrt{\frac{R^2M-2H(0)}{\alpha E} + \frac{H'(0)^2}{\alpha^2E^2}} .$$

This completes the proof of Theorem 3.

§4. Remarks

First, if a solution does not admit any regular continuation across $t=T$, one may ask: What happens at $t = T$? Since the proof of Theorem 3 is carried out by reduction ad absurdum, it does not answer this question. Probably a shock appear on the boundary of the support. However the verification is a subject of the future study.

It is desireble to remove the condition ii) of the definition of the regular solution, since it is a technical condition in order to symmetrize the equation (1)(2). For the necessity of this improvement we refer to §6 of [5].

References

[1] T. Kato, The Cauchy problem for quasi-linear symmetric hyperbolic systems, Arch. Rational Mech. Anal., 58(1975), 181-205.

[2] S. Klainerman and A. Majda, Compressible and incompressible fluids, Comm. Pure Appl. Math., 35(1982), 629-651.

[3] P. D. Lax, Hyperbolic systems of conservation laws and the mathematical theory of shock waves, SIAM Conf. Lecture No.11, Phi§adelphia, 1973.

[4] A. Majda, Compressible fluid flow and systems of conservation laws in several space variables, Appl. Math. Sci. 53, Springer-Verlag, 1984.

[5] T. Makino, On a local existence theorem for the evolution equations of gaseous stars, to appear in "Pattern and Wave", North-Holland, 1986.

[6] T. Makino, S. Ukai et S. Kawashima, Sur la solution à support compact de l'équation d'Euler compressible, to appear in Japan J. Appl. Math.

[7] T. Sideris, Formation of singularities in solutions to nonlinear hyperbolic equations, Arch. Rational Mech.Anal., 86(1984), 369-381.

[8] T. Sideris, Formation of singularities in three-dimensional compressible fluids, Comm. Math. Phys., 101(1985), 475-485.

Recent Topics in Nonlinear PDE III, Tokyo, 1986
Lecture Notes in Num. Appl. Anal., 9, 185–218 (1987)

On a Nonlinear Eigenvalue Problem

Ken'ichi NAGASAKI

Department of Mathematics, Faculty of Engineering

Chiba Institute of Technology

and

Takashi SUZUKI

Department of Mathematics, Faculty of Science

University of Tokyo

§1. Introduction.

In this paper we are concerned with the nonlinear boundary value problem (P):

(1.1) $$\Delta u + \lambda e^{u(x)} = 0 \qquad \text{for} \quad x \in \Omega ,$$

(1.2) $$u(x) = 0 \qquad \text{for} \quad x \in \partial\Omega .$$

Here Ω is a simply connected and bounded domain in $\mathbb{R}^2$ with smooth boundary $\partial\Omega$, $x = (x_1, x_2)$ and $\Delta = \frac{\partial^2}{\partial x_1^2} + \frac{\partial^2}{\partial x_2^2}$. We deal with classical solutions (u, λ) of (P) only for non-negative λ, so that u is nonnegative in Ω by the maximum principle.

Nonlinear problems of this type arise in the theory of thermal self-ignition of a chemically active mixture, in the theory of nonlinear heat generation, in the study of abstract surface with constant Gaussian curvature.

To begin with, we review briefly the results which have been known till now.

Generally speaking, when Ω is a disk, radially symmetric solutions of partial differential equations are reduced to those of ordinary ones, and in this way Gel'fand [7] studied radially symmetric solutions for (1.1) with (1.2) on $\Omega = \{|x| < R\}$. However, in our case, any nontrivial solution u is positive so that is radially symmetric from Gidas-Ni-Nirenberg [8]. Gel'fand [7] has proved consequently that there exists a positive λ^* such that (P) has no solution if $\lambda > \lambda^*$, a unique solution if $\lambda = \lambda^*$ and exactly two solutions if $0 < \lambda < \lambda^*$. In fact, for $\Omega = \{x \mid |x| < R\}$, the solutions of (P) are given as

$$u(x) = 2 \log \frac{c}{1+\frac{\lambda}{8}c_\pm^2|x|^2} \qquad c_\pm = \frac{4\pm\sqrt{16-8\lambda R^2}}{\lambda R^2}$$

for $\lambda \in (0, \lambda^*)$, where λ^* is equal to $\frac{2}{R^2}$. (On the other hand, Joseph and Lundgren [9] showed curious phenomena about the number of solutions for the same problem (P) with a spherical domain Ω in R^n where $2 < n < 10$).

The nonlinearity $e(u) = e^u : \overline{R}^+ \longrightarrow R^+$ is monotone increasing and convex, where the monotone iteration method works well. Keller and Cohen [11] showed that the spectrum of P, that is the set of nonnegative λ's for which (P) has solutions, is a closed interval $[0, \lambda^*]$. Here, $\lambda = \lambda^*(\Omega) > 0$ is determined by Ω. For every λ in the spectrum, there exists the minimal solution $\underline{u} = \underline{u}_\lambda$, namely the solution satisfying $\underline{u}_\lambda \leq w$ in Ω for any solution w

of (P) for the same λ. Fujita [6] and Laetsch [12] proved the nonexistence of the ordered triple of solutions of (P) for fixed λ.

Nonlinear functional analytic approach to (P) is also feasible (Keener-Keller [10], Crandall-Rabinowitz [4]). First, the implicit function theorem indicates that the minimal solutions $(\underline{u}_\lambda, \lambda)$ form a branch $\underline{\mathcal{S}}$ which originates from (0, 0) and continues up to $\lambda = \lambda^*$ and that $\underline{\mathcal{S}}$ bends back at $(\lambda^*, u_{\lambda^*})$. Secondly, the mountain-pass lemma, a modified version of the Ljusternik-Schnirelman theory, shows the existence of a second solution for every λ in $(0, \lambda^*)$ ([4]). On the other hand, by the theory of Rabinowitz [16], the component $\mathcal{S}$ of the solutions of (P) containing $\underline{\mathcal{S}}$ is unbounded in $C(\bar{\Omega}) \times [0, \infty)$. Nevertheless nothing is known as to whether this component contains the second solution in [4] and whether $\mathcal{S}$ has a branch which goes to infinity as $\lambda \downarrow 0$.

A more detailed and delicate approach is possible with the Liouville integral. Note that the change of variables such as $z = x_1 + ix_2$, $\bar{z} = x_1 - ix_2$ reduces the equation (1.1) into

$$(1.3) \qquad 4 \frac{\partial^2 u}{\partial z \partial \bar{z}} + \lambda e^u = 0 ,$$

where $\frac{\partial}{\partial z} = \frac{1}{2}(\frac{\partial}{\partial x_1} - i\frac{\partial}{\partial x_2})$ and $\frac{\partial}{\partial \bar{z}} = \frac{1}{2}(\frac{\partial}{\partial x_1} + i\frac{\partial}{\partial x_2})$. Owing to Liouville [13], every real solution of (1.3) is expressed in the form

$$(1.4) \qquad u = \log \frac{|f'|^2}{(1+\frac{\lambda}{8}|f|^2)^2} ,$$

where $f(z)$ is meromorphic with at most simple zeros and simple poles in Ω. With this expression, Schwarz' symmetrization and isoperimetric inequalities, Bandle [1-2] derived the lower and upper estimates of $\lambda^* = \lambda^*(\Omega)$. She also gave an a priori estimate for a certain class of solutions, which will be precisely refered to later as Lemma 2. Lastly, we look over the results of Weston [18] and Moseley [14]. For a simply connected domain $\Omega \subset \mathbb{R}^2$ satisfying appropriate conditions, they constructed, by the method of singular perturbations, "large solutions" u^* which exist for positive λ near 0 and blow up as $\lambda \downarrow 0$. More exactly,

$$(1.5) \qquad u^*(x) = 4 \log|1-\bar{\delta}g^{-1}(x)|/|g^{-1}(x)-\delta| + o(1)$$

uniformly in $\bar{\Omega}$ as $\lambda \downarrow 0$. Here,

$$(1.6) \qquad g : D = \{z \,|\, |z| < 1\} \longrightarrow \Omega$$

is a Riemann mapping, that is, one-to-one and conformal mapping having a homeomorphic extension $\bar{g}$; $\bar{D} \longrightarrow \bar{\Omega}$. Moreover, $\delta \in D$ solves the equation

$$(1.7) \qquad \bar{\delta} = \frac{1}{2}(1 - |\delta|^2)g''(\delta)/g'(\delta) .$$

Thus $u^*(x)$ brings about one-point blowing-up at $\kappa = g(\delta) \in \Omega$ as $\lambda \downarrow 0$.

The main object of the present paper is to investigate the possibility of the connectedness between the branch of minimal solutions and that of Weston-Moseley's large solutions. We shall show the existence of a solution branch connecting them when Ω is close to a disc.

In this connection, De Figueiredo-Lions-Nussbaum [5] studied the equation

$$(P_1) \qquad \begin{aligned} \Delta u + \lambda f(u) &= 0 \qquad \text{for} \quad x \in \Omega, \\ u &= 0 \qquad \text{for} \quad x \in \partial\Omega, \end{aligned}$$

where $\Omega \subset R^2$ is bounded and the nonlinearity $f ; \bar{R}^+ \longrightarrow R^+$ is monotone increasing, convex and superlinear (that is, $\lim_{t\to+\infty} \frac{f(t)}{t} = +\infty$) and satisfies a growth condition at infinity: $\lim_{t\to+\infty} \frac{f(t)}{t^\sigma} = 0$, where $\sigma > 0$. They showed that the component $\mathcal{S}_1$ of solutions of (P_1) containing $(0, 0)$ is unbounded in $C(\bar{\Omega}) \times [0, \infty)$ but $\{(u, \lambda) \in \mathcal{S}_1 | \lambda \geq \varepsilon\}$ is bounded for each $\varepsilon > 0$. Further they showed that the spectrum of (P_1) is a closed interval $[0, \lambda^*]$ for some $\lambda^* > 0$ and that for every $\lambda \in (0, \lambda^*)$, (P_1) has at least two solutions on $\mathcal{S}_1$. In their proof employing the topological degree argument, essential are a priori estimates in $L^\infty(\Omega)$-sense of solutions. Those estimates are derived from standard arguements by Sobolev's imbedding and the elliptic estimate. However it seems to be difficult to derive such estimates for solutions of (P) with the nonlinearity e^u, and hence to obtain such a component $\mathcal{S}$ for (P) in that way. Further, even if such a component can be proved topologically to exist, its relation with Weston-Moseley's solutions would be obscure.

§2. Heuristics and Statement of Main Result.

In the beginning of this section, we illustrate the construction of Weston-Moseley's large solutions.

Substitution $F(z)$ for $(\frac{\lambda}{8})^{1/2} f(z)$ in (1.4) yields

$$(2.1) \qquad (\frac{\lambda}{8})^{1/2} e^{u/2} = \frac{|F'|}{1+|F|^2}$$

where $F(z)$ satisfies the same conditions in Ω as those of $f(z)$. Besides, boundary condition (1.2) is reduced to the condition

$$(2.2) \qquad \frac{|F'|}{1+|F|^2} = (\frac{\lambda}{8})^{1/2} \quad \text{for} \quad z \in \partial\Omega.$$

At this point, we recall the Riemann mapping $g : D \longrightarrow \Omega$ of (1.6) and transform (2.2) into

$$(2.3) \qquad \frac{|G'|}{1+|G|^2} = (\frac{\lambda}{8})^{1/2} |g'| \quad \text{for} \quad \zeta \in \partial D,$$

with $G = F \circ g$.

First, asymptotic solutions $G = G(\zeta)$ as $\lambda \downarrow 0$ for (2.3) is constructed in the following way (Weston [18]): Putting $G = \lambda^{-1/2} G_0$ in (2.3), we have

$$(2.4) \qquad \frac{|G_0'|}{|G_0|^2} = \frac{1}{\sqrt{8}} |g'| \quad \text{for} \quad \zeta \in \partial D.$$

modulo-$O(\lambda^{1/2})$, which is the first asymptotic equation for (2.3). The n-th order equation will follow from putting $G = \lambda^{-1/2} \sum_{p \geq 0} \lambda^p G_p$ in (2.3) and making modulo-$O(\lambda^{n/2})$ procedure. We have to solve those asymptotic equations in turn.

The first equation (2.4) is reduced to

(2.5) $\sqrt{8}\,\frac{d}{d\zeta}G_0(\zeta)^{-1} = A(\zeta)g'(\zeta)$ for $\zeta \in \overline{D}$

if $A(\zeta)$ satisfies $|A(\zeta)| = 1$ on $\zeta \in \partial D$. To see how $A = A(\zeta)$ should be taken, let us consider for the moment the case when Ω is a unit disc: $\Omega = \{x = (x_1, x_2) \mid |x| < 1\}$. Then we may take $g = \mathrm{id}$. As is described in §1, the solutions for (P) are given as

(2.6) $$u_\pm(x) = 2\log\frac{C_\pm}{1+\frac{\lambda}{8}C_\pm^2|x|^2} \quad \text{with} \quad C_\pm = \frac{4\pm\sqrt{16-8\lambda}}{\lambda}.$$

Therefore, we can set

(2.7) $$f = \left(\frac{8}{\lambda}\right)^{1/2}F_\pm = -C_\pm\zeta$$

in (1.4). Hence

$$G_+(\zeta) = F_+(\zeta) \sim \lambda^{-1/2}G_0(\zeta) \quad \text{with} \quad G_0(\zeta) = -\sqrt{8}\zeta \quad \text{as} \quad \lambda \downarrow 0,$$

so that (2.5) holds for $A(\zeta) = \frac{1}{\zeta^2}$. In view of this, Weston [18] imposed in (2.5) that

(2.8) $$A(\zeta) = \left(\frac{1-\overline{\delta}\zeta}{\zeta-\delta}\right)^2$$

for some $\delta \in D$. The equation (1.7) follows for the first equation (2.5) to be solvable.

Under certain assumptions for Ω (or $g : D \longrightarrow \Omega$), he showed the sovability of the asymptotic equations of higher order, and obtained the function $u_n = u_n(x)$ on Ω such that

(2.9) $$\Delta u_n + \lambda e^{u_n} = 0 \quad (\text{in } \Omega)$$

and

$$(2.10)\qquad u_n = O(\lambda^n) \quad (\text{on } \partial\Omega), \quad \|u_n\|_{L^\infty} = O(\log \tfrac{1}{\lambda}) \quad \text{as} \quad \lambda \downarrow 0$$

for $n = 1,2,\ldots,$ Moseley [14] adopted another expression of the Liouville integral (1.4), that is

$$(2.11)\qquad e^{-u(z)/2} = |v(z)|^2 + \frac{\lambda}{8}|v(z)\int^z \frac{d\hat{z}}{v(\hat{z})^2}|^2 \quad (z=x_1+ix_2 \in \Omega).$$

Here, $v = v(z)$ is holomorphic with at most simple zeros in Ω and $v''(z_0) = 0$ when $v(z_0) = 0$ $(z_0 \in \Omega)$. He showed that then the assumptions for the solvability of asymptotic equations of any order is reduced to a simple condition, that is $\mathrm{Det}(\delta) \neq 0$, where $\delta \in D$ solves (1.7) and

$$(2.12)\qquad \mathrm{Det}(\zeta) = |g'(\zeta)|^2 - \frac{1}{4}|g'''(\zeta)(1-|\zeta|^2)^2 - 6\bar{\zeta}^2 g'(\zeta)|^2.$$

It is known in the complex function theory that (1.7) has at least a solution $\delta \in D$ for any simply connected domain Ω. Further in the case of a convex domain Ω, $\delta \in D$ and hence $\kappa = g(\delta) \in \Omega$ is unique and $\mathrm{Det}(\delta) > 0$.

Now, the genuine large solutions for (P) are constructed by a modified Newton's iteration taking n-th order asymptotic solution as a starting point. If $n \geq 3$ and $\lambda > 0$ is sufficiently small, the iteration scheme converges to produce a genuine solution, except for a "pathological case". We can show that this pathological case does not hold when $\mathrm{Det}(\delta) > 0$ ([15] c.f. [17]). These conditions can be stated more simply if we note that a solution δ D of (1.7) is reduced to $\delta = 0$ by composing $\varphi(\zeta) = \frac{\zeta+\delta}{1+\delta\zeta}$ to $g = g(\zeta)$ from the right-hand side; $g_N = g \circ \varphi : D \longrightarrow \Omega$. Then, (1.7) reads:

$$g_N''(0) = 0 \tag{2.13}$$

and $\mathrm{Det}(\delta) \gtreqless 0$ is equivalent to

$$|g_N'''(0)/g_N'(0)| \lesseqgtr 2. \tag{2.14}$$

Thus, we have arrived at the point to illustrate our idea.

From the complex analytic viewpoint, the equation (2.2) can be interpreted as follows. Let K denote the Riemann sphere with unit diameter, tangent to w-plane at the origin, and let ω be the point on K corresponding to $F(z)$. Further, let the linear elements on Ω and on K at corresponding points by F be denoted by $d\sigma = |dz|$ and $d\tau$, respectively. Then the relation $d = \frac{|F'|}{1+|F|^2}\, d\sigma$ holds. In this situation, the equality (2.2) implies that the length of $F(\partial\Omega)$ on K is equal to

$$\ell \equiv \int_{\partial\Omega} \frac{|F'|}{1+|F|^2}\, d\sigma = \left(\frac{\lambda}{8}\right)^{1/2} |\partial\Omega|. \tag{2.15}$$

Similarly, from (2.1) the area of $F(\Omega)$ on K is given by

$$s \equiv \int_{\Omega} \left(\frac{|F'|}{1+|F|^2}\right)^2 dx = \frac{\lambda}{8} \int_{\Omega} e^u dx, \tag{2.16}$$

which plays a key role in our theory.

When Ω is a unit disc, we can show that all solutions of (P) is parametrized by s, where s varies from 0 to π. In fact, the value s for $u_\pm$:

$$u_\pm(x) = 2 \log \frac{C_\pm}{1+\frac{\lambda}{8}C_\pm^2|x|^2}$$

is equal to

(2.17) $$s = \frac{\pi}{2}\{1 \pm \sqrt{1 - \frac{\lambda}{2}}\}.$$

Inspired by the above example, we conceive to analyze the solution branch of (P) by the parametrization with s in (2.16). To state our result, let $\omega \subset \mathbb{R}^2$ be a simply connected domain with a smooth boundary $\partial\omega$ and let

$$g_1 : D \longrightarrow \omega$$

be a Riemann mapping such that $g_1''(0) = 0$. Then, for sufficiently small $|\varepsilon|$,

$$g_{N,\varepsilon} = g_{N,\varepsilon}(\zeta) = \zeta + \varepsilon g_1(\zeta) : D \longrightarrow \Omega_\varepsilon$$

becomes a Riemann mapping such that $g_{N,\varepsilon}''(0) = 0$, where $\Omega_\varepsilon = g_{N,\varepsilon}(D)$. In fact, the univalentness follows from Dorboux's theorem.[1)] Then, a criterion for the existence of large solutions, $|g_{N,\varepsilon}'''(0)/g_{N,\varepsilon}'(0)| < 2$, holds when $|\varepsilon|$ is sufficiently small. Further,

Theorem 1. The branch of Weston-Moseley's large solutions connects to that of minimal solutions provided that $|\varepsilon|$ is sufficiently small.

§3. Lemmas and Proofs.

In this section, we present five lemmas and afterwards complete the proof of Theorem 1. These lemmas are irrelevant to the simple connectedness of Ω.

The first lemma concerning a priori estimates of solutions in question is due to C. Bandle [3]. However we will give another proof.

Lemma 1. If a solution (u, λ) of (P) satisfies that $0 < s < \pi$, where s is the right-hand side of (2.16), then

$$\|u\|_{L_\infty} \leq -2 \log(1-\frac{s}{\pi}) \tag{3.1}$$

Proof. For $t \geq 0$, $\Gamma(t)$ and $\Omega(t)$ denote the sets $\{x \in \Omega | u(x) = t\}$ and $\{x \in \Omega | u(x) > t\}$ respectively. In this case $\Gamma(t)$ is obviously the boundary of $\Omega(t)$. From the argument in §2, the length $L(t)$ of $F(\Gamma(t))$ and the area $D(t)$ of $F(\Omega(t))$ on the sphere K are defined such as

$$L(t) = \int_{\Gamma(t)} \frac{|F'|}{1+|F|^2} d\sigma = (\frac{\lambda}{8})^{1/2} e^{\frac{t}{2}} \int_{\Gamma(t)} d\sigma ,$$

and

$$D(t) = \int_{\Omega(t)} \frac{|F'|^2}{(1+|F|^2)^2} dx = \frac{\lambda}{8} \int_{\Omega(t)} e^u dx ,$$

where F is the function in (2.1).

From the fact that (u, λ) solves (P),

$$D(t) = \frac{1}{8} \int_{\Omega(t)} - \Delta u dx = \frac{1}{8} \int_{\Gamma(t)} - \frac{\partial u}{\partial n} d\sigma , \tag{3.2}$$

n being the outer normal of $\Omega(t)$.

Owing to the co-area formula [3], we have the relation

$$D'(t) = \frac{\lambda}{8} \frac{d}{dt} \int_{\Omega(t)} e^u dx = - \frac{\lambda}{8} e^t \int_{\Gamma(t)} \frac{1}{-\frac{\partial u}{\partial n}} d\sigma . \tag{3.3}$$

With Schwarz' inequality we get from (3.2) and (3.3) the inequality

$$(3.4)\qquad -D(t)D'(t) \geq \frac{\lambda}{64} e^{t}\left(\int_{\Gamma(t)} d\sigma\right)^2 = \frac{1}{8}\{L(t)\}^2 .$$

The isoperimetric inequality on the sphere K with unit diameter means that

$$(3.5)\qquad L(t)^2 \geq 4D(t)\{\pi - D(t)\} .$$

From (3.4) and (3.5), we find

$$-\frac{D'(t)}{\pi - D(t)} \geq \frac{1}{2}$$

Integration from 0 to $\|u\|_{L_\infty}$ with respect to t yields the desired estimate. Note that $D(0) = s$. □

For $p \in C^0(\overline{\Omega})$, we introduce the eigenvalue problem

$$(3.6)\qquad -\Delta\varphi - p\varphi = \mu\varphi \qquad \text{for} \quad x \in \Omega ,$$

$$(3.7)\qquad \varphi = 0 \qquad \text{for} \quad x \in \partial\Omega .$$

The set $\{\mu_j(p)\}_{j=1}^{\infty}$ $(-\infty < \mu_1(p) < \mu_2(p) \leq \mu_3(p) \leq \cdots \to \infty)$ denotes its eigenvalues. Further, A_p denotes the differential operator $-\Delta - p$ on Ω with the zero Dirichlet condition.

We note that the linearized eigenvalue problem of (P) with respect to u at (u, λ) is reduced to the above problem with $p = \lambda e^u$. It is known about the least eigenvalue $\mu_1(p)$ with $p = \lambda e^u$ that

$$\mu_1(p) > 0 \quad (\text{respectively, } \mu_1(p) = 0)$$

for the minimal solution (u, λ) of (P) with $0 < \lambda < \lambda^*$ $= \lambda^*(\Omega)$, (respectively, $\lambda = \lambda^*$),

$$\mu_1(p) < 0$$

for any non-minimal solution (u, λ). For these facts, we refer to Crandall-Rabinowitz [4].

The following lemma is also due to C. Bandle [1], from which we find that the solution (u, λ) with small s is the minimal one.

<u>Lemma 2</u>. If (u, λ) solves (P) and $s < \frac{\pi}{2}$, then

$$\mu_1(p) > 0$$

with $p = \lambda e^u$.

<u>Proof</u>. This is an immediate consequence of Proposition A. In fact, set $q = e^u$, $K_0 = \frac{\lambda}{2}$ and $M = \lambda \int_\Omega e^u \, dx$, then

$$K_0 M = 4s < 2\pi .$$

This means that the assumption of Proposition A is satisfied. Therefore we know that the least eigenvalue ν_1 of the following problem:

$$-\Delta\psi - \nu e^u \psi = 0 \qquad \text{for} \quad x \in \Omega ,$$

$$\psi = 0 \qquad \text{for} \quad x \in \partial\Omega ,$$

is greater than $2K_0 = \lambda$. Obviously this fact proves the assertion. □

Lemma 3. If (u, λ) solves (1.1) and $s < \pi$, then

$$\mu_2(p) > 0$$

with $p = \lambda e^u$.

Proof. Denote the eigenfunction of (3.6) with (3.7) corresponding to $\mu_2(p)$ by ϕ_2, then it has two nodal domains Ω_1 and Ω_2. Either

$$s_1 \equiv \frac{\lambda}{8}\int_{\Omega_1} e^u dx < \frac{\pi}{2}$$

or

$$s_2 \equiv \frac{\lambda}{8}\int_{\Omega_2} e^u dx < \frac{\pi}{2}$$

holds for $s = s_1 + s_2$, while $\mu_2(p)$ coincides with the least eigenvalue of $-\Delta - p$ on Ω_1 or Ω_2 under the Dirichlet boundary condition. Moreover, the corresponding eigenfunction is $\phi_2|_{\Omega_1}$ or $\phi_2|_{\Omega_2}$. Hence the lemma follows from the previous one. □

The next lemma is useful in parametrizing the solution (u, λ) of P in terms of $s = \frac{\lambda}{8}\int_\Omega e^u dx$ with the aid of implicit function theorem. We introduce the nonlinear function

$$\Phi = \Phi(h, s) : \hat{X} \times \mathbb{R} \longrightarrow \hat{Y}$$

for $h = \binom{u}{\lambda} \in \hat{X} \equiv \begin{matrix} X \\ \times \\ \mathbb{R} \end{matrix}$ as

$$(3.8) \qquad \Phi(h,\ s) = \begin{pmatrix} \Delta u + \lambda e^{u} \\ \int_{\Omega} e^{u}dx - \frac{8s}{\lambda} \end{pmatrix} \in \hat{Y} \equiv \begin{matrix} Y \\ \times \\ \mathbb{R} \end{matrix} .$$

Here $X = C^{2+\alpha}(\overline{\Omega}) \cap C_0(\overline{\Omega})$ and $Y = C^{\alpha}(\overline{\Omega})$ with $0 < \alpha < 1$. Then its zero characterizes the solution (u, λ) of (1.1) such that $s = \frac{\lambda}{8}\int_{\Omega} e^{u}dx$.

Note that its Fréchet derivative $d_h\Phi : \hat{X} \longrightarrow \hat{Y}$ at (h, s) with respect to h is given by the matrix

$$d_h\Phi = \begin{pmatrix} \Delta + \lambda e^{u} & e^{u} \\ \int_{\Omega} e^{u}\cdot dx & \frac{8s}{\lambda 2} \end{pmatrix}.$$

For this operator, we claim the following.

<u>Lemma 4</u>. $d_h\Phi : \hat{X} \longrightarrow \hat{Y}$ is invertible at any zero (h, s) of Φ, whenever $\mu_1(p) \geq 0$.

<u>Proof</u>. Supposing that $d_h\Phi(h, s)[f] = 0$ with $f = \begin{pmatrix} v \\ \rho \end{pmatrix} \in \hat{Y}$ we have

$$(3.9) \qquad \Delta v + pv + \rho e^{u} = 0 \quad (\text{in } \Omega), \qquad v = 0 \quad (\text{on } \partial\Omega)$$

and

$$(3.10) \qquad \int_{\Omega} p\{v + \tfrac{\rho}{\lambda}\}\, dx = 0,$$

where $p = \lambda e^{u}$ $\left(h = \begin{pmatrix} u \\ \lambda \end{pmatrix}\right)$. In the case of $\mu_1(p) > 0$, we have $v = \frac{\rho}{\lambda} A_p^{-1}(p)$, so that

$$\frac{\rho}{\lambda}\int_{\Omega} p\{1 + A_p^{-1}(p)\}dx = 0.$$

Further, $A_p^{-1}(p) > 0$ (in Ω), and hence we get $\rho = 0$ and $v = 0$.

If $\mu_1(p) = 0$, we get from (3.9) that

$$\frac{\rho}{\lambda}\int_\Omega p\varphi_1 dx = 0,$$

where $\varphi_1 > 0$ is the first eigenfunction. Since $p > 0$, we have $\rho = 0$ and hence $v = \text{constant} \times \varphi_1$. Now $v = 0$ follows from (3.10). □

From the above proof, we see that $0 \in \sigma(d_h\Phi)$ is equivalent to $I = 0$ in the case of $0 \notin \sigma(A_p)$, where

$$I = -\int_\Omega p\{1 + A_p^{-1}(p)\}dx. \tag{3.11}$$

Since $\varphi^* = 1 + A_p^{-1}(p)$ satisfies $\Delta\varphi^* + p\varphi^* = 0$ in Ω, we have

$$I = \int_{\partial\Omega} \frac{\partial}{\partial n} A_p^{-1}(p)d\sigma,$$

Here, we note

<u>Lemma 5</u>. In the case of $0 \notin \sigma(A_p)$, we have

$$\frac{\partial s}{\partial\lambda} = -\frac{1}{8\lambda} I, \tag{3.12}$$

where s is the right-hand side of (2.16).

<u>Proof</u>. By virtue of $0 \notin \sigma(A_p)$, the relation $v \equiv \frac{\partial}{\partial\lambda} u = \frac{1}{\lambda} A_p^{-1}(p)$ is obtained by differentiating

$$-\Delta u = \lambda e^u \quad (\text{in } \Omega), \qquad u = 0 \quad (\text{on } \partial\Omega)$$

in λ. Hence we have

$$\frac{\partial s}{\partial \lambda} = \frac{1}{8}\int_\Omega \{e^u + \lambda e^u v\}dx = \frac{1}{8\lambda}\int_\Omega p\{1 + A_p^{-1}(p)\}dx = -\frac{1}{8\lambda} I. \qquad \square$$

We prove Theorem 1 under these preparations;

<u>Outline of Proof of Theorem 1</u>: Recall the Riemann mapping $g_{N,\varepsilon} = g_{N,\varepsilon}(\zeta) = \zeta + \varepsilon g_1(\zeta) : D \longrightarrow \Omega_\varepsilon$ with $g_{N,\varepsilon}''(0) = 0$. From the Weston-Moseley theory, there exist positive constants ε_0 and δ such that the large solutions $u^*_{\lambda,\varepsilon}$ of

$$(3.13) \qquad -\Delta u = \lambda e^u \quad (\text{in } \Omega_\varepsilon) \quad \text{and} \quad u = 0 \quad (\text{on } \partial\Omega_\varepsilon)$$

arise for $0 < \lambda < \delta$ and $|\varepsilon| < \varepsilon_0$. We set $\mathscr{S}^*_\varepsilon = \{(u^*_{\lambda,\varepsilon}, \lambda) \mid 0 < \lambda < \delta\}$.

As is described above, (3.13) is re-formulated as

$$\Phi_\varepsilon(h, s) = 0$$

through the mapping $\Phi_\varepsilon : \hat{X}_\varepsilon \times \mathbb{R} \longrightarrow \hat{Y}_\varepsilon$ defined as

$$\Phi_\varepsilon(h, s) = \begin{pmatrix} \Delta u + \lambda e^u \\ \int_{\Omega_\varepsilon} e^u dx - \frac{8s}{\lambda} \end{pmatrix}$$

for $h = \begin{pmatrix} u \\ \lambda \end{pmatrix}$, where $\hat{X}_\varepsilon = X_\varepsilon \times \mathbb{R}$, $\hat{Y}_\varepsilon = Y_\varepsilon \times \mathbb{R}$, $X_\varepsilon = C^{2+\alpha}(\overline{\Omega}_\varepsilon) \cap C^\alpha_0(\overline{\Omega}_\varepsilon)$ and $Y_\varepsilon = C^\alpha(\overline{\Omega}_\varepsilon)$ with $0 < \alpha < 1$. Putting

$$(3.14) \qquad s^*(\lambda, \varepsilon) = \frac{\lambda}{8}\int_{\Omega_\varepsilon} e^{u^*_{\lambda,\varepsilon}} dx \quad \text{and} \quad h^*_{\lambda,\varepsilon} = \begin{pmatrix} u^*_{\lambda,\varepsilon} \\ \lambda \end{pmatrix},$$

we have $\Phi_\varepsilon(h^*_{\lambda,\varepsilon}, s^*(\lambda, \varepsilon)) = 0$ $(0 < \lambda < \delta, |\varepsilon| < \varepsilon_0)$. In terms of the diffeomorphism $g^{-1}_{N,\varepsilon} : \Omega_\varepsilon \longrightarrow \Omega_0 = D$, the problem (3.13) on Ω_ε is transformed into that on Ω_0. Let it be (P_ε). Then, Φ_ε will be transformed into another mapping from $\hat{X}_0 \times \mathbb{R}$ into $\hat{Y}_0 \times \mathbb{R}$, which is denoted by F_ε. Then, setting $U^*_{\lambda,\varepsilon} = u^*_{\lambda,\varepsilon} \circ g_{N,\varepsilon}$ and $H^*_{\lambda,\varepsilon} = \begin{pmatrix} U^*_{\lambda,\varepsilon} \\ \lambda \end{pmatrix}$, we have

$$F_\varepsilon(H^*_{\lambda,\varepsilon}, s^*(\lambda, \varepsilon)) = 0$$

for $0 < \lambda < \delta$ and $|\varepsilon| < \varepsilon_0$.

<u>Step 1</u>. As for (P_0), every solution $U_\pm = u_{\pm,\lambda}$ is given explicitly as in (2.6) and is parametrized by $s = \frac{\lambda}{8}\int_\Omega e^u dx$ with $0 < s < \pi$. Let it be

$$h_{s,0} = \begin{pmatrix} u_0(s) \\ \lambda_0(s) \end{pmatrix} \qquad (0 < s < \pi).$$

We have $\Phi_0(h_{s,0}, s) = 0$ $(0 < s < \pi)$. Further, $d_h\Phi_0(h_{s,0}, s)$ $(0 < s < \pi)$ is invertible by Lemmas 4 and 5, and the expression (2.17).

The inverse mapping of $\lambda = \lambda_0(s)$ is two-valued. Let it be $s = s_\pm(\lambda)$, where $s_+(\lambda) \longrightarrow \pi$ and $s_-(\lambda) \longrightarrow 0$ as $\lambda \to 0$.

<u>Step 2</u>. For each $\lambda \in (0, \delta)$, $\{U^*_{\lambda,\varepsilon} \mid |\varepsilon| < \varepsilon_0\}$ is bounded in L^∞-sense, so that $U^*_{\lambda,\varepsilon}$ converges to a solution of (P_0) as $\varepsilon \to 0$ from the elliptic estimate. Further, the L^∞-norm of the limit function goes to ∞ as $\lambda \downarrow 0$, and hence it ought to be $u_{+\lambda}$:

$$\| U^*_{\lambda,\varepsilon} - u_{+\lambda} \|_{C^0(\bar{D})} \longrightarrow 0 \quad (\text{as } \varepsilon \to 0).$$

Consequently,

$$s^*(\lambda,\ \varepsilon) = \frac{\lambda}{8} \int_{\Omega_\varepsilon} e^{u^*_{\lambda,\varepsilon}} dx \longrightarrow s_+(\lambda) \quad (= \frac{\lambda}{8} \int_{\Omega_0} e^{u_{+\lambda}} dx)$$

as $\varepsilon \to 0$.

Step 3. On the other hand, a branch $h = \underline{h}_{s,\varepsilon} = \begin{pmatrix} \underline{u}_{s,\varepsilon} \\ \underline{\lambda}_{s,\varepsilon} \end{pmatrix}$ of solutions of $\Phi_\varepsilon(h,\ s) = 0$ exists for $0 < s < \pi$, originating from $(h,\ s) = (0,\ 0)$ by Lemmas 1 and 3. We set $\mathscr{S}_\varepsilon = \{(\underline{u}_{s,\varepsilon},\ \underline{\lambda}_{s,\varepsilon}) \mid 0 < s < \pi\}$. Through the diffeomorphism $g^{-1}_{N,\varepsilon} : \Omega_\varepsilon \longrightarrow \Omega_0$, let $\underline{h}_{s,\varepsilon}$ be transformed into $\underline{H}_{s,\varepsilon} = \begin{pmatrix} \underline{U}_{s,\varepsilon} \\ \underline{\lambda}_{s,\varepsilon} \end{pmatrix}$. Then, we have $F_\varepsilon(\underline{H}_{s,\varepsilon},\ s) = 0 \quad (0 < s < \pi)$.

In the same way as in Step 2, we see that

$$\| \underline{H}_{s,\varepsilon} - h_{s,0} \| \ (= \| \underline{U}_{s,\varepsilon} - u_0(s) \|_{C^0(\overline{D})} + |\underline{\lambda}_{s,\varepsilon} - \lambda_0(s)|) \to 0$$

as $\varepsilon \to 0$ for each $s \in (0,\ \pi)$. Further, the convergence is uniform in s on each compact interval contained in $(0,\ \pi)$.

Step 4. Take an s_0 close to π such that $\lambda_0(s_0) \in (0,\ \delta)$. Then, there exist constants ε_1 and $\rho_1 > 0$ such that $d_H F_\varepsilon(\underline{H}_{s,\varepsilon},\ s)$ is invertible for $|\varepsilon| < \varepsilon_1$ and $|s - s_0| < \rho_1$ from Steps 1 and 3. Consequently, the branch $\{(\underline{H}_{s,\varepsilon},\ s) \mid |s - s_0| \leq \rho_1/2\}$ has a local uniqueness property as a solution set of $F_\varepsilon(H,\ s) = 0$. Namely there exists a $\kappa > 0$ such that $|\varepsilon| \leq \varepsilon_1/2$, $|s_1 - s_0| \leq \rho_1/2$, $F_\varepsilon(H_1,\ s_1) = 0$

and $\|H_1-\underline{H}_{s_0,\varepsilon}\|<\kappa$ imply $(H_1,s_1)\in\{(\underline{H}_{s,\varepsilon},s)\,|\,|s-s_0|\leq\rho_1/2\}$.

On the other hand, Step 2 implies that

$$\|H^*_{\lambda_0(s_0),\varepsilon}-\underline{H}_{s_0,\varepsilon}\|\leq\|H^*_{\lambda_0(s_0),\varepsilon}-h_{s_0,0}\|+\|\underline{H}_{s_0,\varepsilon}-h_{s_0,0}\|$$

$$=\|U^*_{\lambda_0(s_0),\varepsilon}-u_{+\lambda_0(s_0)}\|_{C^0(\overline{D})}+\|\underline{H}_{s_0,\varepsilon}-h_{s_0,0}\|\longrightarrow 0$$

and

$$|s^*(\lambda_0(s_0),\,\varepsilon)-s_0|\longrightarrow 0$$

as $\varepsilon\to 0$. Further we have $F\,(H^*_{\lambda_0(s_0),\varepsilon},\ s^*(\lambda_0(s_0),\,\varepsilon))=0$, so that $(H^*_{\lambda_0(s_0)},\ s^*(\lambda_0(s_0),\,\varepsilon))\in\{(\underline{H}_{s,\varepsilon},\ s)\,|\,|s-s_0|\leq\rho_1/2\}$ (as $\varepsilon\to 0$). Hence $\mathcal{S}^*_\varepsilon$ connects with $\underline{\mathcal{S}}_\varepsilon$, provided that $|\varepsilon|$ is sufficiently small.

§4. Concluding Remarks.

1. If Ω is star-shaped, for instance, with respect to the origin, and if (u,λ) solves (P), then Rellich's identity yields that

$$\frac{1}{B}\,(4s-B)^2\leq B-\lambda A, \tag{4.1}$$

where $s=\frac{\lambda}{8}\int_\Omega e^u dx$, $A=|\Omega|$ and $B=\int_{\partial\Omega}\frac{1}{n\cdot x}\,d\sigma$. (Bandle [1]). We always have $B\geq 2\pi$. In case $B\leq 4\pi$ and $s\geq\pi$, we get

$$\frac{1}{B}\,(4\pi-B)^2\leq\frac{1}{B}\,(4s-B)^2\leq B-\lambda A,$$

and hence $\lambda\leq 8\pi(B-2\pi)/AB$. In other words, $s<\pi$ holds when $B \leq 4\pi$ and $\lambda > \underline{\lambda} \equiv 8\pi(B - 2\pi)/AB$. From Lemmas 1 and 3, we can show that

<u>Theorem 2</u>. Suppose that $B \leq 4\pi$ and $\underline{\lambda} = 8\pi(B - 2\pi)/AB < \lambda^* = \lambda^*(\Omega)$. Then, the problem (P) has exactly two solutions on $(\underline{\lambda}, \lambda^*)$. They form a branch which connects to that of minimal solutions and bends at $\lambda = \lambda^*$.

2. It is convenient to regard the operator

$$d_h \Phi = \begin{bmatrix} \Delta + \lambda e^u & e^u \\ \int_\Omega e^u \cdot dx & \frac{8s}{\lambda 2} \end{bmatrix} \tag{4.2}$$

as that in $\begin{matrix} L^2(\Omega) \\ \times \\ \mathbb{R} \end{matrix}$ under the Dirichlet condition for the first component, rather than as that on $\begin{matrix} X \\ \times \\ \mathbb{R} \end{matrix}$ into $\begin{matrix} Y \\ \times \\ \mathbb{R} \end{matrix}$. Then, with the domain $D(d_h \Phi) = \begin{matrix} H^2(\Omega) \cap V \\ \times \\ \mathbb{R} \end{matrix}$ it becomes self-adjoint and has a positivity-preserving and compact resolvent, V being $H_0^1(\Omega)$. The associated symmetric bilinear form $\mathfrak{a}(\ ,\ )$ is defined on $\begin{matrix} V \\ \times \\ \mathbb{R} \end{matrix}$ through the relation

$$\langle (d_h \Phi)(f), g \rangle_{\begin{matrix} L^2(\Omega) \\ \times \\ R \end{matrix}} = \mathfrak{a}(f,g) \quad \left(f \in D(d_h \Phi) \subset \begin{matrix} V \\ \times \\ \mathbb{R} \end{matrix},\ g \in \begin{matrix} V \\ \times \\ \mathbb{R} \end{matrix}\right). \tag{4.3}$$

Actually for $f = \begin{pmatrix} v \\ \kappa \end{pmatrix} \in \begin{matrix} V \\ \times \\ \mathbb{R} \end{matrix}$ and $g = \begin{pmatrix} w \\ \rho \end{pmatrix} \in \begin{matrix} V \\ \times \\ \mathbb{R} \end{matrix}$,

$$\mathfrak{a}(f,g) = -\int_\Omega \nabla v \cdot \nabla w dx + \int_\Omega p(v + \frac{\kappa}{\lambda})(w + \frac{\rho}{\lambda}) dx \tag{4.4}$$

with $p = \lambda e^{u}$.

We identify $\begin{matrix} V \\ \times \\ \mathbb{R} \end{matrix}$ with $V^{*} = \{v \in H^{1}(\Omega) \mid \frac{\partial}{\partial \tau} v = 0 \text{ on } \partial\Omega\}$, τ being the unit tangent vector on $\partial\Omega$, through the isomorphism

$$f = \begin{bmatrix} v \\ \kappa \end{bmatrix} \in \begin{matrix} V \\ \times \\ \mathbb{R} \end{matrix} \longrightarrow \tilde{f} = v + \frac{\kappa}{\lambda} \in V^{*}.$$

Then, the identity (4.3) reads

$$(4.5) \qquad \mathfrak{A}(f,g) = - a(\tilde{f}, \tilde{g}) \qquad (\text{for } f, g \in \begin{matrix} V \\ \times \\ \mathbb{R} \end{matrix}),$$

where $a(\cdot, \cdot)$ is the symmetric bilinear form on $H^{1}(\Omega)$:

$$a(v, w) = \int_{\Omega} (\nabla v \cdot \nabla w - pvw)dx \qquad (v, w \in H^{1}(\Omega)).$$

Now we can introduce the self-adjoint operator A_{p}^{*} in $L^{2}(\Omega)$ associated with the form $a|_{V^{*} \times V^{*}}$ such as

$$(4.6) \qquad (A_{p}^{*}\tilde{v}, \tilde{w})_{L^{2}(\Omega)} = a(\tilde{v}, \tilde{w}) \qquad (\tilde{v} \in D(A_{p}^{*}) \subset V^{*}, \quad \tilde{w} \in V^{*}).$$

Namely,

$$A_{p}^{*} = - \Delta - p$$

with

$$D(A_{p}^{*}) = \{v \in H^{2}(\Omega) \mid \frac{\partial}{\partial \tau} v = 0 \text{ on } \partial\Omega \text{ and } \int_{\partial\Omega} \frac{\partial}{\partial n} v = 0\}.$$

Because of the relation (4.3), (4.5) and (4.6), the invertibility of $d_{h}\Phi$ in $\begin{matrix} L^{2}(\Omega) \\ \times \\ \mathbb{R} \end{matrix}$ is equivalent to that of A_{p}^{*}

in $L^2(\Omega)$. Henceforth, $\{\mu_j^*(p)\}_{j=1}^{\infty}$ $(-\infty < \mu_1^*(p) < \mu_2^*(p) \leq \mu_3^*(p) \leq \ldots.)$ denotes the set of eigenvalues of A_p^*.

For the constant function $C = \frac{1}{|\Omega|^{1/2}}$, we have $a(c, c) < 0$. On account of the mini-max principle, this means that $\mu_1^*(p) < 0$. Since the codimension of V in V^* is one, we have

$$\mu_2^*(p) \geq \mu_1(p) \qquad \text{and} \qquad \mu_3^*(p) \geq \mu_2(p)$$

also from the mini-max principle. Therefore, $\mu_3^*(p) > 0$ if $s < \pi$ by Lemma 3. Also, by virtue of Lemma 4 we have $\mu_2^*(p) > 0$ if $\mu_1(p) \geq 0$. Further, we have

Lemma 6. For the case of $\mu_1(p) < 0 < \mu_2(p)$, the relation $\mu_2^*(p) \gtreqless 0$ is equivalent to $I = \int_{\partial\Omega} \frac{\partial}{\partial n} A_p^{-1}(p) \, d\sigma \gtreqless 0$.

Outline of Proof: We see that

$$\varphi^* = 1 + A_p^{-1}(p) \in V^*$$

satisfies

$$a(\varphi^*, \varphi_j) = 0 \qquad (j = 1,2,\ldots),$$

where φ_j denotes the j-th eigenfunction of A_p and also that

$$I = a(\varphi^*, \varphi^*) = - \int_{\Omega} p\varphi^* dx.$$

Further, the equivalence between $0 \in \sigma(d_h \Phi)$ and $I = 0$ follows directly. In the case of $I > 0$, the closed subspace

$V_1^* = \langle \varphi^*, \varphi_j | j \geq 2 \rangle \subset V^*$ satisfies $\dim(V^*/V_1^*) = 1$ and

$$\inf_{\substack{v \in V_1^* \\ \|v\|_{L^2}=1}} a(v, v) > 0,$$

so that $\mu_2^* > 0$. In the case of $I < 0$, on the other hand, any closed subspace $V_1^* \subset V^*$ of codimension 1 contains an element $v = \xi_1 \varphi_1 + \xi_2 \varphi^*$ such that $\xi = (\xi_1, \xi_2) \in \mathbb{R}^2 \backslash \{0\}$. For this v, we have $a(v, v) < 0$, so that $\mu_2^* \leq 0$. However, the case $\mu_2^* = 0$ holds only if $I = 0$. Hence we have $\mu_2^* < 0$. □

Appendix. Generalized Schwarz Symmetrization and the estimates of eigenvalues.

The estimate of the eigenvalue $\mu_1(p)$ in (3.6) and (3.7) with $p = \lambda e^u$ was derived by C. Bandle as an application of generalized Schwarz Symmetrization. We review briefly the theory for reader's convenience.

Definition A.1. Let D be a domain in $\mathbb{R}^2$ with Riemannian metric $d\sigma^2 = p(x)ds^2$, where $ds^2 = dx_1^2 + dx_2^2$. For real constants K_0 and $b(> 0)$, the generalized symmetrized domain $D^*_{K_0,b}$ with Riemannian metric

$$d\hat{\sigma}^2 = \frac{b}{(1+\frac{b}{4}K_0|r|^2)^2} ds^2 \equiv \hat{v}(r: K_0, b)ds^2, \quad \text{where } r = |x|,$$

is a disk $\{ x | |x| < R \}$ such that

$$\int_D p(x)dx = \int_{D^*_{K_0,b}} \hat{v}(r: K_0, b)dx.$$

For a closed domain D, we define $D^*_{K_0,b}$ as a closed disk $\{x \mid |x| \leq R\}$.

The area elements of Riemann surfaces $(D, d\sigma)$ and $(D^*_{K_0,b}, d\hat{\sigma})$ are denoted by $d\tau$ and $d\hat{\tau}$ respectively, that is, $d\tau = p(x)dx$ and $d\hat{\tau} = \hat{v}(r;\ K_0,\ b)dx$. We note that Gaussian curvatures of $(D, d\sigma)$ and $(D^*_{K_0,b}, d\hat{\sigma})$ are equal to $k(x) \equiv \dfrac{\Delta \log p(x)}{-2p(x)}$ and K_0 respectively.

Definition A.2. For a function $u : D \longrightarrow \mathbb{R}$, we define a function $u^*_{K_0,b} : D^*_{K_0,b} \longrightarrow \mathbb{R}$ as follows:

$$u^*_{K_0,b}(x) = \sup\{t \mid x \in D(t)^*_{K_0,b}\}, \text{ where } D(t) = \{x \in D \mid u(x) > t\}.$$

The function $u^*_{K_0,b}$, which is radially symmetric, is called a generalized symmetrized function of u.

Henceforth $D^*_{K_0,b}$, $\hat{v}(r;\ K_0, b)$ and $u^*_{K_0,b}$ may be abbreviated to D^*, $\hat{v}(r)$ and u^* for simplicity.

Among the many interesting properties of the generalized symmetrized function, we take up two of them, which will be needed later.

Lemma A.1. Let $g(x)$ and $h(x)$ be continuous in $\overline{D}$, then

$$\int_D g(x)h(x)d\tau \leq \int_{D^*} g^*(x)h^*(x)d\hat{\tau}. \tag{A.1}$$

Proof. Let $h_0 = \min_{\overline{D}} h(x)$, $h_1 = \max_{\overline{D}} h(x)$ and $D(t) = \{x \in D, | h(x) > t\}$, then we have

$$\int_D g(x)h(x)d\tau = h_0 \int_D g(x)d\tau + \int_{h_0}^{h_1} \left(\int_{D(t)} g(x)d\tau \right) dt$$

and

$$\int_{D^*} g^*(x)h^*(x)d\hat{\tau} = h_0 \int_{D^*} g^*(x)d\hat{\tau} + \int_{h_0}^{h_1} \left(\int_{D(t)^*} g^*(x)d\hat{\tau} \right) dt.$$

On account of $\int_D g(x)d\tau = \int_{D^*} g^*(x)d\hat{\tau}$ and

$\int_{D(t)} g(x)d\tau \le \int_{D(t)^*} g^*(x)d\hat{\tau}$,

the inequality (A.1) follows.

<u>Lemma A.2</u>. Let D be a domain in $\mathbb{R}^2$ and $k(x)$ be Gaussian curvature of $(D, d\sigma) = (D, \sqrt{p(x)}\, ds)$. Under the assumption that $k(x) \le K_0$ and $K_0 M < 4$, where K_0 is that in Definition A.1, and $M = \int_D d\tau = \int_D p(x)dx$, the inequality

$$\text{(A.2)} \qquad \int_D |\nabla u|^2 dx \ge \int_{D^*} |\nabla u^*|^2 dx$$

holds for a real analytic function $u(x)$ such that $u(x) \ge 0$ in D and $u(x) = 0$ on ∂D.

Before proving the above lemma, we recall an isoperimetric inequality on a Riemann surface, that is, Bol's inequality:

For any subdomain B of D, let $M_B = \int_B d\tau = \int_B p(x)dx$ and $L_B = \int_{\partial B} d\sigma = \int_{\partial B} \sqrt{p(x)}\, ds$ denote the area of B and the length of ∂B, then

(A.3) $$L_B^2 \geq (4\pi - K_0 M_B)M_B.$$

Proof of Lemma A.2. For $t \geq 0$, we define $D(t)$, $\Gamma(t)$, $a(t)$ and $\ell(t)$ as follows:

$$D(t) = \{x \in D | u(x) > t\},$$

$$\Gamma(t) = \{x \in D | u(x) = t\},$$

$$a(t) = \int_{D(t)} d\tau = \int_{D(t)} p(x)dx,$$

$$\ell(t) = \int_{\Gamma(t)} d\sigma = \int_{\partial D(t)} \sqrt{p(x)}ds.$$

For a real analytic function u, the inverse function of $t(a)$ of $a(t)$ is well-defined because $a(t)$ is strictly decreasing in $(0, u_{max})$. Moreover, $a(t)$ and $t(a)$ are differentiable.

On account of a co-area formula $-\frac{da}{dt} = \int_{\Gamma(t)} \frac{p(x)}{|\nabla u|} ds$ and Schwarz's inequality, we have

$$-\frac{da}{dt} \geq \ell(t)^2 \left(\int_{\Gamma(t)} |\nabla u| ds \right)^{-1}.$$

From an application of Bol's inequality follows

(A.4) $$\int_{\Gamma(t)} |\nabla u| ds \geq \{4\pi - K_0 a(t)\}\, a(t) \left(-\frac{dt}{da} \right).$$

Combining (A.4) with another co-area formula

$$-\frac{d}{dt}\int_{D(t)}|\nabla u|^2 dx = \int_{\Gamma(t)}|\nabla u| ds ,$$

and integrating in $[0, u_{max}]$ with respect to t, we get

$$\text{(A.5)} \qquad \int_D |\nabla u|^2 dx \geq \int_0^M (4\pi - K_0 a) a \left(-\frac{dt}{da}\right)^2 da .$$

In the right-hand side of (A.5), the substitution r for a with the relation $a = \int_{|x|<r} d\hat{\tau} = \frac{\pi b r^2}{1+\frac{b}{4}K_0 r^2}$ yields the equality

$$\text{(A.6)} \qquad \int_0^M (4\pi - K_0 a) a \left(-\frac{dt}{da}\right)^2 da = \int_0^R \left|\frac{du^*}{dr}\right|^2 2\pi r\, dr = \int_{D^*} |\nabla u^*|^2 dx ,$$

where we use the fact that $|\nabla u^*| = -\frac{du^*}{dr} = -\frac{dt}{da} \; \frac{2\pi b r}{(1+\frac{b}{4}K_0 r^2)^2}$ and $M = \int_{D^*} d\hat{\tau} = \frac{\pi b R^2}{1+\frac{b}{4}K_0 R^2}$.

The assertion follows from (A.5) and (A.6).

We derive some estimates of the minimal eigenvalues ν_1, ν_1^* of the following eigenvalue problems:

$$\text{(E.P)} \qquad \begin{cases} \Delta\varphi + p(x)\varphi = 0 & \text{for} \quad x \in D , \\ \varphi = 0 & \text{for} \quad x \in \partial D , \end{cases}$$

$$(E.P)^* \quad \begin{cases} \Delta\psi + \nu\hat{v}(r)\psi = 0 & \text{for} \quad x \in D^* , \\ \psi = 0 & \text{for} \quad x \in \partial D^* . \end{cases}$$

The comparison of ν_1 with ν_1^* is given in the following.

Lemma A.3. If $K_0 M < 4\pi$, where K_0 and M are the same in Lemma A.2, we have

$$\nu_1 \geq \nu_1^* .$$

Proof. We introduce Rayleigh quotients

$$R[\varphi] = \frac{\int_D |\nabla\varphi|^2 dx}{\int_D \varphi^2 d\tau} \qquad \text{for} \quad \varphi \in H_0^1(D)$$

and

$$R^*[\psi] = \frac{\int_{D^*} |\nabla\psi|^2 dx}{\int_{D^*} \psi^2 d\hat{\tau}} \qquad \text{for} \quad \psi \in H_0^1(D^*).$$

According to the variational characterization of the minimal eigenvalue, we have

$$\nu_1 = \inf_{\varphi \in H_0^1(D)} R[\varphi] \quad \text{and} \quad \nu_1^* = \inf_{\psi \in H_0^1(D^*)} R^*[\psi] .$$

On account of the positivity of the eigenfunction corresponding to ν_1 and the denseness in $C_0^1(\bar{D})$ of real analytic functions, the minimizing sequence $\{\varphi_n\}$ of $R[\varphi]$ can be chosen such that every φ_n $(n = 1, 2, \ldots)$ satisfies the assumptions in Lemma A.2. Hence, the application of Lemma A.1

and A.2 to φ_n yields the estimate

$$R[\varphi_n] \geq R[\varphi_n^*] : \tag{A.7}$$

The assertion follows immediately from (A.7).

Next we will calculate the minimal eigenvalue of (E.P) for particular p and D.

Lemma A.4. For a disk $B_\rho = \{x \mid |x| < \rho\}$, we denote by $\nu_1(B_\rho)$ the minimal eigenvalue of the eigenvalue problem:

$$(E.P)_\rho \quad \begin{cases} \Delta\varphi + \nu \dfrac{4C^2}{(1+r^2)^2}\varphi = 0 & \text{for } x \in B_\rho , \\ \varphi = 0 & \text{for } x \in \partial B_\rho , \end{cases}$$

where $r = |x|$ and C is a positive constant.

Then we have

$$\nu_1(B_1) = \frac{2}{C^2} \qquad \text{for } \rho = 1$$

and

$$\nu_1(B_\rho) > \frac{2}{C^2} \qquad \text{for } \rho \in (0, 1).$$

Proof. In polar coordinates $(E.\ P)_\rho$ can be expressed as follows.

$$\frac{1}{r}(r\varphi_r)_r + \frac{1}{r^2}\varphi_{\theta\theta} + \nu\frac{4C^2}{(1+r^2)^2}\varphi = 0 \quad \text{for } r < \rho , \tag{A.8}$$

$$\varphi = 0 \quad \text{for } r = \rho . \tag{A.9}$$

Setting $\varphi(r, \theta) = u(r)\Phi(\theta)$ in (A.8), we get

$$\Phi(\theta) = a_n \sin n\theta + b_n \cos n\theta \quad (n = 0, 1, 2, \ldots).$$

On the other hand, $u(r)$ is a solution of

(A.10) $$\frac{1}{r}(ru_r)_r - \frac{n^2}{r^2} u + \nu \frac{4C^2}{(1+r^2)^2} u = 0 \quad \text{for} \quad r \quad (0, \rho),$$

(A.11) $$u(0) < \infty, \quad u(\rho) = 0 .$$

By the substitution of $z = \frac{r^2-1}{r^2+1}$ and $v(z) = u(r)$, we transform (A.10,11) into the associated Legendre equation:

(A.12) $$\frac{d}{dz}\{(1-z^2)\frac{dv}{dz}\} - \frac{n^2}{1-z^2} v + \nu c^2 v = 0 \quad \text{for} \quad z \in (-1, \frac{\rho^2-1}{\rho^2+1})$$

(A.13) $$v(-1) < \infty, \quad v(\frac{\rho^2-1}{\rho^2+1}) = 0 .$$

In case $\rho = 1$, the equation (A.12) is satisfied with $n = 0$, $\nu = \frac{2}{C^2}$ and $v(z) = - z$. This means that $\frac{2}{C^2}$ is an eigenvalue of $(E.P)_1$ with the corresponding eigenfunction $\varphi(x) = \frac{1-r^2}{1+r^2}$. Moreover $\frac{2}{C^2}$ must be the minimal eigenvalue $\nu_1(B_1)$ because of the positivity of $\varphi(x) = \frac{1-r^2}{1+r^2}$ in B_1.

The latter part of the assertion is a consequence of the monotonity of the minimal eigenvalue of (E.P) with respect to the size of the domain B_ρ, that is, ρ.

Lastly we reach the position to state the main proposition in this Appendix.

<u>Proposition A</u>. If $K_0 > 0$ and $K_0 M < 2\pi$, where K_0 and

M are the same as in Lemma A.2., then

$$\nu_1 > 2K_0,$$

ν_1 being the minimal eigenvalue of (E.P).

Proof. Setting b equal to $4K_0^{-1}$ in $v(r: K_0, b)$, we can reduce the problem $(E.P)^*$ to the problem $(E.P)_R$ in Lemma A.4 with K_0^{-1} instead of C^2. In this situation, $R < 1$ follows from the assumption $K_0 M < 2\pi$.

The application of Lemma A.3 and A.4 provides that

$$\nu_1 \geq \nu_1^* = \nu_1(B_R) > 2K_0 .$$

Note:

1) The complex number $t_\varepsilon(\theta) = g'_{N,\varepsilon}(e^{i\theta})/|g'_{N,\varepsilon}(e^{i\theta})|$ $(e^{i\theta} \in S^1 = \partial D)$ indicates the unit normal vector of $\partial\Omega_\varepsilon$ at the point $g_{N,\varepsilon}(e^{i\theta}) \in \partial\Omega_\varepsilon$. Therefore, the univalentness of $g_{N,\varepsilon}$ on the boundary ∂D follows if the winding number of the mapping

$$t_\varepsilon : e^{i\theta} \in S^1 \longmapsto T_\varepsilon(\theta) \in S^1$$

is $+1$ and

$$\frac{\partial}{\partial\theta} \operatorname{Arg} T_\varepsilon(\theta) > 0 \quad (0 \leq \theta \leq 2\pi).$$

Both hold for $\varepsilon = 0$ and hence when $|\varepsilon|$ is sufficiently small.

References

[1] Bandle, C., Existence theorems, qualitative results and a priori bounds for a class of a nonlinear Dirichlet problems, Arch. Rat. Mech. Anal., 58 (1975) 219-238.

[2] Bandle, C., Isoperimetric inequalities for a nonlinear eigenvalue problem, Proc. Amer. Math. Soc., 56 (1976) 243-246.

[3] Bandle, C., Isoperimetric Inequalities and Applications, Pitman, Boston/London/Melbourne, 1980.

[4] Crandall, M.G., Rabinowitz, P.H., Some continuation and variational methods for positive solutions of nonlinear elliptic eigenvalue problems, Arch. Rat. Mech. Anal., 58 (1975) 207-218.

[5] De Figueiredo, D.G., Lions, P.L., Nussbaum, R.D., A priori estimates and existence of positive solutions of nonlinear elliptic equations, J. Math. Pure Appl., 61 (1982) 41-63.

[6] Fujita, H., On the nonlinear equations $\Delta u+e^u=0$ and $\partial v/\partial t =\Delta v+e^v$, Bull. Amer. Math. Soc., 75 (1969) 132-135.

[7] Gel'fand, I.M., Some problems in the theory of quasilinear equations, Amer. Math. Soc. Transl., 1(2) 29 (1963) 295-381.

[8] Gidas, B., Ni Wei-Ming, Nirenberg, L., Symmetry and related properties via the maximum principle, Comm. Math. Phys., 68 (1979) 209-243.

[9] Joseph, D.D., Lundgren, T.S., Quasilinear Dirichlet problems driven by positive sources, Arch. Rat. Mech. Anal., 49 (1973) 241-269.

[10] Keener, J.P., Keller, H.B., Positive solutions of convex nonlinear eigenvalue problem, J. Diff. Equations, 16 (1974) 103-125.

[11] Keller H.B., Cohen, D.S., Some positive problems suggested by nonlinear heat generation, J. Math. Mech., 16 (1967) 1361-1376.

[12] Laetsch, T., On the number of solutions of boundary value problems with convex nonlinearities, J. Math. Anal. Appl., 35 (1971) 389-404.

[13] Liouville, J., Sur l'equation aux derivees partielles $(\partial^2 \log \lambda)/\partial u \partial v \pm 2\lambda a^2=0$, J. de Math., 18 (1853) 71-72.

[14] Moseley, J.L., Asymptotic solutions for a Dirichlet problem with an exponential nonlinearity, SIAM J. Math. Anal., 14 (1983) 719-735.

[15] Nagasaki, K., Suzuki, T., in preparation.

[16] Rabinowitz, P.H., Some aspects of nonlinear eigenvalue problems, Rocky Mountain J. Math., 3 (1973) 161-202.

[17] Wente, H., Counter example to a conjecture of H. Hopf, Pacific J. Math., 121 (1986) 193-244.

[18] Weston, V.H., On the asymptotic solution of a partial differential equation with an exponential nonlinearity, SIAM J. Math. Anal., 9 (1978) 1030-1053.

Recent Topics in Nonlinear PDE III, Tokyo, 1986
Lecture Notes in Num. Appl. Anal., 9, 219–239 (1987)

On an Estimate for Solutions of Nonlinear Elliptic Variational Inequalities

Haruo NAGASE

Suzuka College of Technology
Suzuka 510-02, Japan

Introduction

Let Ω be a bounded domain in R^n with the boundary Γ of class $C^{0,1}$ and E be a compact subset(or a compact subset on a (n-1)-dimensional hypersurface of class $C^{0,1}$) in Ω.

The first constraint condition is given by the following set:

(1) $$K_1 = \left\{ v \in W_0^{1,p}(\Omega);\ v(x) \in \mathbb{K}(x) \quad \text{a.e.(or p.p.)} \quad x \in E \right\},$$

where $\mathbb{K}(x)$ is a closed convex set in R^1 depending on x.

Next let Γ_1 and Γ_2 be two disjoint open subsets of Γ such that $\Gamma = \overline{\Gamma}_1 \cup \overline{\Gamma}_2$ and $\Gamma_1 \neq \emptyset$. We set

$$C^1_{(0)}(\overline{\Omega}) = \left\{ v \in C^1(\overline{\Omega});\ v = 0 \text{ in a neighborhood of } \overline{\Gamma}_1 \right\} .$$

The completion of $C^1_{(0)}(\overline{\Omega})$ with respect to the norm $\| u \|_{1,p} = \| u \|_p + \| \nabla u \|_p$ is denoted by $W^{1,p}_{(0)}(\Omega)$, where for the sake of simplicity we write $\| \cdot \|_{L^p(\Omega)} = \| \cdot \|_p$ and $(\partial_{x_1} u, \partial_{x_2} u, \cdots, \partial_{x_n} u) = \nabla u$. The following set

K_2 defines the second constraint condition:

$$(2) \qquad K_2 = \left\{ v \in W^{1,p}_{(0)}(\Omega);\ v(x) \in \mathbb{k}(x) \quad \text{p.p. } x \in \overline{\Gamma_2} \right\},$$

where $\mathbb{k}(x)$ is also a closed convex set in R^1 depending on x.

The aim of this paper is to establisch an estimate for the solution $u \in K_i$ of the following variational inequality:

$$(3) \qquad \sum_{j=1}^{n} \left\langle a_j(x,\nabla u),\ \partial_{x_j}(u - v)\right\rangle + (a_0(x,u), u - v) \leqq (f, u - v)$$

for any $v \in K_i$,

where we denote the pairing between $W^{1,p}_0(\Omega)$ $(W^{1,p}_{(0)}(\Omega))$ and its dual by $\langle\,,\,\rangle$, and the inner product of $L^2(\Omega)$ by $(\ ,\ )$.

In the case when $K = K_1$ (resp. $K = K_2$) and $E = \Omega$ (resp. $\Gamma_1 = \phi$), many authors obtained a number of results with respect to the properties of solutions of (3) for the operators a_j and for $\mathbb{K}(x)$ (resp. $\mathbb{k}(x)$) of various types. Here we do not refer explicitly to such cases.

Before stating our theorem, we will refer to the results related to our problems. At first we mention the results for the cases when a_j does not degenerate. D. Kinderlehrer ([7]) proved the existence of a Lipschitz continuous solution when the dimension n = 2 and E is a segment. For the case when the dimension n is general, J.Frehse([5]) discussed the continuity of the first order derivatives of solutions for a (n-1)-dimensional manifold E in Ω and G.H.Williams ([18]) proved the existence of a Lipschitz continuous solution for a subset E in Ω. In the above three cases $\mathbb{K}(x)$ is only of the type $\mathbb{K}(x) = \{v(x) \geqq \phi(x)\}$ for a given function $\phi(x)$. Additionally when $n = 2$ and $\Gamma_2 = (a,b) \times \{x_2 = 0\}$ particularly, D.Kinderlehrer([8]) showed that solutions belong to the class $C^{1,\alpha}(\Omega \cup \Gamma_2)$ with the assumption that $\mathbb{k}(x) = \{v(x) \geqq \psi(x)\}$ for some function $\psi(x)$.

Secondly for the cases when a_j degenerates, H.Beirão da Veiga obtained the $L^\infty(\Omega)$ estimate under the constraint condition $u(x) \geqq \phi_i(x)$ on $E_i (i=1,\cdots,m)$ in [15] and moreover in [16] he establisched the $L^\infty(\Omega)$ estimate and the $C^\alpha(\bar{\Omega})$ estimate for the constraint condition $K = \{v \in W^{1,p}(\Omega);\ v(x) \geqq \psi(x) \text{ on } \Gamma,\ v(x) = \psi(x) \text{ on } \Gamma_1\}$. H.Beirão da Veiga-F.Conti([17]) proved that solutions belong to $C^\alpha(\bar{\Omega})$ with the constraint condition $u(x) \geqq \phi(x)$ on E. A.Domarkas ([2],[3]) obtained the same result for the constraint condition K:

$K = \{v \in W_0^{1,p}(\Omega);\ v(x) \geqq \phi_1(x) \text{ on } E_1 \text{ and } v(x) \leqq \phi_2(x) \text{ on } E_2\}$ or

$K = \{v \in W^{1,p}(\Omega);\ v(x) \geqq \psi_1(x) \text{ on } \Gamma_1 \text{ and } v(x) \leqq \psi_2(x) \text{ on } \Gamma_2\}$. In the above works E and E_i are subsets of Ω and Γ_i are subsets of Γ, additionally $\phi_i(x)$, $\psi(x)$ and $\psi_i(x)$ are some given functions.

Throughout this paper let $p \geqq 2$ and let us assume that $\alpha \geqq 0$ if $p \geqq n$ $0 \leqq \alpha < n(p - 1)/(n - p) - 1$ if $p < n$.

Now we impose the following assumption on $a_j (j = 0, 1, \cdots, n)$. At first we consider the function $a_j(x,z,\eta)$ defined on $\Omega \times R^1 \times R^n$ in place of operator $a_j(x,u,\nabla u)$

Assumption A. For $x \in \Omega$, $z \in R^1 - \{0\}$, $\eta \in R^n - \{0\}$ and $\xi \in R^n$, the followings hold;

(I) (i) $a_j = a_j(x,\eta) \in C^0(\Omega \times R^n) \cap C^1(\Omega \times (R^n - \{0\}))$, $a_j(x,0) = 0$,

$$(j = 1, \cdots, n) .$$

(ii)
$$\sum_{i,j=1}^{n} \frac{\partial a_j}{\partial \eta_i}(x,\eta)\xi_i \xi_j \geqq \gamma(\kappa_0 + |\eta|^{p-2})|\xi|^2 ,$$

$$\left|\frac{\partial a_j}{\partial \eta_i}(x,\eta)\right| \leqq \Lambda(\kappa_0 + |\eta|^{p-2}) \quad (i = 1,\cdots, n) ,$$

$$\left|\frac{\partial a_j}{\partial x_k}(x,\eta)\right| \leqq \Lambda(\kappa_0|\eta| + |\eta|^{p-1}) \quad (k = 1,\cdots, n) .$$

(II) (i) $a_0 = a_0(x,z) \in C^0(\Omega \times R^1) \cap C^1(\Omega \times (R^1 - \{0\}))$, $a_0(x,0) = 0$.

(ii)
$$\frac{\partial a_0}{\partial z}(x,z) \geqq 0 , \quad \left|\frac{\partial a_0}{\partial z}(x,z)\right| \leqq \Lambda(|z|^{\alpha} + 1) ,$$

$$\left|\frac{\partial a_0}{\partial x_k}(x,z)\right| \leqq \Lambda(|z|^{\alpha+1} + 1) \quad (k = 1,\cdots, n) .$$

Here κ_0 is a non-negative constant, γ and Λ are some positive constants.

Hereafter we write by the same C all constants independent of u and f, which appear in (3). We define the following function $\Phi(x)$ in R^n:

$$\Phi(x) = \begin{cases} \text{dis.}(x, E \cup \Gamma) & \text{for the case of } K = K_1, \\ \text{dis.}(x, \Gamma) & \text{for the case of } K = K_2, \end{cases}$$

where dis.(A,B) is the distance between A and B.

Our theorem is as follows.

Theorem. Under the assumption A if $f \in W^{1,p^*}(\Omega)$ (resp. $L^2(\Omega)$) in the case of $\kappa_0 = 0$ (resp. $\kappa_0 \neq 0$), the following assertions hold for the solution u of the nonlinear variational inequality (3).

(I) In any case, $\Phi(x) a_j(x, \nabla u) \in W^{1,p^*}(\Omega)$, $\Phi(x) |\nabla u|^{p/2} \in W^{1,2}(\Omega)$, $j = 1, \cdots, n$.

(II) If $\kappa_0 = 0$,

$$\| \Phi(\cdot) a_j(\cdot, \nabla u) \|_{1,p^*}^{p^*} + \| \Phi(\cdot) |\nabla u|^{p/2} \|_{1,2}^{2} \leqq C(1 + \| f \|_{1,p^*}^{p^*} + \| f \|_{p^*}^{(\alpha+2)/(p-1)}).$$

(III) If $\kappa_0 \neq 0$, $\Phi(x) \nabla u \in W^{1,2}(\Omega)$ and

$$\| \Phi(\cdot) \nabla u \|_{1,2}^{2} + \| \Phi(\cdot) a_j(\cdot, \nabla u) \|_{1,p^*}^{p^*} + \| \Phi(\cdot) |\nabla u|^{p/2} \|_{1,2}^{2} \leqq C(1 + \| f \|_{2}^{2\beta/p}),$$

where $\beta = \max.(p,\alpha+2)$ and p^* is the dual number of p, i.e., $1/p + 1/p^* = 1$.

In connection to the estimates in our theorem the following results were obtained by G.H.Yakovlev. He gave first the estimate of $\| \partial_{x_j}(|\partial_{x_i} u|^{p/2}) \|_{L^2(\Omega_\delta)}$ for solutions of the variational problem in [19]. And he also obtained estimates of $\| a_j(\cdot,u,\nabla u) \|_{W^{1,p^*}(\Omega_\delta)}$ and $\| \frac{\partial a_j}{\partial x_k}(\cdot,u,\nabla u) \|_{W^{1,p^*}(\Omega_\delta)}$ for weak solutions of the nonlinear elliptic equation $\sum_{j=1}^{n} \partial_{x_j}(a_j(x,u,\nabla u)) = a_0(x,u,\nabla u)$ under weaker assumptions than ours([21]). Here $\Omega_\delta = \{ x \in \Omega;\ \text{dis.}(x,\Gamma) > \delta \}$. The method in [19] and [21] is to use the quotient of differentials with the usual parallel transformation, namely,

$$h^{-1}[u(x_1, x_2, \cdots, x_{i-1}, x_i + h, x_{i+1}, \cdots, x_n) - u(x)] ,$$

which implies that the estimate of the norm is obliged to be restricted in Ω_δ. In this paper we use a transformation with weight function $\Phi(x)$, so we can estimate the norm in the whole Ω. Moreover our estimates are very similar to that of G.H.Yakovlev([20]), where a nonlinear elliptic equation with the Dirichlet boundary condition was treated. He prepared the estimate for smooth solutions and applied the Galerkin's method, so his technique can not be applied to our variational inequality.

Finally we refer to the regularity of weak solutions of the nonlinear elliptic equation. Let us put $v = u \pm \phi$ in (3) for a solution u and any function ϕ in $C_0^\infty(\Omega \setminus E)$ (resp. $C_0^\infty(\Omega)$) in the case of $K = K_1$ (resp. $K = K_2$), then we see that u is a weak solution of the nonlinear elliptic equation

(4) $$-\sum_{j=1}^{n} \partial_{x_j} (a_j(x,\nabla u)) + a_0(x,u) = f \quad ,$$

in $\Omega \setminus E$(resp.Ω).

J.C.Evans([4]) and J.L.Lewis([10]) proved that weak solutions of (4) belong to $C^{1,\alpha}_{loc}(\Omega \setminus E)$(resp.$C^{1,\alpha}_{loc}(\Omega)$) when $a_j = |\nabla u|^{p-2}\partial_{x_j} u$ and $a_0 = 0$. Besides E.DiBenedetto([1]) and P.Tolksdorf([14]) showed the same results under weaker assumptions on a_j and a_0 than those of [4] and [10].

In Section 1 and Section 2 we give some lemmas without proof, which are used in the proof of our theorem and proposition. In Section 3 we state the main proposition and describe the outline of the proof for our theorem. The detailed proof will be given in the forthcoming paper [13].

1.

Lemma 1.1 Under the assumption A the following assertions hold:

(i) $a_j(j = 0, 1,\cdots, n)$ are estimated in such a way that

(1.1) $$|a_j(x,\eta)| \leq C(\kappa_0 + |\eta|^{p-2})|\eta| \qquad (j = 1,\cdots, n) \quad ,$$

(1.2) $$|a_0(x,z)| \leq C(1 + |z|^{\alpha})|z| \quad .$$

(ii)(P.Tolksdorf[14, p.129] and P.Lindqvist[11, p.310]) There exists a positive number γ_0 depending only on γ and p such that

$$(1.3) \qquad \sum_{j=1}^{n} (a_j(x,\eta) - a_j(x,\eta'))(\eta_j - \eta_j')$$

$$\geqq \gamma_0(\kappa_0 + |\eta|^{p-2} + |\eta'|^{p-2})|\eta - \eta'|^2 ,$$

$$(1.4) \qquad (a_0(x,z) - a_0(x,z'))(z - z') \geqq 0 .$$

Here $x \in \Omega$, η, $\eta' \in R^n$ and z, $z \in R^1$.

Remark. The following inequality is verified from (1.3):

$$(1.5) \qquad \sum_{j=1}^{n} (a_j(x,\eta) - a_j(x,\eta'))(\eta_j - \eta_j') \geqq \gamma_0(\kappa_0 + |\eta - \eta'|^{p-2})|\eta - \eta'|^2 .$$

This is due to K.L.Kuttler Jr.([9]).

Lemma 1.2 For u, $v \in W_0^{1,p}(\Omega)\,(W_{(0)}^{1,p}(\Omega))$ we define the operator A in such a way that $(A(u),v) = \sum_{j=1}^{n} \langle a_j(x,\nabla u), \partial_{x_j} v\rangle + (a_0(x,u),v)$, then the operator A is psuedo-monotone and coercive from $W_0^{1,p}(\Omega)\,(W_{(0)}^{1,p}(\Omega))$ to its dual space.

The existence of solutions for the variational inequality (3) is derived from Lemma 1.2 for any $f \in (W_0^{1,p}(\Omega))'\,((W_{(0)}^{1,p}(\Omega))')$ (J.L.Lions[12, p.247]). And the uniqueness of solutions follows from (1.3) and (1.4).

The estimate for the gradient of the solution u is given in the next lemma.

Lemma 1.3 Under the assumption A if $f \in L^{p^*}(\Omega)$ (resp. $L^2(\Omega)$) and $\kappa_0 = 0$ (resp. $\kappa_0 \neq 0$), the gradient of the solution u of the variational inequality (3) is estimated as follows:

$$(1.6) \qquad \kappa_0 \| \nabla u \|_2^2 + \| \nabla u \|_p^p \leqq C(1 + \| f \|_{p^*}^{p^*}) \qquad (\text{resp. } C(1 + \| f \|_2^2)) .$$

We give a sufficient condition to assure that a sequence of functions converges weakly in $L^q(\Omega)$ $(1 < q < \infty)$.

Lemma 1.4 Let u be a distribution in Ω and let $\{u_\nu\}_{\nu=1}^{\infty}$ be a sequence in $L^q(\Omega)$ $(1 < q < \infty)$ such that the norms $\| u_\nu \|_q$ are uniformly bounded. If for any $\phi \in C_0^\infty(\Omega)$,

$$(u_\nu, \phi) \longrightarrow (u, \phi) \quad \text{as} \quad \nu \longrightarrow \infty ,$$

then u belongs to $L^q(\Omega)$ and the sequence u_ν converges weakly to u in $L^q(\Omega)$.

2.

We introduce a coordinate transformation with the weight function $\Phi(x)$ and give some results with respect to it.

Let $\mathbb{h}$ be a non-zero vector in R^n with the length $h = |\mathbb{h}|$. Hereafter h is assumed to be sufficiently small. As mentioned in the introduction we put $\Phi(x) = \text{dis.}(x,\Gamma\cup E)$ (resp. $\text{dis.}(x,\Gamma)$) for $K = K_1$ (resp. $K = K_2$) and we consider the transformation of the coordinates:

$$\Phi_{\mathbb{h}} : \quad y = x + \Phi(x)\,\mathbb{h}\,. \tag{2.1}$$

We write $\mathbb{h} = (h_1, h_2, \cdots, h_n)$ and $\mathbf{J} = \partial(y_1, y_2, \cdots, y_n)/\partial(x_1, x_2, \cdots, x_n)$, then we have

$$\mathbf{J} = \begin{pmatrix} 1 + h_1\partial_{x_1}\Phi & h_2\partial_{x_1}\Phi & \cdots & h_n\partial_{x_1}\Phi \\ h_1\partial_{x_2}\Phi & 1 + h_2\partial_{x_2}\Phi & \cdots & h_n\partial_{x_2}\Phi \\ \vdots & \vdots & \ddots & \vdots \\ h_1\partial_{x_n}\Phi & h_2\partial_{x_n}\Phi & \cdots & 1 + h_n\partial_{x_n}\Phi \end{pmatrix} \tag{2.2}$$

Let us put $\mathbb{e} = h^{-1}\mathbb{h}$ and let $\mathbb{e}$ be arbitrarily fixed. Noting that $|\partial_{x_j}\Phi| \leqq 1$ (see [6, p.57]), we see that the determinant J of $\mathbf{J}$ is not zero for sufficiently small h, therefore the mapping $\Phi_{\mathbb{h}}$ and its inverse $\Phi_{\mathbb{h}}^{-1}$ are both one-to-one from R^n onto itself. If we set $\Psi(y) = -\Phi(x) (= -(\Phi_{\mathbb{h}}^{-1}(y)))$, it is written

$$(2.3) \qquad \Phi_{\mathbb{h}}^{-1} : \quad x = y + \Psi(y)\,\mathbb{h} \quad .$$

Here we remark that from (2.2) we can put $J = 1 + hJ_1$ and the determinant J^{-1} of the Jacobian $\mathbb{J}^{-1}$ connected with the inverse transformation $\Phi_{\mathbb{h}}^{-1}$ can be described in the form $J^{-1} = 1 + hJ_2$, where J_1 and J_2 are uniformly bounded in $x \in \Omega$ and $\mathbb{h} \in R^n$. Furthermore the transformation $\Phi_{\mathbb{h}}$ maps $x \in \Omega$ to $y \in \Omega$ and $x \in \Omega^c$ to $y \in \Omega^c$ respectively, so it is a one-to-one mapping from Ω onto itself.

Now we define

$$(2.4) \quad \begin{cases} (S_{\mathbb{h}}u)(x) = u(x + \Phi(x)\,\mathbb{h}), \qquad (T_{\mathbb{h}}u)(y) = u(y + \Psi(y)\,\mathbb{h}) \ , \\[2ex] (P_{\mathbb{h}}u)(x) = h^{-1}[(S_{\mathbb{h}}u)(x) - u(x)] \quad , \\[2ex] (Q_{\mathbb{h}}u)(y) = h^{-1}[(T_{\mathbb{h}}u)(y) - u(y)] \quad . \end{cases}$$

Hereafter we write simply by $S_{\mathbb{h}}u$, $T_{\mathbb{h}}u$, $\cdots$ the functions $(S_{\mathbb{h}}u)(x)$, $(T_{\mathbb{h}}u)(y)$, $\cdots$, respectively.

Lemma 2.1 ([6, p.58, p.59])

(i) We have

$$
(2.5)\quad
\begin{cases}
\nabla_x(S_{\mathbb{h}}u) = S_{\mathbb{h}}\nabla_x u + h(\mathbb{e}\cdot S_{\mathbb{h}}\nabla_x u)\nabla_x\Phi\ , \\[2ex]
\nabla_y(T_{\mathbb{h}}u) = T_{\mathbb{h}}\nabla_y u + h(\mathbb{e}\cdot T_{\mathbb{h}}\nabla_y u)\nabla_y\Psi\ , \\[2ex]
\nabla_x(P_{\mathbb{h}}u) = P_{\mathbb{h}}\nabla_x u + (\mathbb{e}\cdot S_{\mathbb{h}}\nabla_x u)\nabla_x\Phi\ , \\[2ex]
\nabla_y(Q_{\mathbb{h}}u) = Q_{\mathbb{h}}\nabla_y u + (\mathbb{e}\cdot T_{\mathbb{h}}\nabla_y u)\nabla_y\Psi\ .
\end{cases}
$$

(ii) If $u \in W^{1,q}(\Omega)\,(1 < q < \infty)$, there exists a constant C independent of $\mathbb{h}$ and u such that

$$
(2.6)\qquad \|P_{\mathbb{h}}u\|_q\ ,\ \|Q_{\mathbb{h}}u\|_q \leqq C\|\nabla u\|_q\ .
$$

Lemma 2.2 If $u \in L^q(\Omega)\,(1 < q < \infty)$, then for any function ϕ in $C_0^\infty(\Omega)$ it holds that

$$
(P_{\mathbb{h}}u - J_2u,\phi) \longrightarrow ((\mathbb{e}\cdot\nabla)(\Phi u),\phi) \quad \text{as} \quad h \longrightarrow 0\ ,
$$

where the derivative $(\mathbb{e}\cdot\nabla)(\Phi u)$ of Φu is in the sense of the distribution.

3.

At first we state the main proposition without proof. It is essential in the proof of our theorem.

Proposition. Let us assume the assumption A. Then the following estimates hold for the solution u of the variational inequality (3):

(i) If $\kappa_0 = 0$ and $f \in W^{1,p^*}(\Omega)$,

$$\| |S_{\mathbb{h}} \nabla u|^{(p-2)/2} P_{\mathbb{h}} \nabla u \|_2^2 + \| |\nabla u|^{(p-2)/2} P_{\mathbb{h}} \nabla u \|_2^2$$

$$\leq C(1 + \|f\|_{1,p^*}^{p^*} + \|f\|_{p^*}^{(\alpha+2)/(p-1)}) .$$

(ii) If $\kappa_0 \neq 0$ and $f \in L^2(\Omega)$,

$$\| P_{\mathbb{h}} \nabla u \|_2^2 + \| |S_{\mathbb{h}} \nabla u|^{(p-2)/2} P_{\mathbb{h}} \nabla u \|_2^2 + \| |\nabla u|^{(p-2)/2} P_{\mathbb{h}} \nabla u \|_2^2$$

$$\leq C(1 + \|f\|_2^{2\beta/p}) ,$$

where $\beta = \max.(p, \alpha+2)$.

Now we briefly sketch the proof for our theorem.

First step. We give the unifrom $L^{p^*}(\Omega)$ estimate for the sequence $\{P_{\mathbb{h}}(a_j(x,\nabla u)) - J_2 a_j(x,\nabla u)\}_{h>0}$, where h is sufficiently small. We write $P_{\mathbb{h}}(a_j(x,\nabla u))$ in the form

$$(3.1) \qquad P_{\mathbb{h}}(a_j(x,\nabla u)) = [a_j(S_{\mathbb{h}}x, S_{\mathbb{h}}\nabla u) - a_j(x, S_{\mathbb{h}}\nabla u)]h^{-1}$$

$$+ [a_j(x,S_{\mathbb{h}}\nabla u) - a_j(x,\nabla u)]h^{-1}.$$

Using the inequality in the assumption A and the equality

$$a_j(S_{\mathbb{h}}x,S_{\mathbb{h}}\nabla u) - a_j(x,S_{\mathbb{h}}\nabla u) = \int_0^1 \sum_{k=1}^{n} \frac{\partial a_j}{\partial x_k}(x + \theta\Phi(x)\mathbb{h},S_{\mathbb{h}}\nabla u)h_k\Phi(x)d\theta \quad ,$$

we see that

$$(3.2) \qquad \| [a_j(S_{\mathbb{h}}x,S_{\mathbb{h}}\nabla u) - a_j(x,S_{\mathbb{h}}\nabla u)]h^{-1}\|_{p^*}^{p^*} \leqq C(\kappa_0^{p^*}\|\nabla u\|_{p^*}^{p^*} + \|\nabla u\|_p^p).$$

For the second term of (3.1), we get the inequality

$$(3.3) \qquad \| [a_j(x,S_{\mathbb{h}}\nabla u) - a_j(x,\nabla u)]h^{-1}\|_{p^*}^{p^*}$$

$$\leqq C\Big\{\kappa_0^{p^*}\|P_{\mathbb{h}}\nabla u\|_2^{p^*} + \|\nabla u\|_p^p + (\| |S_{\mathbb{h}}\nabla u|^{(p-2)/2} P_{\mathbb{h}}\nabla u\|_2^2$$

$$+ \| |\nabla u|^{(p-2)/2} P_{\mathbb{h}}\nabla u\|_2^2)\Big\}.$$

In the above estimate we have used the assumption A and the equality

$$a_j(x,S_{\mathbb{h}}\nabla u) - a_j(x,\nabla u) = \int_0^1 \sum_{i=1}^{n} \frac{\partial a_j}{\partial \eta_i}(x,\theta S_{\mathbb{h}}\nabla u + (1-\theta)\nabla u)\cdot$$

$$(S_{\mathbb{h}}\partial_i u - \partial_i u)d\theta \quad ,$$

where we write simply $\partial_{x_j} u = \partial_j u$.

Because of (3.1)- (3.3) it holds that

$$\|P_{\mathbb{I}h}(a_j(x,\nabla u))\|_{p^*}^{p^*} \leqq C\left\{\kappa_0^{p^*}(\|\nabla u\|_{p^*}^{p^*} + \|P_{\mathbb{I}h}\nabla u\|_2^{p^*}) + \|\nabla u\|_p^p\right.$$
$$\left. + (\|\,|S_{\mathbb{I}h}\nabla u|^{(p-2)/2} P_{\mathbb{I}h}\nabla u\|_2^2 + \|\,|\nabla u|^{(p-2)/2} P_{\mathbb{I}h}\nabla u\|_2^2)\right\}. \tag{3.4}$$

Therefore if $\kappa_0 = 0$,

$$\|P_{\mathbb{I}h}(a_j(x,\nabla u))\|_{p^*}^{p^*} \leqq C(1 + \|f\|_{1,p^*}^{p^*} + \|f\|_{p^*}^{(\alpha+2)/(p-1)}),$$

from (3.4), Proposition and Lemma 1.3. We write the right-hand side by $C\gamma_f^0$.

Moreover if $\kappa_0 \neq 0$, we have similarly

$$\|P_{\mathbb{I}h}(a_j(x,\nabla u))\|_{p^*}^{p^*} \leqq C(1 + \|f\|_2^{2\beta/p}),$$

where $\beta = \max.(p,\alpha+2)$. The right-hand side is written by $C\gamma_f$.

On the other hand the functions J_2 are uniformly bounded in x and h. Thus by Lemma 1.1

$$\|J_2 a_j(x,\nabla u)\|_{p^*}^{p^*} \leqq C(\kappa_0^{p^*}\|\nabla u\|_{p^*}^{p^*} + \|\nabla u\|_p^p). \tag{3.5}$$

Applying the estimate for ∇u in Lemma 1.3 to each term on the right-hand side of (3.5), the $L^{p^*}(\Omega)$ norms of functions $J_2 a_j(x,\nabla u)$ are estimated as follows: if $\kappa_0 = 0$(resp. $\kappa_0 \neq 0$),

$$\| J_2 a_j(x,\nabla u) \|_{p^*}^{p^*} \leqq C\gamma_f^0 \qquad (\text{resp.} C\gamma_f) .$$

From the above the $L^{p^*}(\Omega)$ norms of the sequence $\{P_{\mathbb{h}}(a_j(x,\nabla u)) - J_2 a_j(x,\nabla u)\}_{h>0}$ are estimated. That is, if $\kappa_0 = 0$(resp. $\kappa_0 \neq 0$),

$$(3.6) \qquad \| P_{\mathbb{h}}(a_j(x,\nabla u)) - J_2 a_j(x,\nabla u) \|_{p^*}^{p^*} \leqq C\gamma_f^0 \qquad (\text{resp.} C\gamma_f) .$$

<u>Second step.</u> Because $a_j(x,\nabla u) \in L^{p^*}(\Omega)$, we conclude on account of Lemma 2.2 that for any $\phi \in C_0^\infty(\Omega)$,

$$(P_{\mathbb{h}}(a_j(x,\nabla u)) - J_2 a_j(x,\nabla u), \phi) \longrightarrow ((\mathbb{C}\cdot\nabla)(\Phi a_j(x,\nabla u)), \phi) ,$$

$$\text{as } h \longrightarrow 0 .$$

Hence Lemma 1.4 and (3.6) yield that the distribution $(\mathbb{C}\cdot\nabla)(\Phi a_j(x,\nabla u))$ belongs to $L^{p^*}(\Omega)$ and that

$$(3.7) \qquad P_{\mathbb{h}}(a_j(x,\nabla u)) - J_2 a_j(x,\nabla u) \longrightarrow (\mathbb{C}\cdot\nabla)(\Phi a_j(x,\nabla u)) \quad \text{in } L^{p^*}(\Omega) ,$$

$$\text{as } h \longrightarrow 0 ,$$

where "$\rightharpoonup$" means the weak convergence.

Therefore from (3.6) and (3.7) we derive that if $\kappa_0 = 0$ (resp. $\kappa_0 \neq 0$),

$$\| (\mathbb{C}\cdot\nabla)(\Phi a_j(x,\nabla u)) \|_{p^*}^{p^*} \leqq C\gamma_f^0 \qquad (\text{resp.} C\gamma_f) .$$

In this way the proof of the part for $\Phi(x)a_j(x,\nabla u)$ is finished.

Third step. The assertion concerning $\Phi(x)|\nabla u|^{p/2}$ can be treated more easily. By simple calculations we deduce the inequality

$$|P_{\mathbb{I}h}(|\nabla u|^{p/2})| \leqq C|P_{\mathbb{I}h}\nabla u|(|S_{\mathbb{I}h}\nabla u|^{(p-2)/2} + |\nabla u|^{(p-2)/2}).$$

From this inequality and the estimate in Proposition we have for the case of $\kappa_0 = 0$ (resp. $\kappa_0 \neq 0$)

$$\| P_{\mathbb{I}h}(|\nabla u|^{p/2}) \|_2^2 \leqq C\gamma_f^0 \qquad (\text{resp.} C\gamma_f) .$$

Since the functions J_2 are uniformly bounded, we get from Lemma 1.3

$$\| J_2|\nabla u|^{p/2} \|_2^2 \leqq C\gamma_f^0 \qquad (\text{resp.} C\gamma_f) ,$$

if $\kappa_0 = 0$ (resp. $\kappa_0 \neq 0$).

Thus the $L^2(\Omega)$ norms of the sequence $\left\{P_{\mathbb{h}}(|\nabla u|^{p/2}) - J_2|\nabla u|^{p/2}\right\}_{h>0}$ are estimated as follows: if $\kappa_0 = 0$(resp. $\kappa_0 \neq 0$),

$$(3.8) \qquad \| P_{\mathbb{h}}(|\nabla u|^{p/2}) - J_2|\nabla u|^{p/2} \|_2^2 \leqq C\gamma_f^0 \qquad (\text{resp.} C\gamma_f) \ .$$

Using the same method as in the second step, we can show from (3.8) that $(\mathbb{e}\cdot\nabla)(\Phi|\nabla u|^{p/2})$ belongs to $L^2(\Omega)$ and its $L^2(\Omega)$ norm is estimated as follows:

$$\| (\mathbb{e}\cdot\nabla)(\Phi|\nabla u|^{p/2}) \|_2^2 \leqq C\gamma_f^0 \qquad (\text{resp.} C\gamma_f) \ .$$

Finally we briefly explain the proof of the part for $\Phi(x)\nabla u$. On account of the estimate (ii) in Proposition, $\| P_{\mathbb{h}} u \|_{1,2}$ are uniformly bounded in h, more precisely,

$$\| P_{\mathbb{h}} u \|_{1,2} \leqq C\gamma_f^{1/2} \ ,$$

if $\kappa_0 \neq 0$.

Applying the same way as in Lemma 5 in [6], we can conclude from the above estimate that $\Phi(x)(\mathbb{e}\cdot\nabla)u$ belongs to $W^{1,2}(\Omega)$ and its norm is estimated as follows:

$$\| \Phi(\mathbb{e}\cdot\nabla)u \|_{1,2} \leqq C\gamma_f^{1/2}$$

Thus the proof is finished.

— Bibliography —

[1]E.DiBendetto, $C^{1+\alpha}$ local regularity of weak solutions of degenerate elliptic equations, Nonlinear Anal.T.M.A., 7(1983), 827-850.

[2]A.Domarkas, Regularity of solutions of quasilinear elliptic equations with unilateral boundary conditions, Lihtu.Math.Jour., 20(1980), 8-15.

[3]————, Unilateral problems for quasilinear elliptic equation, ibid., 21(1981), 317-327.

[4]L.C.Evans, A new proof of local $C^{1,\alpha}$ regularity for solutions of certain degenerate elliptic P.D.E., Jour.Differ.Eq., 45(1982), 356-373.

[5]J.Frehse, On Signorini's problem and variational problems with thin obstacles, Ann.Scuola Norm.Pisa, 4(1977), 343-362.

[6]K.Hayasida-H.Nagase, On solutions of variational inequalities constrained on a subset of positive capacity, Nagoya Math.Jour., 97(1985), 51-69.

[7]D.Kinderlehrer, Variational inequalities with lower dimensional obstacles, Israel Jour.Math. 16(1971), 339-348.

[8]————, The smoothness of the solution of the boundary obstacle problem, Jour.math.pures appl., 60(1980), 193-212.

[9]K.L.Kuttler Jr., Degenerate variational inequalities of evolution, Nonlinear Anal.T.M.A., 8(1984), 837-850.

[10]J.L.Lewis, Regularity of the derivatives of solutions to certain degenerate elliptic equations, Indiana Univ.Math.Jour., 32(1983), 849-858.

[11]P.Lindqvist, On the growth of the solutions of the differential equation div.($|\nabla u|^{p-2}\nabla u$) = 0 in n-dim. space, Jour.Differ.Eq., 58(1985), 307-317.

[12]J.L.Lions, Quelques méthodes de résolution des problèmes aux limites nonlinéaries, Dunod Gautyier-Villars, 1969.

[13]H.Nagase, On an estimate for solutions of nonlinear elliptic variational inequalities(in preparation).

[14]P.Tolksdorf, Regularity for a more general class of quasilinear elliptic equation, Jour.Differ.Eq., 51(1984), 126-150.

[15]H.Beirão da Veiga, Proprietà di sommabilità e di limitatezza per soluzioni di disequazioni variazionali ellittiche, Rend.Sem.Nat.Padova, 46 (1971), 141-171.

[16] ——————, Sur la régularité des solutions de l'équation div.A(x,u,∇u) = B(x,u,∇u) avec des conditions aux limites unilatérales et mêlées, Ann.Mat.Pure Appl., 93(1972), 173-230.

[17]——— -F.Conti, Equazioni ellittiche non lineari con ostacoli sottili applicazioni allo studio dei punti regolari, Ann.Scuola Norm.Sup.Pisa, 26(1972), 533-562.

[18]G.H.Williams, Lipschitz continuous solutions for nonlinear obstacle problems, Math.Zeit., 154(1977), 51-65.

[19]G.H.Yakovlev, A variational problem, Differ.Eq., 5(1969), 960-966.

[20]—————, The first boundary value problem for quasilinear elliptic equations of second order, Proc.Steklov Inst.Math., 117(1972), 381-403.

[21]—————, Some properties of solutions of quasilinear elliptic equations, ibid., 134(1975), 441-458.

Recent Topics in Nonlinear PDE III, Tokyo, 1986
Lecture Notes in Num. Appl. Anal., 9, 241–246 (1987)

On the Boundedness of Cyclic Predator-prey Systems of Volterra and Lotka

Yorimasa OSHIME
Junior College of Economics, Wakayama University

1. Introduction.

It was Volterra[5] and Lotka[3] that proposed the systems of differential equations of the form:

$$du_i/dt = u_i(e_i + \sum_{j=1}^{n} p_{ij}u_j), \ p_{ii} \leq 0 \quad \text{for all} \quad i=1,2,\ldots,n,$$

$$u_i(0) > 0 \quad \text{for all} \quad i=1,2,\ldots,n$$

to analyze the variation of the biomass in ecological systems. Here each $u_i(t)$ represents the biomass of the i-th species at time t. In this system, p_{ij} and p_{ji} represent the relation between the i-th and j-th species. For instance, $p_{ii}<0$ means the self-limiting effect of the i-th, $p_{ij}>0$ and $p_{ji}<0$ mean the i-th is the predator and the j-th is the prey, $p_{ij}<0$ and $p_{ji}<0$ mean the i-th and the j-th compete for the food or the niches. Note that because each equation has the form: $du_i/dt=u_if(t)$ and $u_i(0)>0$, we have $u_i(t)>0$ for all time as long as the solution can be continued. And it is also natural to consider only the solutions with $u_i>0$ for all i because each u_i represents the biomass.

Volterra[5] himself solved the behavior of the soltions completely for the case $n=2$ (2 components). And other people, Kolmogorov for instance, considered the generalized systems. However few systems with $n \geqq 3$ have been fully analyzed. One of the unsolved systems is

$$du_i/dt = U_i(e_i + \sum_{j=1}^{n} p_{ij}u_j) \quad \text{for all} \quad i=1,2,\ldots,n$$

where $p_{ii}<0$, $p_{ii+1} \geqq 0$ for all $i=1,2,\ldots,n$ (p_{nn+1} means p_{n1}) and $p_{ij} \leqq 0$ for the other (i,j). This system means the 1-st species eats the 2-nd, the 2-nd the 3-rd, ... and the n-th the 1-st. So it is called cyclic predator-prey system. Concerning it, even the boundedness condition has not been solved definitely. We shall study this problem completely in the present paper.

We explain here the special usage of the suffixes in the sequel. We identify the suffixes modulo n . For instance, u_{n+1} , u_{n+2} , ... mean u_1 , u_2 , ... and p_{nn+1} , p_{n+1n+2} , ... mean p_{n1} , p_{12} ... etc.

2. Boundeness Condition.

The system we consider is the following:

$$(2.1) \quad du_i/dt = u_i(e_i + \sum_{j=1}^{n} p_{ij}u_j) \quad i=1,2,\ldots,n$$

where $p_{ii}<0$ and $p_{ii+1} \geqq 0$ for all $i=1,2,\ldots,n$ and $p_{ij} \leqq 0$ for the other (i,j).

Theorem 1. With e_i , p_{ij} of (2.1), we set

$$(r_{ij}) = \begin{pmatrix} e_1 & p_{12} & \cdots & p_{1n} \\ e_2 & p_{22} & \cdots & p_{2n} \\ \vdots & \vdots & & \vdots \\ e_n & p_{n2} & & p_{nn} \end{pmatrix}.$$

Let λ_{min} be the minimal real eigenvalue (which, in this case, has the minimal real part) of

$$\begin{pmatrix} p_{12} & p_{13} & \cdots & p_{1n} & p_{11} \\ p_{22} & p_{23} & & p_{2n} & p_{21} \\ \vdots & \vdots & & \vdots & \vdots \\ p_{n2} & p_{n3} & & p_{nn} & p_{n1} \end{pmatrix}.$$

Then the following holds for (2.1).

i) Let $\lambda_{min} > 0$. Then the solution with sufficiently large $x_1(0), x_2(0), \ldots x_n(0)$ are unbounded. And every unbounded solution blows up at some finite time $t = t_0$ in the following way:

$$C^{-1}(t_0 - t)^{-1} \leqq x_i(t) \leqq c(t_0 - t)^{-1} \quad \text{for all} \quad t \varepsilon (t_0 - \delta, t_0)$$

and for all $i = 1, 2, \ldots, n$. Here $C > 1$ is uniform for the unbounded solutions. For the bounded solutions, if they exist,

$$\limsup_{t \to \infty} \max_i x_i(t) \leqq M$$

Here M is a uniform constant for the bounded solutions.

ii) Let $\lambda_{min}<0$. Then every solution remains bounded. More precisely,

$$\limsup_{t\to\infty} \max_{i} x_i(t) \leqq M .$$

Here M is a constant independent of solutions.

iii-a) Let $\lambda_{min}=0$ and $(-1)^{n-1}\det(r_{ij})>0$. Then every solution exponentially grows up:

$$C_1^{-1} e^{C_2(t - t_0)} \leqq x_i(t) \leqq c_1 e^{c_2(t - t_0)}$$

for all $t\varepsilon(t_0, \infty)$ and all $i=1,2, \ldots ,n$. Here $C_1>1$ and $c_2>0$ are constants independent of solutions and t_0 is a constant depending on solutions.

iii-b) Let $\lambda_{min}=0$ and $(-1)^{n-1}\det(r_{ij})<0$. Then every solution remains bounded. More precisely,

$$\limsup_{t\to\infty} \max_{i} x_i(t) \leqq M .$$

Here M is a constant independent of solutions.

iii-c) Let $\lambda_{min}=0$ and $(-1)^{n-1}\det(r_{ij})=0$. Then every solution remains bounded both from above and away from zero. But the upper and the lower bounds depend on solutions. As a matter of a fact, the equilibrium points form a straight ray with positive direction.

3. Asymptotic Direction of Unbounded Solutions.

In [2] ,Krikorian made the following conjecture for n=3 : The ratio of components of every unbounded solution to (2.1) converges. In this section, we state the results concerning this propblem for (2.1).

Theorem 2. Let n=3 . Then the ratio of components of every unbounded solution converges to a certain one independent of the unbounded solutions as the solution diverges.

Theorem 3. Let $n \geqq 4$. For appropriate α_i ,every solution to

$$du_i/dt = u_i \left(\sum_{j=1}^{n} \alpha_{i-j} u_j \right) \qquad i = 1, 2, \ldots, n$$

is unbounded and ratio of the components does not converge as it blows up.

REFERENCES

[1] Kolmogorov,A.N. : Sulla teoria di Volterra della lotta per l'esistenza, Giorn. Instituto Ital. Attuari 7, 74-80(1936).

[2] Krikorian,N: The Volterra model for three species predator-prey systems:Boundedness and stability, j. Math. Biol. 7, 117-132 (1979).

[3] Lotka,A. : Elements of Mathematical Biology, Dover(1956).

[4] Takeuchi,Y., Adachi,N. and Tokumaru,H. : Global stability of ecosystems of the generalized Volterra type, Math. Biosciences 42, 119-136(1978).

[5] Volterra,V : Lecons sur la theorie mathematique de la lutte pour la vie, Gathier-Villars (1931).

Recent Topics in Nonlinear PDE III, Tokyo, 1986
Lecture Notes in Num. Appl. Anal., 9, 247–266 (1987)

Forced Vibrations for a Superlinear Vibrating String Equation

Kazunaga TANAKA

Department of Mathematics, Faculty of Science, Nagoya University
Chikusa-ku, Nagoya 464, Japan

0. Introduction and statement of results

In this article we shall study the nonlinear vibrating string equation:

(0.1) $$v_{tt} - v_{xx} + g(v) = f(x,t), \qquad (x,t) \in (0,\pi)\times\mathbb{R},$$

(0.2) $$v(0,t) = v(\pi,t) = 0, \qquad t \in \mathbb{R},$$

(0.3) $$v(x,t+2\pi) = v(x,t), \qquad (x,t) \in (0,\pi)\times\mathbb{R},$$

where $f(x,t)$ is a 2π-periodic function of t and $g\colon \mathbb{R} \to \mathbb{R}$ is a continuous function such that

(0.4) $$\frac{g(\xi)}{\xi} \to \infty \quad \text{as} \quad |\xi| \to \infty.$$

The function $g(\xi)$ that satisfies (0.4) is called of superlinear growth.

Many mathematicians are concerned with free vibrations; that is, assume $f(x,t) = 0$ and find nontrivial solutions. Especially P. H. Rabinowitz [15] proved that (0.1)-(0.3) possesses an unbounded sequence of weak solutions under the following assumptions:

(g_1) $g(\xi)$ is a strictly increasing function of ξ,

and

(g_2) there exist $\mu > 2$ and $\ell \geqq 0$ such that for $|\xi| \geqq \ell$,

$$0 < \mu\int_0^\xi g(\tau)\, d\tau \leqq \xi g(\xi).$$

See also the earlier works by P. H. Rabinowitz [13], H. Brezis, J. M. Coron and L. Nirenberg [7] and J. M. Coron [9]. Note that under the condition (g_2) there are $a_1, a_2 > 0$ such that

$$\xi g(\xi) \geqq a_1|\xi|^\mu - a_2 \qquad \text{for } \xi \in \mathbb{R}.$$

Hence $g(\xi)$ is of superlinear growth.

We shall deal with the existence of forced vibrations; that is, for a given $f(x,t)$ find solutions of (0.1)-(0.3). In case $g(\xi)$ is of linear growth, many existence results are obtained (see H. Brézis [5] and its references). But forced vibrations for superlinear equations are not well studied and it seems that the existence of at least one solution of (0.1)-(0.3) is not obtained when $g(\xi)$ is of superlinear growth and $f(x,t)$ depends on t.

Our main result is as follows:

Theorem 1 ([18]). Suppose that $g(\xi) \in C(\mathbb{R},\mathbb{R})$ satisfies (g_1), (g_2) and

(g_3) there are constants $s > 1$ and $C > 0$ such that

$$|g(\xi)| \leqq C(|\xi|^s + 1) \qquad \text{for all } \xi \in \mathbb{R}.$$

Moreover, assume that $f(x,t) \in L^\infty([0,\pi]\times\mathbb{R})$ is 2π-periodic and s satisfies

(g_4) $$\frac{2}{s-1} > \frac{\mu}{\mu-1}.$$

Then (0.1)-(0.3) possesses an unbounded sequence of weak solutions in $L^\infty([0,\pi]\times\mathbb{R})$.

As a special case, we have

Theorem 2 ([17]). Assume that $g(\xi) = |\xi|^{s-1}\xi$ ($s \in (1, 1+\sqrt{2})$) and $f(x,t) \in L^{(s+1)/s}_{loc}([0,\pi]\times\mathbb{R})$ is a 2π-periodic function of t. Then (0.1)-(0.3) possesses an unbounded sequence of weak solutions in $L^{s+1}_{loc}([0,\pi]\times\mathbb{R})$.

Remarks. (a) By a weak solution of (0.1)-(0.3) we mean a function $v(x,t)$ which is 2π-periodic and satisfies

$$\int_0^{2\pi}\int_0^{\pi} v(\phi_{tt}-\phi_{xx})\ dxdt + \int_0^{2\pi}\int_0^{\pi} g(v)\phi\ dxdt = \int_0^{2\pi}\int_0^{\pi} f\phi\ dxdt$$

for all smooth ϕ satisfying (0.2) and (0.3).

(b) In addition to the assumptions of Theorem 1, if $g(\xi)$ and $f(x,t)$ are C^∞, then the solutions are also C^∞ (see Theorem 2 of H. Brézis and L. Nirenberg [8]).

The problem (0.1)-(0.3) is closely related to the problem of elliptic type:

(0.5) $$-\Delta u = g(u) + f(x), \qquad x \in D,$$

(0.6) $$u = 0, \qquad x \in \partial D,$$

where $D \subset \mathbb{R}^N$ is a bounded domain with a smooth boundary ∂D, $f(x) \in L^2(D)$ and $g(\xi)$ is a continuous function such that

(g_5) $\qquad g(-\xi) = -g(\xi) \qquad$ for all $\xi \in \mathbb{R}$.

A. Bahri and H. Berestycki [3], M. Struwe [16] and P. H. Rabinowitz [14] obtained the conditions on $g(\xi)$ which ensure the existence of infinitely many solutions of (0.5)-(0.6) for all $f(x)$. They considered the following functional on $H_0^1(D)$:

$$F(u) = \frac{1}{2}\int_D |\nabla u|^2 \, dx - \int_D G(u) \, dx - \int_D fu \, dx,$$

where

$$G(\xi) = \int_0^\xi g(\tau) \, d\tau$$

and sought for critical points of this functional. Since the term $\int_D fu \, dx$ destroys the symmetry (evenness) of the functional, A. Bahri and H. Berestycki [3] and M. Struwe [16] prepared a perturbation result asserting the existence of infinitely many critical points of perturbed symmetric functionals and applied this result to $F(u)$. Here, restricted Lusternik Schnirelman theory and energy estimates played an essential role. On the other hand, P. H. Rabinowitz [14] used the ideas from A. Ambrosetti and P. H. Rabinowitz [1] in conjunction with those of [3] and [16] and obtained better existence result. In particular, in case $N = 2$ under the conditions (g_2)-(g_5), [14] showed the desired existence result. Acting on S^1 symmetry, he also obtained similar existence result for periodic solutions of perturbed second order ordinary differential equations. Moreover his method is applicable to our problems.

To prove our theorems, we convert the problem to a simpler one by a Legendre transformation which is used in H. Brézis, J. M. Coron and L. Nirenberg [7], that is, we use the "dual variational formulation" for (0.1)-(0.3). Next we develop L^p-estimates for the corresponding functional and use the topological tools in P. H. Rabinowitz [14]. We act on S^1 symmetry and prove the existence of solutions without assumption (g_5) for the wave equation (0.1)-(0.3).

In what follows we shall outline the proof of Theorem 2 rather than Theorem 1 for the sake of simplicity. Concerning Theorem 1, we briefly explain the idea of the proof at the end of this paper.

1. Dual variational formulation

We deal with Theorem 2, that is, we consider the equation:

$$v_{tt} - v_{xx} + |v|^{s-1}v = f(x,t), \qquad (x,t) \in (0,\pi)\times\mathbb{R}, \tag{1.1}$$

together with the boundary and periodicity conditions (0.2)-(0.3).

Let $\Omega = (0,\pi)\times(0,2\pi)$ and for $p \in [1,\infty)$ we denote by L^p the space of 2π-periodic functions of t whose p-th powers are integrable, i. e.,

$$\|u\|_p^p = \int_\Omega |u|^p \, dxdt < \infty.$$

Consider the operator $Au = u_{tt} - u_{xx}$ acting on functions in L^1 satisfying (0.2), (0.3). The kernel N of A consists of functions of the form:

$$N = \{\ \rho(t+x)-\rho(t-x);\ \ \rho \text{ is } 2\pi\text{-periodic},\ \ \rho \in L^1_{loc}(\mathbb{R}) \text{ and } \int_0^{2\pi} \rho(\tau)\, d\tau = 0\ \}$$

$$= \overline{\text{span}}\{\ \sin jx \cos jt,\ \sin jx \sin jt;\ \ j \in \mathbb{N}\ \}.$$

(N is closed in L^1.)

Recall that given $v \in L^1$ such that $\int_\Omega v\phi = 0$ for all $\phi \in N\cap L^\infty$, there exists a unique function $u \in C(\bar{\Omega})$ such that $Au = v$ and $\int_\Omega u\phi = 0$ for all $\phi \in N$. Set $u = Kv$ $(= A^{-1}v)$. The following properties of K are well known (c. f. [7]).

$$\|Kv\|_\infty \le C\|v\|_1, \tag{1.2}$$

$$\|Kv\|_{C^{0,\alpha}} \le C\|v\|_p, \qquad \alpha = 1 - \frac{1}{p} \tag{1.3}$$

$$\int_\Omega (Kv_1)v_2 = \int_\Omega v_1(Kv_2) \tag{1.4}$$

Set

$$q = \frac{1}{s} + 1 \in (1,2). \tag{1.5}$$

We shall consider the space:

$$E = \{\ u \in L^q;\ \int_\Omega u\phi = 0 \quad \text{for all} \quad \phi \in N \cap L^{s+1}\ \}$$

with norm $\|\cdot\|_q$.

We denote by $(\cdot,\cdot)$ the duality product between E^* and E or between L^{s+1} and L^q, that is,

$$(v,u) = \int_\Omega vu$$

For a given $f \in L^q$ we define the functional $I(u)$ on E by

$$I(u) = -\frac{1}{2}(-Ku,u) + \frac{1}{q}\|u+f\|_q^q$$

which is C^1 on E and

$$(I'(u),\zeta) = (Ku + |u+f|^{q-2}(u+f),\zeta) \qquad \text{for all} \quad u,\ \zeta \in E.$$

From the Hahn-Banach theorem, we have

$$Ku + |u+f|^{q-2}(u+f) = w + \phi$$

with $w \in L^{s+1}$, $\|w\|_{s+1} = \|I'(u)\|_{E^*}$, $\phi \in N \cap L^{s+1}$.

If $I'(u) = 0$, we have

$$Ku + |u+f|^{q-2}(u+f) = \phi \in N \cap L^{s+1}$$

Set $v = \phi - Ku = |u+f|^{q-2}(u+f)$, then we get

$$Av + |v|^{s-1}v = f.$$

Thus there is one-to-one correspondence between critical points of $I(u)$ and weak solutions of (1.1), (0.2), (0.3). Hence we seek critcal points of $I(u)$. This is so-called dual variational formulation of the problem (1.1), (0.2), (0.3).

2. A modified functional and minimax methods

We replace $I(u)$ by a modified functional $J(u)$ as follows. This replacement is used to solve the elliptic problem (0.5)-(0.6) in [14]. The main reason for introducing $J(u)$ is that the first assertion of the following Proposition 1 holds for $J(u)$ but not for $I(u)$.

Let $\chi \in C^\infty(\mathbb{R},\mathbb{R})$ such that $\chi(t) = 1$ for $t \leq 1$, $\chi(t) = 0$ for $t \geq 2$ and $-2 \leq \chi'(t) \leq 0$, $0 \leq \chi(t) \leq 1$ for $t \in \mathbb{R}$. We set

$$\Phi(u) = a(I(u)^2 + 1)^{1/2},$$

$$\psi(u) = \chi(\Phi(u)^{-1}(-Ku,u)),$$

$$J(u) = -\frac{1}{2}(-Ku,u) + \frac{1}{q}\|u\|_q^q + \frac{1}{q}\psi(u)(\|u+f\|_q^q - \|u\|_q^q),$$

where $a = (6q+4)/(2-q) > 1$.

For $\theta \in [0,2\pi) \simeq S^1$, define S^1-action $T_\theta: E \to E$ by

$$(T_\theta u)(x,t) = u(x,t+\theta).$$

We remark that in case $f = 0$ the functional $J(u)$ $(= I(u))$ is an S^1 invariant functional, i. e., $J(T_\theta u) = J(u)$ for all $u \in E$ and $\theta \in [0, 2\pi)$. But in case $f \neq 0$ the functional $J(u)$ is no longer S^1 invariant on E. The following proposition gives an estimate on its deviation from S^1 symmetry $(J(T_\theta u) - J(u))$ and ensures large critical values of $J(u)$ are also critical values of $I(u)$.

Proposition 1. The functional $J(u) \in C^1(E, \mathbb{R})$ satisfies

(i) There is a constant $\beta = \beta(\|f\|_q) > 0$ such that for all $u \in E$ and $\theta \in [0, 2\pi)$,

$$|J(T_\theta u) - J(u)| \leq \beta(|J(u)|^{(q-1)/q} + 1).$$

(ii) There is a constant $M = M(\|f\|_q) > 0$ such that $J(u) \geq M$ and $\|J'(u)\|_{E^*} \leq 1$ imply that $J(u) = I(u)$ and $I'(u) = J'(u)$.

(iii) $J(u)$ satisfies the Palais-Smale compactness condition on $A_M = \{ u \in E; J(u) \geq M \}$. That is, any sequence (u_j) in E such that

$$M \leq J(u_j) \leq \tilde{M} \qquad \text{for some } \tilde{M},$$

$$J'(u_j) \to 0 \text{ in } E^* \qquad \text{as } j \to \infty$$

is precompact in E.

The proof of these statements can be found in [17, 18]. By (iii), we can use minimax method to obtain critical points of $J(u)$.

Note that K is a compact self-adjoint operator in

$$\{ u \in L^2; \int_\Omega u\phi = 0 \quad \text{for all } \phi \in N \cap L^2 \}$$

$$= \overline{\text{span}} \{ \sin jx \cos kt, \sin jx \sin kt; \; j \in \mathbb{N}, \; k \in \mathbb{N} \cup \{0\}, \; j \neq k \}.$$

Its eigenvalues are $\{1/(j^2-k^2);\ j \neq k\}$ corresponding eigenfunctions are $\sin jx \cos kt$ and $\sin jx \sin kt$. We observe that each negative eigenvalue possesses even multiplicity. We rearrange negative eigenvalues in the following order, denoted by

$$-\mu_1 \leqq -\mu_2 \leqq \cdots < 0.$$

Here for each n, there is a one-to-one correspondence between $-\mu_n$ and a 2-dimensional invariant space:

$$\text{span}\{\ e_n^+ = \sin jx \cos kt,\quad e_n^- = \sin jx \sin kt\ \}\ (\ j^2-k^2 = -\mu_n^{-1}).$$

Next we shall define spaces E_n, $E_n^\perp$ and projection $P_n : E \to E_n$ by

$$E_n = \text{span}\{\ e_1^+,\ e_1^-,\ e_2^+,\ e_2^-,\ \cdots,\ e_n^+,\ e_n^-\ \},$$

$$E_n^\perp = \{\ u \in E;\ (e_i^+,u) = (e_i^-,u) = 0 \quad \text{for}\quad i = 1,\ 2,\ \cdots,\ n\ \},$$

$$P_n u = \frac{1}{2\pi^2}\sum_{i=1}^{n}((e_i^+,u)e_i^+ + (e_i^-,u)e_i^-) \qquad \text{for}\quad u \in E.$$

Since

$$J(u) \leqq -\frac{1}{2}\mu_n\|u\|_2^2 + \frac{1}{q}\|u\|_q^q + \frac{1}{q}\|u+f\|_q^q \qquad \text{for all}\quad u \in E_n,$$

there exists a constant $R_n > 0$ such that

$$J(u) \leqq 0 \quad \text{for all}\quad u \in E_n \quad \text{with}\quad \|u\|_q \geqq R_n.$$

We may assume that $R_n < R_{n+1}$ for all n.

Let

$$B_R = \{\ u \in E;\ \ \|u\|_q \leqq R\ \} \quad \text{for}\quad R > 0,$$

$$D_n = B_{R_n} \cap E_n,$$

$$\Gamma_n = \{ \gamma \in C(D_n, E);\quad \gamma(T_\theta u) = T_\theta \gamma(u) \quad \text{for all} \quad \theta \in [0, 2\pi),\quad u \in D_n,$$
$$\gamma(u) = u \qquad \text{for all} \quad \|u\|_q = R_n \}.$$

Moreover, set

$$U_n = \{ u = \tau \frac{e^+_{n+1}}{\|e^+_{n+1}\|_q} + w;\quad \tau \in [0, R_{n+1}],\quad w \in B_{R_{n+1}} \cap E_n \quad \text{and}$$
$$\|u\|_q \leq R_{n+1} \},$$

$$\Lambda_n = \{ \lambda \in C(U_n, E);\quad \lambda|_{D_n} \in \Gamma_n \quad \text{and}$$
$$\lambda(u) = u \quad \text{if} \quad \|u\|_q = R_{n+1} \quad \text{or} \quad u \in (B_{R_{n+1}} \setminus B_{R_n}) \cap E_n \}.$$

Define minimax values for $n \in \mathbb{N}$,

$$b_n = \inf_{\gamma \in \Gamma_n} \max_{u \in D_n} J(\gamma(u)),$$

$$c_n = \inf_{\lambda \in \Lambda_n} \max_{u \in U_n} J(\lambda(u)).$$

The above definitions of minimax values b_n, c_n are analogous to those of P. H. Rabinowitz [14], which are used to prove the existence of infinitely many periodic solutions of perturbed second order Hamiltonian systems. By the definitions it is clear that $c_n \geq b_n$. Since (ii), (iii) of Proposition 1 hold, we have the following result by P. H. Rabinowitz [14]. He proved this with the aid of standard "Deformation Theorem".

Proposition 2 (Lemma 1.57 of P. H. Rabinowitz [14]). Suppose $c_n > b_n \geq M$. Let $d \in (0, c_n - b_n)$ and

$$\Lambda_n(d) = \{ \lambda \in \Lambda_n;\quad J(\lambda) \leq b_n + d \quad \text{on} \quad D_n \}.$$

Define

$$c_n(d) = \inf_{\lambda \in \Lambda_n(d)} \max_{u \in U_n} J(\lambda(u)) \quad (\geqq c_n).$$

Then $c_n(d)$ is a critical value of $I(u)$.

3. Proof of Theorem 2

By Proposition 2, the existence of subsequence of c_n's which satisfy $c_n > b_n \geqq M$ guarantees the existence of critical values. Therefore, to prove Theorem 2, we shall show the following proposition.

Proposition 3. There exists a subsequence $\{n_j\}_{j=1}^{\infty}$ such that

$$c_{n_j} > b_{n_j} \geqq M \quad \text{for all} \quad j \in \mathbb{N},$$

$$b_n \to \infty \qquad \text{as} \quad n \to \infty.$$

Proof. The proof of Proposition 3 is divided into 3 steps.

Step 1: L^q-estimates for $(-Ku, u)$

Step 2: The growth of the value b_n

Step 3: Conclusion

Step 1: L^q-estimates for $(-Ku, u)$

Let $Q: E \to E$ be a projection defined by

$$(3.1) \qquad (Qu)(x,t) = u(x,t) - \frac{1}{2\pi} \int_0^{2\pi} u(x,\tau)\, d\tau.$$

We can easily see that

$$Q(\sin jx \cos kt) = \sin jx \cos kt \qquad \text{if} \quad k \neq 0,$$

$$(3.2) \qquad Q(\sin jx \sin kt) = \sin jx \sin kt \qquad \text{if} \quad k \neq 0,$$

$$Q(\sin jx) = 0.$$

As a first step of the proof, we need the following

Lemma 1. (c.f. Proposition 3 of [17]). There are constants $a_n > 0$ such that

$$(-Ku,u) \leqq a_n \|Qu\|_q^2 \qquad \text{for all} \quad u \in E_n^\perp.$$

Moreover, for any $\delta > 0$ there exists a constant $C_\delta > 0$ such that

$$a_n \leqq C_\delta n^{-2(q-1)/q + \delta} \qquad \text{for all} \quad n \in \mathbb{N}. \tag{3.3}$$

Proof. Suppose that $u(x,t) \in E_n^\perp$, then by means of Fourier series we can write

$$u = \sum_{i=n+1}^{\infty} (u_i^+ e_i^+ + u_i^- e_i^-) + w,$$

where u_i^+, $u_i^- \in \mathbb{R}$ and

$$w \in E^- \equiv \overline{\text{span}}\{\sin jx \cos kt, \ \sin jx \sin kt; \ j^2 - k^2 > 0\}.$$

By (3.2) we have

$$Qu = \sum_{i=n+1}^{\infty} (u_i^+ e_i^+ + u_i^- e_i^-) + Qw, \tag{3.4}$$

where $Qw \in E^-$.

Since $(-Kw,w) \leqq 0$ for all $w \in E^-$, we have

$$(-Ku,u) = \sum_{i=n+1}^{\infty} \mu_i (|u_i^+|^2 + |u_i^-|^2) + (-Kw,w)$$

$$\leqq \sum_{i=n+1}^{\infty} \mu_i (|u_i^+|^2 + |u_i^-|^2).$$

Using Holder's inequality, we get

$$(-Ku,u) \leq \Big(\sum_{i=n+1}^{\infty} \mu_i^{q/(2-q)}\Big)^{(2-q)/q}$$

$$\times \Big(\sum_{i=n+1}^{\infty} (|u_i^+|^{q/(q-1)} + |u_i^-|^{q/(q-1)})\Big)^{2(q-1)/q}.$$

On the other hand, we have by Hausdorff-Young's inequality and (3.4)

$$\Big(\sum_{i=n+1}^{\infty} (|u_i^+|^{q/(q-1)} + |u_i^-|^{q/(q-1)})\Big)^{(q-1)/q} \leq c_q\|Qu\|_q.$$

Hence we get

$$(-Ku,u) \leq a_n\|Qu\|_q^2 \qquad \text{for} \quad u \in E_n^{\perp},$$

where

$$a_n = c_q\Big(\sum_{i=n+1}^{\infty} \mu_i^{q/(2-q)}\Big)^{(2-q)/q}.$$

From the definition of μ_n, for any $\delta > 0$ we can find a constant $C_\delta > 0$ such that

$$\mu_n \leq C_\delta n^{-1+\delta} \qquad \text{for all} \quad n \in \mathbb{N}.$$

Therefore a_n satisfies the desired property (3.3).

Step 2: The growth of the value b_n

Lemma 2. For all $n \in \mathbb{N}$, $\rho \in (0,R_n)$ and $\gamma \in \Gamma_n$,

$$\gamma(D_n) \cap \{\, w \in E_{n-1}^{\perp};\ \|Qw\|_q = \rho \,\} \neq \phi.$$

Proof. Note that $\{\, T_\theta\ ;\ \theta \in [0,2\pi) \simeq S^1 \,\}$ possesses a fixed point set:

$$\text{Fix } S^1 = \{ u \in E;\ \ T_\theta u = u \quad \text{for all} \quad \theta \in [0,2\pi) \}.$$

It is clear from the definition (3.1) that

$$\text{(3.5)} \qquad \text{Range}(Q) \cap \text{Fix } S^1 = \{0\}.$$

Let $\gamma \in \Gamma_n$, $\rho \in (0,R_n)$. Since $Q\gamma$ is S^1-invariant (i. e., $T_\theta(Q\gamma)(u) = Q\gamma(T_\theta u)$ for all θ and u) and (3.5) holds, $(Q\gamma)^{-1}(B_\rho)$ is an S^1-invariant neighborhood of 0 in D_n. Let V be the component of $(Q\gamma)^{-1}(B_\rho)$ containing 0. Then $P_{n-1}Q\gamma \in C(\partial V, E_{n-1})$ is an S^1-equivariant map and $\text{Fix } S^1 \cap E_{n-1} = \{0\}$. Applying an S^1-version of the Borsuk-Ulam theorem in [10], we get

$$\{ u \in \partial V;\ \ P_{n-1}Q\gamma(u) = 0 \} \neq \phi,$$

that is, we have the desired result.

Using Lemmas 1 and 2, we get

Lemma 3. For any $\delta > 0$, there exist constants $C_\delta > 0$ and $C' > 0$ such that

$$\text{(3.6)} \qquad b_n \geq C_\delta n^{2(q-1)/(2-q) - \delta} - C' \qquad \text{for all} \quad n \in \mathbb{N}.$$

Proof. By Lemma 2 and the definition of b_n, we get

$$b_n = \inf_{\gamma \in \Gamma_n} \max_{u \in D_n} J(\gamma(u)) \geq \sup_{0<\rho<R_n} \inf_{w \in E_{n-1}^\perp:\ \|Qw\|_q = \rho} J(w).$$

Let $w \in E_{n-1}^\perp$ with $\|Qw\|_q = \rho$. By Young's inequality,

$$J(w) = -\frac{1}{2}(-Kw,w) + \frac{1}{q}\|w\|_q^q + \frac{1}{q}\psi(w)(\|w+f\|_q^q - \|w\|_q^q)$$

$$\geq -\frac{1}{2}(-Kw,w) + \frac{1}{2q}\|w\|_q^q - C'.$$

By Lemma 1 and boundedness of the operator $Q: L^q \to L^q$, we get

$$J(w) \geq -\frac{1}{2}a_{n-1}\rho^2 + C\rho^q - C'.$$

Hence we obtain

$$b_n \geq (\frac{1}{q} - \frac{1}{2})(qC)^{2/(2-q)} a_{n-1}^{-q/(2-q)} - C'.$$

Thus we obtain the desired inequality from (3.3).

Step 3: Conclusion

Arguing indirectly, we have

Lemma 4. If $c_n = b_n$ for all $n \geq n_0$, then there is a constant $C = C(n_0) > 0$ such that

(3.7) $\qquad b_n \leq Cn^q \qquad$ for all $n \in \mathbb{N}$.

Proof. Note that $D_{n+1} = \{ T_\theta u;\ u \in U_n,\ \theta \in [0,2\pi) \}$. For a given $\lambda \in \Lambda_n$, we define $\hat{\lambda} \in \Gamma_{n+1}$ by

$$\hat{\lambda}(T_\theta u) = T_\theta \lambda(u) \quad \text{for } u \in U_n \text{ and } \theta \in [0,2\pi).$$

Then we obtain by (i) of Proposition 1,

$$\max_{T_\theta u \in D_{n+1}} J(\hat{\lambda}(T_\theta u)) \leq \max_{u \in U_n,\ \theta} [J(\lambda(u)) + |J(T_\theta\lambda(u)) - J(\lambda(u))|]$$

$$\leq \max_{u \in U_n} [\ J(\lambda(u)) + \beta(|J(\lambda(u))|^{(q-1)/q} + 1)\ ].$$

Therefore we obtain

$$b_{n+1} \leq c_n + \beta(|c_n|^{(q-1)/q} + 1).$$

If $c_n = b_n$ for $n \geq n_0$, we obtain

$$b_{n+1} \leq b_n + \beta(|b_n|^{(q-1)/q} + 1) \quad \text{for } n \geq n_0.$$

An induction argument yields (3.7) (c.f. [3, 16]).

End of the proof of Proposition 3. Comparing (3.6) and (3.7), we see the inequalities are incompatible if $\sqrt{2} < q < 2$, i. e., $1 < s < 1 + \sqrt{2}$ by (1.5). Thus the proof of Proposition 3 is completed.

End of the proof of Theorem 2. By Propositions 2,3, there exists a sequence $\{u_n\}$ of critical points of $I(u)$ such that $I(u_n) \to \infty$ as $n \to \infty$. In particular $\|u_n\|_q \to \infty$ as $n \to \infty$. On the other hand, corresponding solutions of (1.1), (0.2), (0.3) to u_n are

$$v_n = |u_n + f|^{q-2}(u_n + f).$$

Therefore

$$\|v_n\|_{s+1} = \|u_n + f\|_q^{q-1} \to \infty \quad \text{as} \quad n \to \infty.$$

Thus the proof of Theorem 2 is completed.

4. Sketch of the proof of Theorem 1.

Set $q = \mu/(\mu - 1)$ and define space E and operator $K: E \to E$ as in § 1. Next we set $h(\xi)$ = the inverse function of $g(\xi)$ and

$$H(\xi) = \int_0^{\xi} h(\tau)\, d\tau.$$

For a given $f \in L^\infty$ we define functional $I(u) \in C^1(E, \mathbb{R})$ by

$$I(u) = -\frac{1}{2}(-Ku, u) + \int_\Omega H(u+f) \qquad \text{for} \quad u \in E.$$

As in §1, $u \in E$ is a critical point of $I(u)$ if and only if $v = h(u+f)$ is a weak solution of (0.1)-(0.3).

In case $g(\xi) = |\xi|^{s-1}\xi$, we can verify the Palais-Smale compactness condition (P.S.) for $I(u)$. But for general $g(\xi)$ it is difficult to verify (P.S.). So we introduce a modified functional, in a sense, a truncation of $g(\xi)$ as follows.

We choose a convex function $\omega(\xi) \in C^\infty(\mathbb{R}, \mathbb{R})$ such that $\omega(\xi) = |\xi|^q$ for $|\xi| \geqq 1$ and $\omega(\xi) = 0$ in a neighborhood of 0. For $\varepsilon \in [0,1]$, we set

$$I(\varepsilon;u) = I(u) + \int_\Omega \omega(\varepsilon u) \in C^1(E, \mathbb{R}).$$

Then $I(\varepsilon:u)$ satisfies (P.S.) for $\varepsilon > 0$.

To construct critical points of $I(u) = I(0;u)$, first we obtain critical points of $I(\varepsilon;u)$ for $\varepsilon > 0$. As in §2, we define modified functionals $J(\varepsilon;u)$ and minimax values $b_n(\varepsilon) = \inf_{\gamma \in \Gamma_n} \max_{u \in D_n} J(\varepsilon;\gamma(u))$, $c_n(\varepsilon) = \inf_{\lambda \in \Lambda_n} \max_{u \in U_n} J(\varepsilon;\lambda(u))$. We have to show $c_{n_j}(\varepsilon) > b_{n_j}(\varepsilon)$ for suitable subsequence $\{n_j\}_{j=1}^\infty$. In fact, using uniform estimates and continuity of $b_n(\varepsilon)$, $c_n(\varepsilon)$ with respect to the parameter $\varepsilon \in [0,1]$, we have the following proposition under the condition (g_2)-(g_4).

Proposition 4.(Proposition 3 of [18]). There exists a subsequence $\{n_j\}_{j=1}^\infty$ such that for some constants $\delta_j \in (0,1]$ and $d_j > 0$,

$$c_{n_j}(\varepsilon) - 2d_j \geqq b_{n_j}(\varepsilon) \geqq M \qquad \text{for all} \quad \varepsilon \in (0, \delta_j].$$

Moreover there exist sequences $\{m_j\}_{j=1}^{\infty}$ and $\{M_j\}_{j=1}^{\infty}$ which are independent of ε and

$$m_j \to \infty \quad \text{as} \quad j \to \infty, \qquad m_j \leq c_{n_j}(\varepsilon;d_j) \leq M_j \quad \text{for} \quad \varepsilon \in (0,\delta_j],$$

where $c_{n_j}(\varepsilon;d_j)$ is a critical value of $I(\varepsilon;u)$ defined by

$$c_{n_j}(\varepsilon;d_j) = \inf_{\lambda \in \Lambda_{n_j}(\varepsilon;d_j)} \max_{u \in U_{n_j}} J(\varepsilon;\lambda(u)),$$

$$\Lambda_{n_j}(\varepsilon;d_j) = \{ \lambda \in \Lambda_{n_j};\ \ J(\varepsilon;\lambda) \leq b_{n_j}(\varepsilon) + d_j \quad \text{on} \quad D_{n_j} \}.$$

On the other hand, we have the following L^{∞}-estimates for critical points with the aid of the argument which is essentially due to H. Brézis, J. M. Coron and L. Nirenberg [7].

Proposition 5. Assume that $u \in E$ and $\varepsilon \in (0,1]$ satisfy $I'(\varepsilon;u) = 0$ and $I(\varepsilon;u) \leq L$. Then there is a constant $C = C(L,\|f\|_{\infty}) > 0$ which is independent of ε such that $\|u\|_{\infty} \leq C$.

By Proposition 4, there is a critical point $u_{n_j}(\varepsilon)$ of $I(\varepsilon;u)$ such that $I(\varepsilon;u_{n_j}(\varepsilon)) = c_{n_j}(\varepsilon,d_j) \leq M_j$. Using Proposition 5 and the fact $\omega(\xi) = 0$ in a neighborhood of 0, we deduce that $u_{n_j}(\varepsilon)$ is a critical point of $I(u)$ for sufficiently small $\varepsilon > 0$.

Note. Very recently, the author [19] has improved the results of this paper. In case $g(\xi) = |\xi|^{s-1}\xi$, he has proved the existence of infinitely many periodic solutions of (0.1)-(0.3) for all $s \in (1,\infty)$ and $f \in L^{(s+1)/s}$.

References

[1] A. Ambrosetti and P. H. Rabinowitz, Dual variational methods in a critical point theory and applications, J. Funct. Anal., **14** (1973), 345-381.

[2] A. Bahri, Topological results on a certain class of functionals and application, J. Funct. Anal., **41** (1981), 397-427.

[3] A. Bahri and H. Berestycki, A perturbation method in critical point theory and applications, Trans. Amer. Math. Soc., **267** (1981), 1-32.

[4] A. Bahri and P. L. Lions, Remarques sur la théorie variationnelle des points critiques et applications, C. R. Acad. Sc. Paris, Sér I, **301** (1985), 145-147.

[5] V. Benci and D. Fortunato, The dual methods in critical point theory. Multiplicity results for indefinite functionals, Annali. Mat. Pura Appl. **32** (1982), 215-242.

[6] H. Brézis, Periodic solutions of nonlinear vibrating strings and duality principles, Bull. Amer. Math. Soc. (N. S.), **8** (1983), 409-426.

[7] H. Brézis, J. M. Coron and L. Nirenberg, Free vibrations for a nonlinear wave equation and a theorem of P. Rabinowitz, Comm. Pure Appl. Math., **33** (1980), 667-689.

[8] H. Brézis and L. Nirenberg, Forced vibrations for a nonlinear wave equation, Comm. Pure Appl. Math., **31** (1978), 1-30.

[9] J. M. Coron, Periodic solutions of a nonlinear wave equation without assumption of monotonicity, Math. Ann., **262** (1983), 273-285.

[10] E. R. Fadell, S. Y. Husseini and P. H. Rabinowitz, Borsuk-Ulam theorem for arbitrary S^1 actions and applications, Trans. Amer. Math. Soc., **274** (1982), 345-360.

[11] J. P. Ollivry, Vibrations forcees pour une equation d'onde nonlineaire, C. R. Acad. Sc. Paris, Ser I, **297** (1983), 29-32.

[12] P. H. Rabinowitz, Variational methods for nonlinear eigenvalue problems, in Eigenvalues of Nonlinear Problems, Edizioni, Cremonese, Rome, 1974, 141-195.

[13] P. H. Rabinowitz, Free vibrations for a semilinear wave equation, Comm. Pure Appl. Math., **31** (1978), 31-68.

[14] P. H. Rabinowitz, Multiple critical points of perturbed symmetric functionals, Trans. Amer. Math. Soc., **272** (1982), 753-769.

[15] P. H. Rabinowitz, Large amplitude time periodic solutions of a semilinear wave equation, Comm. Pure Appl. Math., **37** (1984), 189-206.

[16] M. Struwe, Infinitely many critical points for functionals which are not even and applications to superlinear boundary value problems, Manuscripta Math., **32** (1980), 335-364.

[17] K. Tanaka, Infinitely many periodic solutions for the equation: $u_{tt} - u_{xx} \pm |u|^{s-1}u = f(x,t)$, Proc. Japan Acad., **61** (1985), 70-73 and Comm. in P. D. E., **10** (1985), 1317-1345.

[18] K. Tanaka, Infinitely many periodic solutions for a superlinear forced wave equation, Proc. Japan Acad., **61** (1985), 341-344 and Nonlinear Analysis: T. M. A. (to appear).

[19] K. Tanaka, in preparation.